THE DARK TOWER

THE
DARK TOWER

and

other radio scripts

by

LOUIS MACNEICE

FABER AND FABER LIMITED
24 Russell Square
London

First published in Mcmxlvii
by Faber and Faber Limited
24 Russell Square London W.C. 1
Printed in Great Britain by
R. MacLehose and Company Limited
The University Press Glasgow
All rights reserved

CONTENTS

GENERAL INTRODUCTION

THE interest shown in such few radio scripts as have been published (the most notable recent example being *The Rescue* by my friend Mr. Edward Sackville-West) has encouraged me to publish some more of my own. I do this not only because like all radio writers I feel frustrated each time a script has been broadcast but in the hope that a selection of dissimilar pieces may throw some light on the medium. I have chosen *The Dark Tower* because I think it the best radio script I have written; the others are included as fairly clear-cut examples—I would certainly not say models—of different types of programme. All of them seem to me worth reading.

Having in my Introduction to *Christopher Columbus* essayed a general exposition of radio-dramatic writing, I will not labour again those main points which I still consider valid, e.g. that 'the first virtue of a radio script is construction'. But I would like in some respects to correct myself. That the radio writer 'must move on a more or less primitive plane' is, I think now, an over-statement or at least misleadingly expressed. What the radio writer must do, if he hopes to win the freedom of the air, is to appeal *on one plane*—whatever he may be doing on the others—to the more primitive listener and to the more primitive elements in anyone; i.e. he must give them (what Shakespeare gave them) entertainment.[1]

In the same Introduction I wrote: 'As compared with most contemporary literature, the objective elements will preponderate over the subjective, statement over allusion, synthesis over analysis.' This again I want to qualify; the comparison with contemporary *literature* may have misled me. The 'psychological' novel, concerned chiefly with 'subjective' experiences, deals

[1] The reception of *The Dark Tower* supports this. Many listeners said that they enjoyed it, found it 'beautiful', 'exciting' etc.—but had 'no idea what it was about.' In fact they were caught by the 'story' but I flatter myself that, in passing, the story 'slipped over' some meaning on them.

9

largely in *oratio obliqua*; even that kind of *oratio recta* used to represent 'the stream of consciousness' is usually not much more than a shorthand for the page. But when no character can be presented except through spoken words, whether in dialogue or soliloquy, that very *spokenness* makes this distinction between subjective and objective futile. A character in a radio play, as in a stage play, may say things that actually he never would or could say—the author may be making him utter what is only known to his unconscious—but once he has said them, there they are! As objective as Ben Jonson's Humours are objective. To take an extreme example, Virginia Woolf's novel *The Waves* is often quoted as subjective writing *par excellence*; the characters, thinking in the first person, say things they never could have formulated, being even as small children endowed with the brilliant introspection and the sad philosophy of their creator. I am confident that this method, though probably not this application of it, would be feasible on the air. Listeners might not accept Virginia Woolf's long-windedness, her preciousness, the sameness of her characters, the lack of a 'story'—but that in no way proves them 'allergic' to subjectivity. Once your characters speak speakable lines—once, to use a horrible piece of jargon, the subjective is objectified—you can get away with anything *so long as you entertain*.

Similarly, the distinctions made in my quotation between statement and allusion and between synthesis and analysis are perhaps equally worthless. It would have been safer to say that in radio dialogue we need a number of things which *sound like* statements—but in spoken dialogue that goes without saying; no two people can keep up a conversation which is one *hundred* per cent surrealist. As for allusion, not only is it difficult in any context to make any statement which is not also an allusion, i.e. suggestive of something beyond its own definitive meaning, but in all *dramatic* writing a word, let alone a phrase, pulls more than its dictionary weight; the pun is only the crudest example of a procedure familiar to, though not of course formulated by, every-one. In characterisation equally, Mr. X, who may appear to be talking at random and naturalistically, can really be talking succinctly and also symbolically, revealing himself—or whatever else is meant to be revealed—by a process of implicit logic. 'Implicit' is here, as in other creative writing, a key-word. Even in the psychological novel, if it is a good one, the psychology is implicit; for explicit psychology we go to the textbooks. This is all I meant in subordinating analysis to synthesis—but this too could have gone without saying or at least I ought so to have expressed it as not to preclude 'psychological' characterisation from the sphere of radio drama.

But criticism comes after the event; it is no good talking about radio until you have experienced it. It may therefore be instructive if, dropping generalities, I make a short confession of my own experiences as listener, script-writer, and producer. Before I joined the B.B.C. I was, like most of the intelligentsia, prejudiced not only against that institution but against broadcasting in general; I rarely listened to anything except concerts and running commentaries on sports events. These latter, which gave me a pleasure distinct from that which lies in *seeing* a game or race, should have provided a hint of radio's possibilities; my prejudice, however, prevented me from exploring the possible pleasures in wireless plays and features. Since then I have listened to many examples of both and must confess that often they give me no pleasure at all—but this proves nothing; we have all met the same disappointment with books, plays, and films. What does prove a point to me is that *some* plays and features have excited, amused, moved me. So the wireless *can* be worth listening to. But next: is it worth writing for?

Many writers are deterred from radio drama by fear of the middlemen and by dislike of actors. They expect their work to be doctored from the start and travestied in the presentation (which has of course sometimes happened—as it has happened both on the stage and page). But while no production will ever seem perfect to the author, the questions are whether one can gamble on a reasonably good production and whether such a production is better than none. Your answers depend on whether you really have an itch for drama; if you have, you must want sooner or later to write dialogue to be spoken somewhere—and it is no more likely to be spoken badly on the air than anywhere else (the wireless lacks the body of the stage—but also some of its impurities). If *you* provide a good script, the odds are that it will gain by being broadcast; in fact, if it loses, while it may be the fault of the production, the more likely inference is that your script was not radiogenic (a handy word, though jargon). The predominance of adapted stage-plays in B.B.C. programmes has probably discouraged a number of writers, for many of these plays do lose on the air (at least as compared with the stage); few of them are radiogenic. Transposition from one medium to another is usually unfair to both. Which is why we must remember that the script-writer is a peculiar species.

The all-important difference between visual and non-visual drama, while discouraging some, may encourage others towards radio, for here and here alone can one listen to calculated speech divorced from all visual supports or interferences—even from a printed page. It would be a great pity if television were ever completely to supersede sound broadcasting as the talkies super-seded the silent films. That cinema revolution was inevitable but through it we lost the unique pleasure of watching a story told visually, dispensing with people's voices. But sound alone is for most people more potent, more pregnant, more subtle, than pictures alone and for that reason—regardless of the material pros and cons of television—I hope that sound broadcasting will survive, dispensing with people's faces. As with many other media its narrow limits are also its virtue, while within those limits it can give us something unobtainable from print (though print of course will always retain its proper autonomy). When I first

General Introduction

heard a piece, which I had written for broadcasting, broadcast, I was irritated by details of presentation but excited and delighted by the total effect (there was more to my script, I felt, than I myself had realised). The mere fact that one's words issue from other people's mouths, while gratifying no doubt to an author's vanity, is also a welcome release from his involuntary egotism. Most novelists and poets, I think, envy the playwright that specious present and that feeling of *sharedness* which are given to a play by every fresh production, just as they envy the painter as composer-executant the excitement of his manual craftsmanship and the immediate impact of his completed work (which also can be shared by several people at once). When you have written for the page, you do not see your readers reading you; which is just as well as you could never tell if in their heads they were 'hearing' you properly. But in broadcasting you can, given the right speakers, force your listeners at least to hear the words as they should. The point is that here we have a means by which written lines can emulate the impact of a stage or of a painting and give the writer that excitement of a sensuous experience simultaneously shared with many which is one of the joys of life. This pleasure in a thing-being-performed-and-shared, while obtainable in all sports and some of the arts, is sadly lacking in the world of literature today. It is a pleasure I have often received, though mixed at times with mortification, when hearing my own scripts broadcast. It is succeeded, as I said before, by a feeling of frustration—because it is 'over'; but in that it is not of course unusual.

I have stressed this fact of pleasure because some people assume that writing for the wireless must be hackwork. It often is—for the salaried script-writer because he must turn his hand to many things, some of them dull, for the occasional writer (less forgivably) when he deals with an uncongenial subject for money or writes badly because he is merely writing for money. But it often is not. Broadcasting is plastic; while it can ape the Press, it can also emulate the arts. Yes, people will say, that is theoretically true but in practice you will never get art—or anything like it— out of a large public institution, encumbered with administrators, which by its nature must play for safety and to the gallery. This is not the place to dispute this at length but I would maintain that in this country such an institution cannot be really authoritarian; with ingenuity and a little luck a creative person can persuade (or fool) at least some of the administrators some of the time.[1] And, thinking of the vexed question of commercial broadcasting, I would add that many of the more original programmes by my friends and myself (this book shows examples in *The Dark Tower* and the 'March Hare' scripts) would have been no more acceptable to sponsored radio than to the biggest and vulgarest profit-making film company. For its acceptance of such experiments I am very grateful to the B.B.C.

In this age of irreconcilable idioms I have often heard writers hankering for some sort of group life, a desire doomed to dis-appointment; the modern writer—at any rate the modern poet— is *ipso facto* a spiritual isolationist who will lose far more than he will gain by trying to pool his mentality with those of his colleagues. Thus of the several dozen poets whom I know there are very few with whom I would wish to discuss poetry and only, I think, one from whom I would often accept criticism. This solitude (which incidentally has nothing to do with the Ivory Tower; there are Group Towers too, remember) is *in our time* salutary—but here again we cannot but envy playwrights, actors or musical executants. And here again I for one have found this missing group experience, in a valid form, in radio. Radio writers and producers *can* talk shop together because their shop is not, as with poets, a complex of spiritual intimacies but a matter of craftsmanship. Though the poet of course is also—or should be—a craftsman, the lyrical poet's technique is—or

[1] I am not suggesting that, as things are, all our administrators need per-suading or fooling.

should be—closely wedded to his unique personality and there is no more point in defending your own personality than in impugning your friend's. But radio craftsmanship, like stage craftsmanship, is something much less private; we are fully entitled to discuss whether dialogue rings true, whether the dramatic climax is dramatic, how well the whole thing works. This is refreshing for a writer.

The popular assumption that all radio professionals resemble civil servants (resting on that other assumption that civil servants are automata) is flatly untrue. The department to which, at the date of writing, I belong in the B.B.C., would compare very well for intelligence with almost any contemporary salon of literati; my radio colleagues would be found on the whole quicker-witted, more versatile, less egocentric, less conventional, more humane. But, apart from these relishes to discussion, the reason why we can work together enjoyably and effectively is that in every case our work must go through the same mill, i.e. into a microphone and out at the other end through a wireless set. This very simple physical fact is such a bond of union as is rare among creative writers, playwrights again excepted. For we share the excitements and anxieties of *the performance*. This is especially so if we are our own executants, i.e. writer-producers. There are obvious drawbacks to this combination of functions—Mr. A as writer may see so clearly what he means that Mr. A as producer will fail to notice when the meaning is not coming over—but it does put a writer more closely in touch with his work-in-performance than he can be anywhere else unless he is Mr. Noel Coward. We know what happens to a film script when the multitude of 'experts' gets hold of it. On the stage there is no such multitude but there still is considerable interference and few writers have the chance, the time, the knowledge, or the capacity, to become stage-producers. But radio production being comparatively simple, not a few writers can learn to handle it— at any rate well enough to gain more than they lose (this especially applies to 'experimental' scripts where the pioneer, though an amateur, has an advantage over the professional geographer).

The script itself, after all, is only half the battle and the writer who merely sends in a script and does not go near the studios is working largely in the dark; whereas a writer who produces his own scripts will cut his coat according to his cloth. Since I have been producing my own programmes, I find that I both avail myself of facilities which I previously overlooked and avoid awkwardnesses which I previously imposed on my producer. Thus an earlier version of *Sunbeams in his Hat*, entitled *Dr. Chekhov*, was so written as to be almost unproduceable in places[1] at least without the use of multiple studios, as I typically had not envisaged the studio set-up. When I came to rewrite it for my own production I eliminated these difficulties and in so doing found I had made the script not only more manageable but more compact, more lucid, more convincing. Similarly, as regards both music and actors, the writer-producer has the advantage of being able to decide at an early stage who is going to do what. Thus, when he has a composer to write special music, he can not only get this music to fit the script but adjust his script on occasion to fit the music. He also has the say in casting, which is especially important in broadcasting both because of the shortness of rehearsals and because of the microphone's transparency to anything ham or unintelligent. In writing my more recent scripts I have always had an eye on the kinds of actor available and so avoided demanding the impossible and, when I could, the improbable; sometimes I have, from its conception, written a part for a particular actor, e.g. the Soldier in *The Nosebag* for Roy Emerton and the March Hare for Esmé Percy.

The preceding paragraph was intended to amplify my point about work-in-performance. While it is obviously not normally feasible for 'outside writers' to produce their own work, it is

[1] For which I now apologise to Mr. Stephen Potter—who in producing it saved the situation.

desirable, if not necessary, that they should be studio-minded; then they can explain to their producer what they want done without being embarrassing or nonsensical. I would like finally, since the chief object of this introduction was to disprove the assumption that broadcasting is 'inhuman', to inform my readers that every transmission of a play or feature, however unimportant the programme, should have—and usually has—the feeling of a First Night; it is something *being made* by a team of people.

For each of the scripts in this book I have written a separate introduction; but they all have this in common that, whatever my sins in either respect, I enjoyed both writing and producing them. The programme on Tchehov was suggested to me by my employers but the others I proposed myself. This gives me the opportunity of expressing my gratitude to the head of my department, Mr. Laurence Gilliam, who is as willing to accept such spontaneous suggestions as he is to allow an elastic treatment of those other programmes which 'have to be done'.

NOTES

The dialogue in these scripts is as broadcast but the directions have been re-written and considerably amplified.

The foregoing Introduction was written before the B.B.C. 'Third Programme' came into being. This new programme—for the first time, I believe, in radio history—assumes that its audience is going to *work* at its listening. So there is less question than ever of playing 'for safety and to the gallery'.

THE DARK TOWER

a radio parable play

TO

BENJAMIN BRITTEN

CAST

The Dark Tower was first broadcast in the B.B.C. Home Service on January 21st, 1946. The main parts, in order of their appearance, were played as follows:

SERGEANT-TRUMPETER	HARRY HUTCHINSON*
GAVIN	FRANK PARTINGTON*
ROLAND	CYRIL CUSACK
MOTHER	OLGA LINDO
TUTOR	MARK DIGNAM
SYLVIE	LUCILLE LISLE*
BLIND PETER	IVOR BARNARD
SOAK	ROBERT FARQUHARSON
STEWARD	HOWARD MARION-CRAWFORD
NEAERA	VERA MAXIME
SHIP'S OFFICER	CHARLES MAUNSELL*
PRIEST	ALEXANDER SARNER*
ROLAND'S FATHER	LAIDMAN BROWNE*
PARROT	MARJORIE WESTBURY*
RAVEN	STANLEY GROOME*
CLOCK VOICE	DUNCAN MCINTYRE*

Special music was composed by Benjamin Britten and conducted by Walter Goehr.

The production was by the author.

* A star denotes membership of the B.B.C. Repertory Company at the time of the broadcast. It will be seen from this and the other lists of cast in the book how useful this institution is.

INTRODUCTORY NOTE

The Dark Tower is a parable play, belonging to that wide class of writings which includes *Everyman*, *The Faerie Queene* and *The Pilgrim's Progress*. Though under the name of allegory this kind of writing is sometimes dismissed as outmoded, the clothed as distinct from the naked allegory is in fact very much alive. Obvious examples are *Peer Gynt* and the stories of Kafka but also in such books as *The Magic Mountain* by Thomas Mann, where the disguise of 'realism' is maintained and nothing happens that is quite inconceivable in life, it is still the symbolic core which makes the work important. My own impression is that pure 'realism' is in our time almost played out, though most works of fiction of course will remain realistic *on the surface*. The single-track mind and the single-plane novel or play are almost bound to falsify the world in which we live. The fact that there is method in madness and the fact that there is fact in fantasy (and equally fantasy in 'fact') have been brought home to us not only by Freud and other psychologists but by events themselves. This being so, reportage can no longer masquerade as art. So the novelist, abandoning the 'straight' method of photography, is likely to resort once more not only to the twist of plot but to all kinds of other twists which may help him to do justice to the world's complexity. Some element of parable therefore, far from making a work thinner and more abstract, ought to make it more concrete. Man does after all live by symbols.

The dual-plane work will not normally be allegory in the algebraic sense; i.e. it will not be desirable or even possible to equate each of the outward and visible signs with a precise or rational inner meaning. Thus *The Dark Tower* was suggested to me by Browning's poem 'Childe Roland to the Dark Tower came', a work which does not admit of a completely rational analysis and still less adds up to any clear moral or message. This poem has the solidity of a dream; the writer of such a poem, though he may be aware of the 'meanings' implicit in his dream, must not take the dream to pieces, must present his characters concretely, must allow the story to persist as a story and not dwindle into a diagram. While I could therefore have offered here an explicit summary of those implicit 'meanings' in *The Dark Tower* of which I myself was conscious, I am not doing so, because it might impair the impact of the play. I would merely say—for the benefit of people like the *Daily Worker's* radio critic, who found the programme pointless and depressing—that in my opinion it is neither. *The Faerie Queene*, *The Pilgrim's Progress*, *Piers Plowman* and the early Moralities could not have been written by men without any beliefs. In an age which precludes the simple and militant faith of a Bunyan, belief (whether consciously formulated or not) still remains a *sine qua non* of the creative writer. I have my beliefs and they permeate *The Dark Tower*. But do not ask me what Ism it illustrates or what Solution it offers. You do not normally ask for such things in the single-plane work; why should they be forced upon something much more complex? 'Why, look you now, how unworthy a thing you make of me!' What is life *useful* for anyway?

Comments on points of detail will be found at the end of this book. The best in this kind are but shadows—and in print they are shadows of shadows. To help the reader to *hear* this piece, I will therefore add this: in production I got the actors to play their parts 'straight', i.e. like flesh and blood (in dreams the characters are usually like flesh and blood too). Out of an excellent cast I am particularly grateful to Cyril Cusack for his most sensitive rendering of 'Roland'. And Benjamin Britten provided this programme with music which is, I think, the best I have heard in a radio play. Without his music *The Dark Tower* lacks a dimension.

THE DARK TOWER

*The Dark Tower. The programme which follows is a parable play—
suggested by Robert Browning's poem 'Childe Roland to the Dark Tower
came'. The theme is the ancient but ever-green theme of the Quest—the
dedicated adventure; the manner of presentation is that of a dream—but
a dream that is full of meaning. Browning's poem ends with a challenge
blown on a trumpet :*

> 'And yet
> Dauntless the slughorn to my lips I set
> And blew. "Childe Roland to the Dark Tower came".'

*Note well the words 'And yet'. Roland did not have to—he did not wish
to—and yet in the end he came to : The Dark Tower.*

(*A trumpet plays through the Challenge Call.*)

SERGEANT-TRUMPETER.
> There now, that's the challenge. And mark this:
> Always hold the note at the end.

GAVIN. Yes, Sergeant-Trumpeter, yes.

ROLAND (*as a boy*).
> Why need Gavin hold the note at the end?

SERGEANT-TRUMPETER.
> Ach, ye're too young to know. It's all tradition.

ROLAND. What's tradition, Sergeant-Trumpeter?

GAVIN. Ask Mother that one (*with a half-laugh*). She knows.

SERGEANT-TRUMPETER.
> Aye, *she* knows.
> But run along, sonny. Leave your brother to practise.
> (*The trumpet begins—but breaks off.*)

SERGEANT-TRUMPETER.
> No. Again.
> (*The trumpet re-begins—breaks off.*)

SERGEANT-TRUMPETER.

Again.

(*The trumpet re-begins and is sustained.*)

SERGEANT-TRUMPETER.

That's it now. But hold that last note—hold it!

(*On the long last note the trumpet fades into the distance.*)

ROLAND. Mother! What's tradition?

MOTHER. Hand me that album. No—the black one.

ROLAND. Not the locked one!

MOTHER. Yes, the locked one. I have the key.

Now, Roland, sit here by me on the sofa.

We'll look at them backwards.

ROLAND. Why must we look at them backwards?

MOTHER. Because then you may recognise—

Now! You know who this is?

ROLAND. Why, that's my brother Michael.

And here's my brother Henry!

Michael and Henry and Denis and Roger and John!

(*He speaks with the bright callousness of children.*)

Do you keep this album locked because they're dead?

MOTHER. No . . . not exactly.

Now—can you guess who this is?

ROLAND. That's someone I saw in a dream once.

MOTHER. It must have been in a dream.

He left this house three months before you were born.

ROLAND. Is it . . . is it my father?

MOTHER. Yes. And this is your grandfather. And this is *his*
father—

For the time being you needn't look at the rest;

This book goes back through seven long generations

As far as George the founder of the family.

ROLAND. And did they all die the same way?

MOTHER. They did, Roland. And now I've answered your question.

ROLAND (*already forgetting*).

>What question, Mother?

>>(*The trumpet call is heard in the distance.*)

ROLAND. Ah, there's Gavin practising.

>He's got it right at last.

>>(*The Call ends and Gavin appears.*)

GAVIN (*excited*).

>Mother! I know the challenge. When can I leave?
>Tomorrow?

MOTHER. Why not today, Gavin?

GAVIN. Today! But I haven't yet checked my equipment;
>I mean—for such a long journey I—

MOTHER. You will travel light, my son.

GAVIN. Well, yes . . . of course . . . today then.

ROLAND. Where are you going, Gavin?

GAVIN. Why, surely you know; I'm—

MOTHER. Hsh!

ROLAND. I know where he's going. Across the sea like Michael.

GAVIN. That's right, Roland. Across the big, bad sea.
>Like Michael and Henry and Denis and Roger and
>John.
>And after that through the Forest.
>And after that through the Desert—

ROLAND. What's the Desert made of?

GAVIN. Well . . . I've never been there.
>Some deserts are made of sand and some are made of
>grit but—

MOTHER (*as if to herself*).

>This one is made of doubts and dried-up hopes.

ROLAND (*still bright*).

>And what do you find at the other end of the desert?

GAVIN. Well, I . . . well . . .

MOTHER. You can tell him.

GAVIN. I find the Dark Tower.

The Dark Tower

(The Dark Tower theme gives a musical transition to the schoolroom.)

TUTOR. Now, Master Roland, as this is our first day of lessons
I trust I shall find you as willing a pupil
As your six brothers before you.

ROLAND. Did you like teaching my brothers?

TUTOR. Like it? It was an honour.
It was teaching to some purpose.

ROLAND. When's my brother Gavin coming back?

TUTOR. What!

ROLAND. Gavin. When's he coming back?

TUTOR. Roland! . . .
I see I must start from the beginning.
I thought your mother'd have told you but maybe
being the youngest—

ROLAND. What would my mother have told me?

TUTOR. You ask when your brother Gavin is coming back?
You must get this straight from the start:
Your family never come back.

(Roland begins to interrupt.)

TUTOR. Now, now, now, don't let me scare you.
Sit down on that stool and I'll try to explain.
Now, Roland—
I said that to teach your brothers was an honour.
Before your mother engaged me to tutor John
I was an usher in a great city,
I taught two dozen lads in a class—
The sons of careerists—salesmen, middlemen, half-
men,
Governed by greed and caution; it was my job
To teach them enough—and only enough—
To fit them for making money. Means to a means.
But with your family it is a means to an end.

ROLAND *(naïvely puzzled).*
My family don't make money?

26

TUTOR. They make history.

ROLAND. And what do you mean by an end?

TUTOR. I mean—surely they told you?
I mean: the Dark Tower.

ROLAND. Will *I* ever go to the Dark Tower?

TUTOR. Of course you will. That is why I am here.

ROLAND (*gaily*).
Oh well! That's different!

TUTOR. It is.

ROLAND. And that means I'll fight the Dragon?

TUTOR. Yes—but let me tell you:
We call it the Dragon for short, it is a nameless force
Hard to define—for no one who has seen it,
Apart from those who have seen its handiwork,
Has returned to give an account of it.
All that we know is there is something there
Which makes the Dark Tower dark and is the source
Of evil through the world. It is immortal
But men must try to kill it—and keep on trying
So long as we would be human.

ROLAND. What would happen
If we just let it alone?

TUTOR. Well . . . some of us would live longer; all of us
Would lead a degraded life, for the Dragon would be
supreme
Over our minds as well as our bodies. Gavin—
And Michael and Henry and Denis and Roger and
John—
Might still be here—perhaps your father too,
He would be seventy-five—but mark this well:
They would not be themselves. Do you understand?

ROLAND. I'm not quite sure, I . . .

TUTOR. You are still small. We'll talk of the Dragon later.
Now come to the blackboard and we'll try some Latin.

You see this sentence?

ROLAND. Per ardúa . . .

TUTOR. Per ardua ad astra.

ROLAND. What does it mean?

TUTOR. It does not go very well in a modern language.

We had a word 'honour'—but it is obsolete.

Try the word 'duty'; and there's another word—
'Necessity'.

ROLAND. Necessity! That's a bit hard to spell.

TUTOR. You'll have to spell it, I fear. Repeat this after me:
N—

ROLAND. N—

TUTOR. E—

ROLAND. E—

(*As they spell it through, their voices dwindle away and a tolling bell
grows up out of the distance.*)

SERGEANT-TRUMPETER.

Ah God, there's the bell for Gavin.

He had the greatest power to his lungs of the lot of
them.

And now he's another name in the roll of honour

Where Michael's is still new gold. Five years it is—

Or would it be more like six—since we tolled for
Michael?

Bells and trumpets, trumpets and bells,

I'll have to be learning the young one next;

Then he'll be away too and my lady will have no more.

MOTHER (*coldly; she has come up behind him*).

No more children, Sergeant-Trumpeter?

SERGEANT-TRUMPETER.

Ach, I beg your pardon. I didn't see you.

MOTHER. No matter. But know this:

I have one more child to bear.

No, I'm not mad; you needn't stare at me, Sergeant.

The Dark Tower

This is a child of stone.

SERGEANT-TRUMPETER.

A child of . . . ?

MOTHER. Stone. To be born on my death-bed.

No matter. I'm speaking in metaphor.

SERGEANT-TRUMPETER (*relieved to change the subject*).

That's all right then. How's young Roland
Making out at his lessons?

MOTHER. I don't know. Roland lacks concentration; he's not
like my other sons,

He's almost flippant, he's always asking questions—

SERGEANT-TRUMPETER.

Ach, he's young yet.

MOTHER. Gavin was his age once.

So were Michael and Henry and Denis and Roger and
John.

They never forgot what they learnt. And they asked
no questions.

SERGEANT-TRUMPETER.

Ah well—by the time that Roland comes to me
When he's had his fill of theory and is all set for
action,

In another half dozen years when he comes to learn
the trumpet call—

MOTHER. Hsh, don't talk of it now.

(*as if to herself*).

Let one bell toll at a time.

(*The bell recedes into nothing, covering a passage of years. Roland is now
grown up.*)

TUTOR. So ends our course on ethics. Thank you, Roland;
After all these years our syllabus is concluded.
You have a brain; what remains to be tried is your will.
Remember our point today: the sensitive man
Is the more exposed to seduction. In six years

29

I have come to know you; you have a warm heart—
It is perhaps too warm for a man with your com-
    mission,
Therefore be careful. Keep to your one resolve,
Your single code of conduct, listen to no one
Who doubts your values—and above all, Roland,
Never fall in love—That is not for you.
If ever a hint of love should enter your heart,
You must arise and go . . . . That's it: Go!
Yes, Roland my son. Go quickly.

(*His last words fade slightly and Sylvie's voice fades in.*)

SYLVIE. But why must you go so quickly? Now that the sun's
    come out.

ROLAND. I have my lesson to learn.

SYLVIE. You're always learning lessons!
    I'll begin to think you prefer your books to me.

ROLAND. Oh, but Sylvie, this isn't books any more.

SYLVIE. Not books? Then—

ROLAND. I'm learning to play the trumpet.

SYLVIE (*irritated*).
    Whatever for? Roland, you make me laugh.
    Is this another idea of your mother's?
    I needn't ask. What's all this leading to?

ROLAND (*quietly*).
    I could tell you, darling. But not today.
    Today is a thing in itself—apart from the future.
    Whatever follows, I will remember this tree
    With this dazzle of sun and shadow—and I will
        remember
    The mayflies jigging above us in the delight
    Of the dying instant—and I'll remember *you*
    With the bronze lights in your hair.

SYLVIE. Yes, darling; but why so sad?
    There will be other trees and—

ROLAND. Each tree is itself, each moment is itself,
    Inviolable gifts of time . . . of God—
    But you cannot take them with you.

SYLVIE. Take them with you where?

ROLAND. Kiss me, Sylvie. I'm keeping my teacher waiting.
    (*The Challenge Call is played through once.*)

SERGEANT-TRUMPETER.
    Nicely blown! Nicely blown!
    You've graduated, my lad.
    But remember—when I'm not here—hold the note
      at the end.

ROLAND. (*a shade bitter*).
    You mean when *I'm* not here.

SERGEANT-TRUMPETER.
    Aye, you're right. But you are my last pupil,
    I'll be shutting up shop, I want you to do me credit.
    When you've crossed the sea and the desert and come
      to the place itself
    I want you to do me credit when you unsling that
      horn.

ROLAND. I hope I will.
    (*He pauses; then slightly embarrassed.*)

ROLAND. Sergeant?

SERGEANT-TRUMPETER.
    Eh?

ROLAND. Do you believe in all this?

SERGEANT-TRUMPETER.
    All what?

ROLAND. Do you think that there really is any dragon to fight?

SERGEANT-TRUMPETER.
    What are you saying! What was it killed Gavin?
    And Michael and Henry and Denis and Roger and John,
    And your father himself and his father before him and
      all of them back to George!

ROLAND. I don't know but . . . nobody's *seen* this dragon.

SERGEANT-TRUMPETER.

> Seen him? They've seen what he's done!
> Have you never talked to Blind Peter?
> I thought not. Cooped up here in the castle—
> Inside this big black ring of smothering yew-trees—
> You never mixed with the folk.
> But before you leave—if you want a reason for leaving—
> I recommend that you pay a call on Peter.
> And his house is low; mind your head as you enter.
>
> (*Another verbal transition.*)

BLIND PETER (*old and broken*).

> That's right, sir; mind your head as you enter.
> Now take that chair, it's the only one with springs,
> I saved it from my hey-day. Well now, sir,
> It's kind of you to visit me. I can tell
> By your voice alone that you're your father's son;
> Your handshake's not so strong though.

ROLAND. Why, was my father—

BLIND PETER.

> He had a grip of iron.
> And what's more, sir, he had a will of iron.
> And what's still more again, he had a conscience—
> Which is something we all need. *I* should know!

ROLAND. Why?

BLIND PETER.

> Why what?

ROLAND. Why do you sound so sad when you talk about having a conscience?

BLIND PETER.

> Because his conscience is something a man can lose.
> It's cold in here, I'll make a long story short.
> Fifty years ago when I had my sight—

But the Dragon was loose at the time—
I had a job and a wife and a new-born child
And I believed in God. Until one day—
I told you the Dragon was loose at the time,
No one had challenged him lately; so he came out
    from his den—
What some people call the Tower—and creeping
    around
He got to our part of the world; nobody saw him of
    course,
There was just like a kind of a bad smell in the air
And everything went sour; people's mouths and eyes
Changed their look overnight—and the government
    changed too—
And as for me I woke up feeling different
And when I looked in the mirror that first morning
The mirror said 'Informer'!

ROLAND (*startled*).

    Informer?

BLIND PETER.

    Yes, sir. My new rôle.
    They passed a pack of laws forbidding this and that
    And anyone breaking 'em—the penalty was death.
    I grew quite rich sending men to their death.
    The last I sent was my wife's father.

ROLAND. But . . . but did you believe in these laws?

BLIND PETER.

    Believe? Aha! Did I believe in anything?
    God had gone round the corner. I was acquiring
      riches.
    But to make a long story short—
    When they hanged my wife's father my wife took
      poison,
    So I was left with the child. Then the child took ill—

Scared me stiff—so I sent for all the doctors,
I could afford 'em then—but they couldn't discover
Anything wrong in its body, it was more as if its soul
Was set on quitting—and indeed why not?
To be a human being, people agree, is difficult.

ROLAND. Then the child . . . ?

BLIND PETER.

Quit.
Yes; she quit—but slowly.
I watched it happen. That's why now I'm blind.

ROLAND. Why? You don't mean you yourself—

BLIND PETER.

When you've seen certain things, you don't want to
see no more.
Tell me, sir. Are people's faces nowadays
As ugly as they were? You know what I mean: evil?

ROLAND. No, not most of them. *Some*, I suppose—

BLIND PETER.

Those ones belong to the Dragon.

ROLAND (*exasperated*).

Why put the blame of everything on the Dragon?
Men have free choice, haven't they?
Free choice of good or evil—

BLIND PETER.

That's just it—
And the evil choice is the Dragon!
But I needn't explain it to you, sir; *you've* made up
your mind,
You're like your father—one of the dedicated
Whose life is a quest, whose death is a victory.
Yes! God bless you! *You've* made up your mind!

ROLAND (*slowly and contemplatively*).

But have I, Peter? Have I?

(*Verbal transition.*)

34

SYLVIE. Have you, Roland dearest? Really made up your
    mind?

ROLAND (*without expression*).
    I go away today.

SYLVIE. That's no answer.
    You go away because they tell you to.
    Because your mother's brought you up on nothing
    But out of date beliefs and mock heroics.
    It's easy enough for her——

ROLAND (*indignantly*).
    Easy for her?
    Who's given her flesh and blood—and I'm the seventh
    son!

SYLVIE. I've heard all that. They call it sacrifice
    But each new death is a stone in a necklace to her.
    Your mother, Roland, is mad.

ROLAND (*with quiet conviction*).
    The world is mad.

SYLVIE. Not all of it, my love. Those who have power
    Are mad enough but there *are* people, Roland,
    Who keep themselves to themselves or rather to each
      other,
    Living a sane and gentle life in a forest nook or a hill
      pocket,
    Perpetuating their kind and their kindness, keeping
    Their hands clean and their eyes keen, at one
      with
    Themselves, each other and nature. I had thought
    That you and I perhaps——

ROLAND.   There is no perhaps
    In my tradition, Sylvie.

SYLVIE. You mean in your family's.
    Isn't it time you saw that you were different?
    You're no knight errant, Roland.

ROLAND. No, I'm not.

But there is a word 'Necessity'—

SYLVIE. Necessity? You mean your mother's orders.

ROLAND (*controlled*).

Not quite. But apart from that,

I saw a man today—they call him Blind Peter—

SYLVIE. Leave the blind to mislead the blind. That Peter

Is where he is because of his own weakness;

You can't help him, Roland.

ROLAND. Maybe not—

(*with sudden insight*).

But maybe I can do something to prevent

A recurrence of Blind Peters.

SYLVIE. Imagination!

ROLAND. Imagination? . . . That things can be bettered?

That action can be worth-while? That there are ends

Which, even if not reached, are worth approaching?

Imagination? Yes, I wish I had it—

I have a little—You should support that little

And not support my doubts.

(*A drum-roll is heard.*)

ROLAND. Listen; there is the drum.

They are waiting for me at the gate.

Sylvie, I—

SYLVIE. Kiss me at least.

(*Pause, while the drum changes rhythm.*)

ROLAND. I shall never—

SYLVIE. See me again?

You will, Roland, you will.

I know you. You will set out but you won't go on,

Your common sense will triumph, you'll come back.

And your love for me will triumph and in the end—

ROLAND. This is the end. Goodbye.

(*The drum swells and ends on a peak. This is the Scene of Departure.*)

TUTOR. To you, Roland, my last message:

    For seven years I have been your tutor.

    You have worked hard on the whole but whether really

    You have grasped the point of it all remains to be seen.

    A man lives on a sliding staircase—

    Sliding downwards, remember; to be a man

    He has to climb against it, keeping level

    Or even ascending slightly; he will not reach

    The top—if there is a top—and when he dies

    He will slump and go down regardless. All the same

    While he lives he must climb. Remember that.

    And I thank you for your attention. Goodbye, Roland.

SERGEANT-TRUMPETER.

    To you, Roland, my last message:

    You are off now on the Quest like your brothers before you

    To take a slap at the Evil that never dies.

    Well, here's this trumpet; sling it around your waist

    And keep it bright and clean till the time comes

    When you have to sound the challenge—the first and the last time—

    And I trust you will do your old instructor credit

    And put the fear of God—or of Man—into that Dragon.

    That's all now. God bless you. But remember—

    Hold that note at the end.

MOTHER. To you, Roland, my last message:

    Here is a ring with a blood-red stone. So long as

    This stone retains its colour, it means that I

    Retain my purpose in sending you on the Quest.

    I put it now on your finger.

ROLAND. Mother! It burns.

MOTHER. That is the heat in the stone. So long as the stone is
red
The ring will burn and that small circle of fire
Around your little finger will be also
The circle of my will around your mind.
I gave a ring like this to your father, Roland,
And to John and Roger and Denis and Henry and
Michael
And to Gavin the last before you. My will was around
and behind them.
Should ever you doubt or waver, look at this ring—
And feel it burn—and go on.

ROLAND. Mother! Before I go—

MOTHER. No more words. Go!
Turn your face to the sea. (*Raising her voice.*) Open
the gates there!
(*aside*) The March of Departure, Sergeant.
Let my son go out—my last. And make the music gay!

(*The March begins at full volume, then gradually dwindles as
Roland and the listener move away. By the time the music has
vanished Roland has reached the Port, where he addresses a
stranger.*)

ROLAND. Forgive me stopping you, sir—

SOAK (*old, alcoholic, leering*).
Forgive you? Certainly not.
I'm on my way to the Tavern.

ROLAND. I'm on my way to the quays. Is it this turning or next?

SOAK. Any turning you like. Look down these stinking
streets—
There's sea at the end of each of 'em.
Yes, young man, but what's at the end of the sea?
Never believe what they said when you booked your
passage.

ROLAND. But I haven't booked it yet.

SOAK. Not booked your passage yet! Why, then there's no
need to hurry.

You come with me to the Tavern; it's only a step.

ROLAND. I cannot spare a step.

SOAK. All right, all right;

If you won't come to the Tavern, the Tavern must
come to you.

Ho there, music!

(*The orchestra strikes up raggedly—continuing while he speaks.*)

SOAK. That's the idea. Music does wonders, young man.

Music can build a palace, let alone a pub.

Come on, you masons of the Muses, swing it,

Fling me up four walls. Now, now, don't drop your
tempo;

Easy with those hods. All right; four walls.

Now benches—tables—No! No doors or windows.

What drunk wants daylight? But you've left out the bar.

Come on—'Cellos! Percussion! All of you! A bar!

That's right. Dismiss!

(*The music ends.*)

SOAK. Barmaid.

BARMAID. Yes, sir?

SOAK. Give us whatever you have and make it triple.

ROLAND. Just a small one for me, please.

SOAK. Oh don't be so objective. One would think,

Looking at your long face, that there's a war on.

ROLAND. But—

SOAK. There is no war on—and you have no face.

Drink up. Don't be objective.

ROLAND. What in the name of—

BARMAID. Look, dearie; don't mind *him*.

He always talks like that. You take my tip;

You're new here and this town is a sea-port,

The tone is rather . . . . You go somewhere inland.

ROLAND. But how can I?

I have to go to sea.

BARMAID (*seriously*).

The sea out there leads nowhere.

SOAK. Come, sweetheart, the same again.

BARMAID. Nowhere, I've warned you. (*In a whisper.*) As for our
friend here,

Don't stay too long in his company.

SOAK. What's that? Don't stay too long in my what?

BARMAID. Company was the word.

SOAK. Company? I have none. Why, how could I?

There's never anyone around where I am.

I exist for myself and all the rest is projection.

Come on, projection, drink! Dance on your strings
and drink!

BARMAID. Oblige him, dearie, oblige him.

SOAK. There! My projection drinks.

I wrote this farce before I was born, you know—

This puppet play. In my mother's womb, dear boy—

I have never abdicated the life of the womb.

Watch, Mabel: my new puppet drinks again—

A pretty boy but I've given him no more lines.

Have I, young man?

(*pause*)

You see, he cannot speak.

All he can do henceforward is to drink—

Look! A pull on the wire—the elbow lifts.

Give him the same again.

BARMAID. Well . . . .

SOAK. There is no well about it. Except the well

That has no bottom and that fills the world.

Triplets, I said. Where are those damned musicians?

Buck up, you puppets! Play!

(*The orchestra strikes up a lullaby, continued behind his speech.*)

The Dark Tower

SOAK (*sleepily*).

> Good. Serenade me now till I fall asleep
> And all the notes are one—and all the sounds are
> silence.
> Unity, Mabel, unity is my motto.
> The end of drink is a whole without any parts—
> A great black sponge of night that fills the world
> And when you squeeze it, Mabel, it drips inwards.
> D'you want me to squeeze it? Right. Piano there.
> Piano—I must sleep. Didn't you hear me?
> Piano, puppets. All right, pianissimo.
> Nissimo . . . nissimo . . . issimo . . . .
> (*The music ends and only his snoring is heard.*)

ROLAND.

> A puppet? . . . A projection? . . . How he lies!
> And yet I've sometimes thought the same, you
> know—
> The same but the other way round.
> There is no evidence for anything
> Except my own existence—he says his.
> But he's wrong anyway—look at him snoring there.
> If I were something existing in his mind
> How could I go on now that he's asleep?

SOAK (*muffled*).

> Because I'm dreaming you.

ROLAND. Dreaming?

BARMAID.

> Yes, sir.
> He does have curious dreams.

SOAK.

> Yes, and the curious thing about my dreams
> Is that they always have an unhappy ending
> For all except the dreamer. Thus at the moment
> You'd never guess, young man, what rôle I've cast
> you for—

ROLAND. What the—

BARMAID. Never mind, dear.

41

Tomorrow he'll wake up.

ROLAND. Tomorrow *he'll* wake up?

And I—Shall I wake up? Perhaps to find

That this whole Quest is a dream. Perhaps I'm still at home

In my bed by the window looking across the valley

Between the yew-trees to where Sylvie lives

Not among yews but apples—

(*He is interrupted by a terrific voice crashing in on the 'Bar' from the outer world.*)

STENTOR. All Aboard!

ROLAND. What's that?

STENTOR. All Aboard!

SOAK. You'd never guess

What happens in my dream . . . .

STENTOR. All Aboard! All Aboard!

Come along there, young man—unless you want to be left.

All Aboard for the Further Side of the Sea,

For the Dead End of the World and the Bourne of No Return!

(*The noise of a crowd materialises, increasing.*)

STENTOR. All Aboard, ladies and gents, knaves and fools, babes and sucklings,

Philistines, pharisees, parasites, pimps,

Nymphos and dipsos—All Aboard!

Lost souls and broken bodies; make it snappy.

That's right, folks. Mind your feet on the gangway.

(*Through the racket of gadarening passengers is heard the mechanical voice of the Ticket Collector.*)

TICKET COLLECTOR.

Ticket? Thank you . . . Ticket? Thank you . . .

Ticket? Thank you . . . Ticket? Thank you . . . .

(*The crowd noises fade out; Roland is now below decks.*)

STEWARD (*with an 'off-straight' accent*).

      This way, sir. Let me show you your stateroom.

      Hot and cold and a blue light over the bed.

      Ring once for a drink, twice for an aspirin.

      Now if you want anything else—a manicure, for example—

ROLAND. No, steward. A sleeping draught.

STEWARD (*archly*).

      Sir! In the morning?

ROLAND. Morning be damned. My head aches.

STEWARD. Drinking last night, sir?

ROLAND. Thinking.

STEWARD (*rattling it off*).

      Thinking? That's too bad, sir.

      But you'll soon get over that, sir.

      In this ship nobody thinks, sir.

      Why should they? They're at sea, sir . . .

      And if your brain's at sea, sir—

ROLAND (*angrily*).

      Listen! I want a sleeping draught.

      How many times do I have to ring for that?

STEWARD (*unperturbed*).

      As many times as you like, sir.

      If you can keep awake, sir.

(*pimpishly*) But talking of sleeping draughts, sir,

      Do you hear that lady playing the fiddle?

ROLAND. Fiddle? No. I don't.

STEWARD. Ah, that's because she plays it in her head.

      But she's a very nice lady, sir.

      Her name, sir, is Neaera.

ROLAND. Why should I care what her name is?

      I tell you, steward—

STEWARD. Of course if you'd rather play tombola—

ROLAND. Tombola?

STEWARD (*throwing it away*).

> Game of chance, sir. They call out numbers.
> Kills the time, sir. Rather like life, sir.
> You can buy your tickets now in the lounge.
> The ship's started, you know, sir.

ROLAND. Oh, so the ship's started?

(*worried*) But I can't hear the engines.

STEWARD. Can't you, sir? I was right then.

ROLAND. Right? What do you mean?

STEWARD. I thought so the moment I saw you.

> You don't, sir; of course you don't.

ROLAND. Don't what, damn you? Don't what?

STEWARD. *You* don't know where you're going, sir.

> (*The ship's engines are heard on the orchestra; from them emerges
> the chatter of the lounge with the banal laughter of tombola
> players.*)

OFFICER. Clickety-click; sixty-six . . .

> Kelly's Eye: Number One . . .
> And we—

CROWD (*raggedly*).

> Shake the Bag!
> (*The orchestral engines give place to a solo violin.*)

NEAERA (*to herself, velvety*).

> . . . Andantino . . . rallentando . . . adagio—
> (*Her violin-playing breaks off.*)

NEAERA (*foreign accent*).

> Mon Dieu! You startled me.

ROLAND. I'm sorry, I—

NEAERA (*cooingly*).

> Do sit down. So you're going Nowhere too?

ROLAND. On the contrary, Madam—

NEAERA. Call me Neaera.

ROLAND. But—

NEAERA. And I'll call you Roland.

ROLAND. How do you know my name?

NEAERA. A little bird told me. A swan, if you want to know;
He sang your name and he died.
That's right, sit down. I've seen your dossier too.

ROLAND. Seen my—

NEAERA. Oh yes, chéri. In the Captain's cabin.

ROLAND. But how can I have a dossier? I've done nothing.

NEAERA. That's just it. It's dull.
But the future part amuses me.
Oh yes, my dear, this dossier includes the future—
And you don't come out of it well.

ROLAND. What do you mean?

NEAERA. You never believed in this Quest of yours, you see—
The Dark Tower—the Dragon—all this blague.
That's why you were so easy to seduce
In the idle days at sea—the days that are just begin-
ning.

(Her violin begins again, then gives way to the lounge chatter, covering a passage of time.)

OFFICER. Key of the Door: Twenty-One!
Eleventh Hour: Eleven!
Ten Commandments: Nine!
Kelly's Eye: Number One!
And we—

CROWD. Shake the Bag!

(The violin re-emerges.)

NEAERA. . . . Lento . . . accelerando . . . presto . . . calando . . .
morendo . . . .

(The violin fades away; it is meant to have established an affaire between Roland and Neaera.)

STEWARD *(slyly)*.
Well, sir? So the lady is still practising.
Golden days, sir, golden days.
At sea, sir, have you noticed

The Dark Tower

One doesn't notice time?
You probably feel you just came on board yesterday
And yet you got your sea-legs weeks ago, sir.

ROLAND. Sea-legs? Why, this trip has been so calm
I've never felt—

STEWARD. That's right, sir; never feel.
There's nothing in life but profit and pleasure.
Allegro assai—some people plump for pleasure
But I now fancy the profit—

(*Receiving a tip.*)

Ah thank you, sir, thank you.
The sea today in the sun, sir, looks like what shall I
say, sir?

ROLAND. The sea today? A dance of golden sovereigns.

NEAERA. The sea today is adagios of doves.

ROLAND. The sea today is gulls and dolphins.

NEAERA. The sea today is noughts and crosses.

OFFICER (*cutting in rapidly*).

And we—

CROWD.   Shake the Bag!

NEAERA. The sea today, Roland, is crystal.

ROLAND. The sea today Neaera, is timeless.

NEAERA. The sea today is drums and fifes.

ROLAND. The sea today is broken bottles.

NEAERA. The sea today is snakes and ladders.

OFFICER (*as before*).

Especially snakes!

CROWD.   Especially snakes!

NEAERA (*wheedling*).

Roland, what's that ring? I've never seen one like it.

ROLAND. There is no other ring like it.

NEAERA. A strange ring for a man . . .
My colour, you know—that red . . .
Why do you twitch your finger?

46

The Dark Tower

ROLAND. Because it burns.

NEAERA. It burns?

Like tingling ears perhaps? Someone is thinking of
you.

ROLAND (*startled—and suddenly depressed*).

What? . . . I hope not.

(*changing the subject*)

Come, darling, let's have a drink.

OFFICER. And we—

CROWD. Shake the Bag!

ROLAND. The sea today is drunken marble.

NEAERA. The sea today is silver stallions.

ROLAND. The sea today is—Tell me, steward:

Where's all this floating seaweed come from?

STEWARD. I imagine, sir—forgive me mentioning it—

That we are approaching land.

ROLAND. Land!

STEWARD. Yes, sir—but *you* won't be landing of course.

The best people never land, sir.

ROLAND. No? . . . (*to himself, fatalistically*) I suppose not.

(*Neaera's violin is heard again.*)

NEAERA (*to herself*).

. . . piu sonoro . . . con forza . . . accelerando . . .

crescendo . . . .

(*The orchestra is added for a final crashing chord and at once we hear the
hubbub of a crowd.*)

STENTOR. Anyone more for the shore? Anyone more for the
shore?

Line up there on the forward deck

All what wants to chance their neck!

Anyone more for the shore?

TICKET COLLECTOR.

This way: thank you—This way: thank you—

This way: thank you—This way: thank you.

STENTOR. Anyone more? Hurry up please!
  But remember this: Once you're off
  You can't come back not ever on board.
  We leave at once. At once!

TICKET COLLECTOR.
  This way: thank you—This way: thank you—This
  way: thank you—This way: thank you.

1ST PASSENGER (*cockney*).
  Here, here, who're you shoving? What's the
  blinkin' hurry?

HIS WIFE. That's right.

1ST PASSENGER.
  Some people seem very keen to land in the future.
  Can't use their eyes—if you ask me!

HIS WIFE. That's right. Look at them vicious rocks.

1ST PASSENGER.
  And that tumble-down shack what thinks it's a
  Customs House.

HIS WIFE. And them horrible mountains behind it.

2ND PASSENGER (*northern*).
  You'd think this country was uninhabited.

TICKET COLLECTOR.
  This way: thank you—This way: thank you— (*with
  finality*) This way: thank *you*!

  (*wearily*) O.K., sir. That's the lot.

STENTOR. Gangway up! Gangway up!
  Clear away there. Mind your heads!

NEAERA. What are you staring at, Roland?
  Come away, chéri; the show's over.
  There goes the gangway; we're moving out now.
  What *are* you staring at, darling?

ROLAND (*to himself*).
  Was that . . . was that . . . I couldn't see in the face of
  the sun but—

Steward, you've sharp eyes.

Did you see over there on the quay, sitting on a rusty bollard—

STEWARD. Hsh, sir, Neaera will hear you.

Yes, sir; a very nice piece.

She was looking at you, sir, too—staring in fact, one might say.

Seems to be staring still—but what's she doing now?

Climbing up on the bollard?

Good Lord, sir, that's bad form; she's making gestures.

SYLVIE (*distant cry*).

Roland! . . . Roland! . . .

ROLAND. Sylvie!

I knew it. Out of my way there!

STENTOR. Here, here, here! Stop him!

Man gone mad there! Don't let him jump!

(*General commotion.*)

NEAERA. Roland! Come back!

(*A loud splash from the orchestra.*)

STENTOR. Man overboard! Man overboard!

(*The crowd reacts excitedly.*)

STENTOR. Lifebuoy! Where's the lifebuoy?

VOICE. Garn! This here ship don't carry no lifebuoys.

Nor he won't need one. Look! He's climbing up on the quay.

(*The orchestral engines start up again.*)

OFFICER (*triumphantly*).

And we—

CROWD. Shake the Bag!

NEAERA (*now revealing her hardness*).

Well, James . . . That's that.

STEWARD. Yes, madam.

NEAERA. You can drop the madam now.

STEWARD. Yes, Neaera—my sweetie-pie.

NEAERA (*matter-of-fact*).

    That's more like it, James, my great big he-man.

    Come to my cabin now; we'll count the takings.

(*The fading engines take the liner to sea; Roland is left on the Shore, with Sylvie sobbing.*)

ROLAND (*dead-pan*).

    There she goes now.

SYLVIE (*echoing him*).

    There she goes now . . . .

                (*then bursting out*)

    Roland, you are a hypocrite!

ROLAND (*quietly—but ashamed*).

    No, Sylvie; merely a sleep-walker.

    Ugh! (*He shivers.*)

SYLVIE (*calm again*).

    The sea must have been cold. Come, let's walk.

ROLAND. How did you get here, Sylvie?

SYLVIE (*a shade bitter*).

    I followed you—but not on a luxury liner.

    Mine was a cargo boat, its limit was seven knots.

ROLAND. And yet you got here first.

    And now I suppose you regret it.

    Are you going to leave me, Sylvie?

SYLVIE. How can I? We're marooned here.

    This is a desolate land. (*With forced control*) I suggest we keep together.

ROLAND. You have the gift of forgiveness.

SYLVIE. I have the gift of common sense.

    As you're bound to be seduced from your so-called Quest,

    In future, Roland, leave the seducing to me.

    Or can't I, perhaps, compete with your ladies of pleasure?

ROLAND. Pleasure ? That was not pleasure.

SYLVIE. It was. But it was not happiness.

ROLAND. And *you* offer me happiness ?

SYLVIE. You doubt that I have it to offer ?

ROLAND. No, I don't doubt that. But my tutor always said
Happiness cannot be taken as a present.

SYLVIE. Forget your tutor. This is a foreign land
Where no one will interfere with us.

ROLAND. No one ? No *man* perhaps.

SYLVIE. What do you mean by that ?

ROLAND. Look round you, Sylvie. See the deserted port,
The ruined shacks, the slag-heaps covered with lichen
And behind it all the frown and fear of the forest.
This is the Dragon's demesne.

SYLVIE. Roland, how childish you are.

ROLAND. You think so ? Look at this notice
That flaps here on the hoarding—
And this one and this one and this one.

SYLVIE (*reading*).
'Wanted for Murder' . . . 'Wanted for Murder' . . .
'Wanted'—

ROLAND. You're reading the words wrong. Not 'for', Sylvie;
'to!'

SYLVIE. 'Wanted to Murder'. You're right.
But what does it mean ?

ROLAND. It means we are on a soil where murder pays.

SYLVIE. It pays in many places.

ROLAND. Yes, but here
The paymaster is the government—and pay-day
Is every day of the week.
The Dragon's doing, I tell you.

SYLVIE. Well, if it is, *you* cannot cure it.
At the best you can cure yourself—

(*tentatively*) And that only through love.

51

ROLAND. Love?

SYLVIE (*stronger*).

    Through me, Roland, through me.

        (*pause*)

ROLAND (*quietly*, *as if solving a problem*).

    Yes, I think you're right.

        (*Then with sudden decisiveness*)

    Sylvie, take this ring; I cannot wear it now,

    I have failed this ring—but this ring will not fail you.

SYLVIE. You mean . . . ?

ROLAND. Yes. Let me put it on your finger.

SYLVIE. Not yet, Roland. That must be done in a church.

ROLAND. And where can we find a church round here?

SYLVIE (*half abstracted*).

    What a strange colour. Like the blood of a child.

ROLAND. I repeat! Where can we find a church or a chapel here?

    (*The Tout pops up. He speaks in broken English.*)

TOUT. 'Scusa. Lady and gentleman want guide to chapel?

ROLAND. God! Where did this come from?

TOUT. Me? Me come from sewer.

    Me accredited guide—very good, very funny.

    Lady and gentleman see chapel today?

ROLAND. Where is this chapel of yours?

TOUT. Chapel not mine, chapel belong to God.

    Me take you there up this road, see.

    Me tell you history, very much history, cheap.

    (*A distant bell is heard, which continues as they speak.*)

TOUT. That chapel bell, tee-hee!

    Ting-a-ling for the wedding!

ROLAND. What wedding?

TOUT. Me not know. No, sir, nobody know.

    Happy pair not come yet.

SYLVIE. Roland, this is a sign.

    Tell him to show us the way.

The Dark Tower

TOUT. Me show you the way sure.

Beautiful lady put best foot first.

Chapel up there in forest.

ROLAND. In the forest?

TOUT. Sure, boss. Chapel old.

Chapel in forest before forest grew.

But needs repairs now bad.

Haunted too—tee-hee!

ROLAND. Haunted!

TOUT. Sure, boss.

Plenty ghosts—tu-whit, tu-whoo.

Me need bonus for them ghosts.

ROLAND. You'll have your bonus. Only get us there quick.

Sylvie, we will exorcise these ghosts.

You know how, my dearest?

SYLVIE (*heart-felt*).

I know how.

(*The bell continues but is gradually submerged by orchestral chapel music. The latter swells to a definite close, leaving Roland and Sylvie in the Haunted Chapel. The voices echo in the emptiness.*)

PRIEST (*old and tired but kindly*).

You have the ring? Good.

Before I complete this ceremony making you man and
   wife

I must deliver a warning.

The original sin is doubt.

And in these days of contempt for the individual

It is also the topical sin.

So if either of you has doubts of the holiness of
   marriage

Or if either of you has doubts of the other

And can conceive a time when he or she

Will think again and wish this thing undone,

Now is your time to speak.

53

(*pause*)

Good. So you have no doubts. There is one other
    formality.

Although there is no congregation present,

Although apart from ourselves and a few sparrows
    and field-mice

This chapel is now empty, I must still put the
    question:

If anyone here know just cause or impediment—

(*He is interrupted by voices with a strange acoustic.*)

BLIND PETER'S VOICE.

    I do!

GAVIN'S VOICE.

    I do!

FATHER'S VOICE.

    I do!

BLIND PETER'S VOICE.

    This young man who's come to you to get married

    Promised me when he left, a week before I died,

    As he would avenge my blindness and bring it about

    How no one should go the way I went in future.

    Well, has he done it? No, and he'll never do it—

    Not if you splice him up to that poor simple girl

    Who only dreams how he and she will be happy.

GAVIN'S VOICE.

    No, Roland, my brother; Blind Peter is right.

    Forget your dreams of a home. You can never be
        happy

    If you forsake the Quest. And if you could—

    Happiness is not all. You must go on—

    Turn your back on this chapel, go on through the
        forest,

    Alone, always alone, and then across the desert,

    And at the other end of that desert—

The Dark Tower

FATHER'S VOICE (*very deep*).

  You will find what I found, Roland.

ROLAND. You?

FATHER'S VOICE.

  You should know my voice though you never heard it.

  Though you had not seen me, you knew my portrait.

ROLAND. My father?

FATHER'S VOICE.

  I am still waiting to be your father.

  While you malinger, you are no son of mine.

ROLAND (*shattered*).

  Sylvie . . . .

SYLVIE. I know what you want . . . Your ring.

 (*She tries to retain self-control in making her renunciation.*)

  There . . . Back on your finger.

  Look how it glows in this darkness.

ROLAND (*bitterly*).

  Glows? It will burn me up.

SYLVIE. Roland, before we part—

PRIEST. This chapel is now closed. I am sorry.

  Goodbye, my daughter; your way lies back,

  Back by the road you came over the hopeless sea,

  Back to your little house and your apple orchard

  And there must you marry one of your own kind

  And spray the trees in spring and raise the ladders in

   autumn

  And spread the shining crop on the spare-room floor

   and—

ROLAND. Sylvie, before we part—

PRIEST. This chapel is now closed. I am sorry.

  Goodbye, my son; your way lies forward,

  Forward through the gibbering guile of the forest,

  Forward through the silent doubt of the desert.

  And here let me warn you: if in the forest

You hear any voices call from the trees,
Pay no attention, Roland, pay no attention . . . .

(*His voice fades as forest music grows up; out of its tangle come the voices of the Birds, harsh and mechanical, speaking in a heavily stressed sing-song rhythm.*)

PARROT. Pretty Polly! Pretty Polly!
Who's this coming now?

RAVEN. Caw-caw! Caw-caw!
Who's a-walkin' in *my* forest?

PARROT. Pretty Polly! The leaves have fallen.

RAVEN. Caw-caw! He's walking late.

PARROT. Pretty Polly! He's looking pale.

RAVEN. Caw-caw! His bones will be paler.

PARROT. Pretty Polly! Here he comes.

RAVEN. Caw-caw! Greet him!

PARROT (*sneeringly*).
Where are you going, Roland, so fast?

RAVEN. Roland, running away from your past?

BOTH. You can't do *that*! You can't do *that*!

PARROT. Still on the road? Still on the Quest?

RAVEN. None achieve it but the best.

BOTH. You're not the sort. You're not the sort.

PARROT. Why not stop, my dear young man?

RAVEN. Let heroes die as heroes can.

BOTH. *You* must *live*! *You* must *live*!
(*The forest music swells up as Roland passes.*)

PARROT. Pretty Polly! He's passed us by.

RAVEN. Caw-caw! The devil take him.

PARROT. Pretty Polly! The devil will.

(*The forest music gives place to desert music and Roland is heard soliloquising.*)

ROLAND (*very tired*).
Oh this desert!
The forest was bad enough but this beats all.

The Dark Tower

When my tutor described it to me, it sounded strange
But now I am here, with the grit of it filling my shoes,
I find that the worst thing about it is this:
The desert is something familiar.
And with no end—no end.
(The music ends. A mechanical voice creeps in.)

CLOCK VOICE.

Tick Tock, Tick Tock,
Sand and grit, bones and waste,
A million hours—all the same,
A million minutes—each an hour,
And nothing stops for nothing starts
But the hands move, the dead hands move,
The desert is the only clock—
Tick Tock, Tick Tock,
Tick Tock, Tick Tock . . . .

*(The Clock Voice recedes but can just be heard ticking as Roland speaks,
with the Desert registering again musically.)*

ROLAND. Flat—No shape—No colour—Only here and there
A mirage of the past—something I've met before—
Figures arising from dust, repeating themselves,
Telling me things that I have no wish to remember.
Mirage . . . mirage . . . mirage . . . .
(The music ends and the Clock comes near again.)

CLOCK VOICE.

Tick Tock, Tick Tock,
Tick Tock, Tick Tock . . . .
(continuing in the background as the first mirage is heard.)

SOAK. A pretty boy—but I've given him no more lines.
He'd never guess what happens in my dream.
Look—a pull on the wire, his feet move forward.
Left Right, Left Right . . . .
*(He synchronises with the Clock Voice as it comes again into the
foreground.)*

CLOCK VOICE.⎱ Tick Tock etc.
SOAK.⎰ Left Right etc.

(They withdraw to the background as the second mirage appears.)

STEWARD. Golden days, sir, golden days.
          In the desert, sir, have you noticed
          One doesn't notice time?
          But I thought so the moment I saw you:
          You don't know where you're going.
          Golden days, golden days . . . .

(He synchronises with the Clock Voice and Soak—the same procedure.)

CLOCK VOICE.⎫ Tick Tock, etc.
SOAK.⎬ Left Right, etc.
STEWARD.⎭ Golden days, etc.

NEAERA. . . . adagio . . . rallentando . . .
          This dossier includes your future—
          You don't come out of it well.
          But kiss me, Roland, kiss me.
          Kiss me, kiss me . . . .
                (synchronises)

CLOCK VOICE.⎫ Tick Tock, etc.
SOAK.⎪ Left Right, etc.
STEWARD.⎬ Golden days, etc.
NEAERA.⎭ Kiss me, etc.

SYLVIE. But why must you go so quickly?
          Now that the sun's come out.
          You, Roland—you're no knight errant.
          Your love for me will triumph, you'll come back,
          Then you and I, you and I . . . .
                (synchronises)

CLOCK VOICE.⎫ Tick Tock, etc.
SOAK.⎪ Left Right, etc.
STEWARD.⎬ Golden days, etc.
NEAERA.⎪ Kiss me, etc.
SYLVIE.⎭ You and I, etc.

The Dark Tower

*(The five voices swell in the foreground, driving as it were at the camera,
till Roland can bear it no longer.)*

ROLAND *(screaming)*.

NO!

(The voices break off as if cut with a knife.)

ROLAND. Shapes of dust and fancy! Unreal voices!

But where is the voice that launched me on my
road?

Where is the shape the first that I remember?

Why doesn't *she* appear—even in fancy?

It is the least she could—Mother, where are you?

Yes, you; I'm calling you—my mother who sent me
forth—

It was all your doing. But for you

I who had no beliefs of my own,

I who had no will of my own,

Should not be here today pursuing

A dark tower that is only dark

Because it does not exist. And Mother!

It is only your will that drives me still

As signified in the blood-red stone

I wear on my finger under my glove

That burns me like a living weal.

(suddenly puzzled)

. . . Burns me? . . . Burns me? . . . . It always has—

But have I gone numb? I can feel nothing.

Off with this glove! I *can't* believe that—

(A chord from the orchestra.)

ROLAND. The ring! The ring!

The colour is gone; the blood has gone out of it.

But that must mean . . . that means . . . .

MOTHER'S VOICE *(in a different acoustic, whispering)*.

It means, my son, that I want you back.

ROLAND. And the Quest then?

MOTHER. Lapses.

> On my deathbed I have changed my mind;
> I am bearing now a child of stone.
> *He* can go on the Quest. But you, Roland—come back!

(A pause while Roland takes in the implications.)

ROLAND. The ring . . . is always right.

> Recall! Reprieve! A thousand years of sunshine!
> And the apples will be in bloom round Sylvie's house.
> Was that my mother's voice? Look at the ring.
> It is as pale as death, there is no more breach of duty,
> Her will is not behind me. Breach of duty?
> If she is dying, *there* is the breach of duty—
> Not to be there. Mother, you sent me out
> And I went out. Now that you call me back
> I will come back! The desert take this ring—
> It serves no further purpose!

(An orchestral clink as he throws away the ring.)

ROLAND *(startled)*.

> What was that?
> It must have struck something hard. That's the first
> Sound I've heard in the desert. Where did I throw
>   that ring?
> A stone? But a carved stone! Looks like a milestone.
> As if the desert had any use for milestones!

(with a hysterical half-laugh)

> How many miles to Babylon? Let's see now;
> These letters are choked with sand, 'To Those . . .
>   To Those . . .'

(He deciphers the inscription, reading it aloud slowly.)

> 'To Those Who Did Not Go Back—
> Whose Bones being Nowhere, their signature is for
>   All Men—
> Who went to their Death of their Own Free Will
> Bequeathing Free Will to Others.'

The Dark Tower

(The Bird Voices cut in, in a different acoustic, jeering.)

PARROT. Pretty Polly! A tall story!

RAVEN. Caw-caw! And not so new!

PARROT. Pretty Polly! Unknown warriors!

RAVEN. Caw-caw! Nobody cares!

PARROT. 'Who went to their death!'—Pretty Polly!

RAVEN. 'Of their own free will!'—Caw-caw!

ROLAND. Of their own free will? It wasn't like that with me.
It was my mother pushed me to this point
And now she pulls me back. Let's see this ring —
Where's it fallen? Hm. Yes, there's no mistake,
Red no longer: my mother wants me back
And indeed it is high time; this desert has no end
Nor even any contour, the blank horizon
Retreats and yet retreats; without either rise or fall
Repeats, retreats, defeats; there is no sign of a
tower—
You could see a tower for miles; there is not even a
knoll,
Flatness is all—and nothing. Own free will?

(He has been speaking quietly but now bursts out.)

As if I Roland had ever . . . . Tutors, trumpeters,
women,
Old soaks and crooked stewards, everyone I have met
Has played his music on me. Own free will!
Three words not one of which I understand!
All right, Mother dear, I'm coming.

(Pause.)

Now . . . Where are my footsteps? Better follow
them back.
Back to the forest and through it and so to the shore
of the sea.
Are these my footsteps? But how small they look!
Well, you're a small man, Roland—Better admit it—

You'll be still smaller now . . . But are these my
    footsteps?
They are so near together—and I thought
I was walking with great strides! O Roland, Roland,
You thought yourself a hero—and you walked
With little steps like that! Now you must watch
These niggling foot-prints all your return journey
To underline your shame. What's shame to me
Who never had free will? . . . 'their own free will
Bequeathing free will to others.' Others indeed!
I begin to think my drunken friend was right
In his subjective tavern; there are no others
Apart from the projections of my mind
And, once that mind is empty, man's a desert.

(*losing his temper*)

Others! Who are these others? Where can I find 'em?

CHILD'S VOICE (*out of the blue*).

Nowhere, Roland. Nowhere.

ROLAND. There! What did I say? There *are* no—

CHILD'S VOICE.

You will never find us if you go forward—
For you will be dead before we are born.
You will never find us if you go back—
For you will have killed us in the womb.

ROLAND. What! So I'm an infanticide now?

CHILD'S VOICE.

Not yet. But if you go back . . .

ROLAND. Who said I was going back?

CHILD'S VOICE.

I thought you had made up your mind.

ROLAND. I never make up my mind!

Didn't I say that my mother—Look, I'll leave it to
    chance;
Chance is as good an arbiter as any.

The Dark Tower

Watch me, you unborn children. See this tiny cactus?
I will strip it leaf by leaf—let that decide—
This Year, Next Year, Eena-Meena—*you* know the
    game, you unborn children.
Now.

(He counts in regular time, but with growing tension, as he picks off the
        leaves.)

Forward—back; forward—back; forward—back—
    forward;
Back—forward; back—forward; back—forward—
    back;
Forward—back; forward—back; forward—back—
    forward;
Back—forward; back—forward; back—forward—
    BACK.
There! The voice of chance. The oracle of the cactus.
Back! Back! That's what the cactus says.
But *I'm* . . .

   (He holds the suspense, then with decision.)
        . . . going forward, children!
Did you think that I'd let a cactus dictate to me?
Mother, don't pull on the string; you must die alone.
Forgive me, dear, but—I tell you I'm going forward.
Forward, Roland . . . into the empty desert,
Where all is flat and colourless and silent.

(He pauses; the orchestra creeps in with a heart-beat rhythm.)

Silent? . . . Then what's this?
Something new! A *sound*! But a sound of what?
Don't say that it's my heart! Why, Roland you poor
    fool,
Who would think you had one? You must be afraid;
It is fear reveals the heart.

            (Heart-beat louder.)

ROLAND. Aha, you piece of clockwork—

63

Trying to have your little say while you can!

Before your wheels run down here in the empty desert.

(*Sudden chord; the heart-beat continues.*)

Empty? . . . Where have those mountains come from?

Closing round in a ring. Hump-backed horrors

That want to be in at the death. And where's the horizon?

A moment ago this was level. What's the game?

A confidence trick? A trap! I am cooped in.

A circle of ugly cliffs—a lobster-pot of rock!

Silence, my stupid heart! This looks like . . . looks like what?

This looks like the great circus in Ancient Rome,

Only there is no audience—and no lions.

(*suddenly noticing*)

No audience?

(*Chord; heart-beat behind—and steadily increasing.*)

No audience! Why, that's Gavin on top of that peak!

And Michael and Denis and Henry and Roger and John!

And men that I've never seen—in outlandish clothes,

Some of them even in armour. And there's Blind Peter—

With sight in his eyes, for he's pointing—

And my father too—I remember him from the album—

And my tutor—he must be dead—looking graver than ever

And—well to the front of course—my dear old Sergeant-Trumpeter.

(*Figure in the music; the succeeding voices, other than Roland's own, sound as if coming from somewhere far-off and above.*)

SERGEANT-TRUMPETER.

Roland! Hold the note at the end.

The Dark Tower

GAVIN. Be ready, old boy. This is it!

BLIND PETER.

> Strike a good blow to avenge Blind Peter.

FATHER. Your heritage, my son. You were born to fight and—

ROLAND. Fight? Fight whom? This circus has no lions.

TUTOR. No lions, Roland? Have you forgotten your lessons?
> I never mentioned lions; it was a dragon—
> And only that for lack of a better name.

ROLAND. Yes, yes, dragon of course—but you told me, my
> good tutor,
> The Dragon would not appear until I came to the
> Tower
> And until I had blown my blast—Well, there is no
> tower!

GAVIN. That fooled *me*, Roland my brother.

FATHER. Look over there, Roland my son.

ROLAND. Where? . . . Oh *that* little thing?
> Like a wart coming out of the ground!

FATHER. It's growing, Roland, it's growing.

TUTOR. You should recognise it from my lectures.

BLIND PETER.

> That's the joker all right.

> (*Figure in the music.*)

GAVIN. The tower! The Dark Tower!

SERGEANT-TRUMPETER.

> Quick now, my lad. Unsling your trumpet.

ROLAND. But—

FATHER. It's growing, my son; waste no time.

ROLAND. It's growing; yes, it's growing.

CHILD'S VOICE.

> Growing! Ooh! Look at it.
> Strike a good blow for us unborn children.

MOTHER (*closer than the rest*).

> And strike a blow for all dead mothers.

E   65

The Dark Tower

GAVIN. Jump to it, Roland.

FATHER. Waste no time.

SERGEANT-TRUMPETER.
    Remember that challenge call.
    Blow it the way I taught you.

ROLAND (*beginning quiet but resolute and building*).
    Yes, dear friends, I will blow it the way you taught
      me.
    I Roland, the black sheep, the unbeliever—
    Who never did anything of his own free will—
    Will do this now to bequeath free will to others.
  (*full out*) Ahoy there, tower, Dark Tower, you're getting big,
    Your shadow is cold upon me. What of that?
    And you, you Dragon or whatever you are
    Who make men beasts, come out—here is a man;
    Come out and do your worst.

(*The heart-beat, having reached its crescendo, ends clean.*)

ROLAND (*restrained, in the sudden silence*).
    Wrist be steady
    As I raise the trumpet so—now fill my lungs—

(*The Challenge Call rings out; the Sergeant-Trumpeter speaks as the last
long note is reached.*)

SERGEANT-TRUMPETER.
    Good lad, Roland. Hold that note at the end.

(*The trumpet holds it, enriched and endorsed by the orchestra. They come
to a full close and that is* THE END.)

SUNBEAMS IN HIS HAT

a study of Tchehov
as a man

TO

LAURENCE GILLIAM

CAST

Sunbeams in his Hat was first broadcast[1] in the B.B.C. Home Service on July 16th, 1944. The main parts, in order of their appearance, were played as follows:

FRAU SCHMIDT	MARCELLA SALZER
OLGA KNIPPER	MARTITA HUNT
TCHEHOV	ALAN WHEATLEY
TCHEHOV'S FATHER	IVOR BARNARD
MASSEUR	RICHARD WILLIAMS*
GENERAL	CYRIL GARDINER*
NURSE	MOLLY RANKIN*
BOY IN SAHALIN	MALCOLM THOMAS
'DORN'	GERALD CASE*
TOLSTOY	ALEXANDER SARNER*
GORKI	DUNCAN MCINTYRE*
'ARTEM'	HARRY HUTCHISON*
NEMIROVICH-DANCHENKO	CHARLES MAUNSELL*
DR. SCHWÖRER	HOWARD MARION-CRAWFORD

Gregori Tcherniak played Russian folk tunes on the balalaika.

Production by the author.

[1] An earlier version entitled *Dr Chekhov* was produced by Stephen Potter for the B.B.C. on September 6th, 1941.

68

INTRODUCTORY NOTE

Sunbeams in his Hat is the only programme in this book which was properly a *feature*.[1] 'Feature', as distinct from 'play', is the B.B.C. name for a dramatised broadcast which is primarily either informative or propagandist (propaganda here being taken to include the emotive celebration of anniversaries and gestures of homage—or of hatred—to anyone or anything dead or alive). Features therefore, having an enormous diversity of subject, have also a great diversity of form. Some of them are as loosely constructed as scrap-books, others come near to the unities and emotional impact of a play. The script here published belongs to the comparatively clearcut type of feature-biography (or feature-historical-portrait). Tchehov was given to me as a subject for homage in 1941, and I rewrote the programme in 1944 for the anniversary of his death. It was assumed that, like all decent feature-biographers, I would give accurate information about him. My own special intention was to correct the popular fallacy which uses the word Tchehov as a synonym for melancholia and which, incidentally, vitiates so many English productions of his plays.

The basic problem of such a portrait is condensation[2]—how to select a few significant 'shots' and put them coherently together in a little space. For this programme I used the method of the *flash-back*. Beginning with Tchehov on the morning of the day of his death I ended with him that evening; phases of his earlier life were presented through flash-backs. This method can be confusing and irritating, though when it comes off it provides tension and unity. The flash-backs in *Sunbeams in his Hat* are not,

[1] The two March Hare programmes, being satirical topical fantasies (negative propaganda or un-homage), were also, I think correctly, classified as features—but they are far from being what the word evokes in the mind of a B.B.C. planner.

[2] In condensing here I fear I omitted much that was very important, e.g. Tchehov's early phase of hard and distasteful hack-work.

I think, confusing but I would not deny that they may irritate. If so, it is not so much the fault of the flash-back scenes themselves as of the lead-ins to them from the preceding scenes; it was in the character of both Tchehov and Olga Knipper to be reminiscent and exchange expressions of homesickness but such reminiscences, just because they come so pat, are only too likely to sound stoogey. Still they remain, I think, preferable to the cold-fish voice of the Narrator.

While in nearly all features some amount of invented detail is necessary—and transpositions in time and place are on occasion permitted—this Tchehov programme is based very closely on fact, even his terms of endearment having been cribbed from his letters. This amount of realism affected of course my writing of dialogue. In my Introduction to *Christopher Columbus* I wrote that 'the radio play (if not the radio feature) can only reach its heights when the subject is slightly larger, or at least simpler, than life and the treatment is to some extent 'stylised' '. I would now italicise that parenthesis and add that even with plays the remark may mislead (especially if 'heights' is taken as equivalent to excellence). Selection of material alone will obviously both simplify and to some extent 'stylise' but larger-than-lifeness need not be part of the recipe; in a programme called *He Had a Date* I attempted the chronicle of a fictitious young man of our time and characterised him throughout by understatement and, while I did not succeed with him, I see nothing wrong in the method (though I admit that *indiscriminate* understatement has ruined the modern theatre).

So with Tchehov, I never made him more articulate—or poetic—than he himself could have been. I aimed at a dialogue that should be easy but exact, that without appearing to press him should give away things to the listener. As to stylisation in the poetic sense, I did fall back at the end of the programme, where such effects seem more needed, on the device of a *dream* (though this dream itself was based on fact). For a dream, besides being of its nature foreboding, allows also the echoing—probably with a 'twist'—of voices heard before. This device, like the flash-back proper, can easily be abused. In another feature-portrait, of Lauro de Bosis, where the hero's whole last Act takes place in the solitude of an aeroplane, I used a similar trick at considerable length because so long a soliloquy was out of the question. But I had not this excuse with Tchehov. My real reason, I think, for introducing the dream of the River was to get a more supple transition, a better prelude to the death itself, than could have been contrived through any further dialogue between Tchehov and his wife—that is, if I kept her in character.

SUNBEAMS IN HIS HAT

(*We hear a band playing in Badenweiler—July 1904. The band ends as the voices begin.*)

FRAU SCHMIDT (*gushing*). Good morning, Madame Tchehov.

OLGA KNIPPER. Good morning, Frau Schmidt.

FRAU SCHMIDT. It's going to be hot again, I think.

OLGA KNIPPER. Hot, Frau Schmidt? Purgatory!

FRAU SCHMIDT. You don't like the heat?

OLGA KNIPPER. Me, Frau Schmidt? Oh, *I* don't mind the heat. It's my husband.

FRAU SCHMIDT. I beg your pardon, how stupid I am. How is your dear husband today?

OLGA KNIPPER. Oh, a bit better, a little bit better, but you know, my dear—well, the last three days have been terrible. Dr. Schwörer came in two days ago and told me I must be prepared . . . .

FRAU SCHMIDT. Prepared . . . for what?

OLGA KNIPPER (*changing the subject*). Exquisite!

FRAU SCHMIDT. What?

OLGA KNIPPER. That shaft of sunlight away over there on the forest. In half an hour or so we'll have sun here on the verandah.

FRAU SCHMIDT. But, Madame Tchehov, you were saying . . . about Dr. Schwörer—?

OLGA KNIPPER. Oh, Dr. Schwörer? A charming man, and he knows when to put his foot down. Anton, you know, wants to pack up his bags. He wants to get out of here at once.

FRAU SCHMIDT. But you have not been long in Badenweiler.

OLGA KNIPPER. My dear Frau Schmidt, we've been three weeks here—and Anton thinks it's eternity.

FRAU SCHMIDT. Your husband doesn't *like* Badenweiler?

OLGA KNIPPER. He's panting to go to Italy. Lake Como, you know. Or, better still, home to Russia.

FRAU SCHMIDT. Geniuses of course are so restless. I always tell my daughter she must never marry a writer.

(*Tinkle of doorbell.*)

OLGA KNIPPER. Quite right, Frau Schmidt. Never marry a writer—especially when he's a genius. There's Anton now.

(*Tinkle of doorbell.*)

The masseur comes to see him at seven-thirty and Anton likes to talk to me first.

FRAU SCHMIDT. Well, remember me to him, Madame Tchehov, and I hope . . . I hope all will be well. If you were to lose him . . . the loss . . . well, the loss, Madame Tchehov, would be a loss to humanity.

(*Tinkle of bell.*)

OLGA KNIPPER. Thank you, Frau Schmidt. I must run.

FRAU SCHMIDT. Goodbye, Madame Tchehov.

OLGA KNIPPER. Goodbye, Frau Schmidt.

FRAU SCHMIDT. Goodbye, Madame Tchehov.

(*The German band begins again—and continues.*)

OLGA. Anton?

TCHEHOV. Ah, there you are, Olga, my poppet. Where have you been?

OLGA. Talking to Frau Schmidt. She wants to be remembered to you.

TCHEHOV. Frau Schmidt? Frau Schmidt? Oh, the woman who's all over braid.

OLGA. Yes. Face like a pudding.

TCHEHOV. Why *do* they dress so badly? German taste, if there *is* such a thing—(*Fit of coughing*)

OLGA. There, Antosha, there!

(*The band continues while he gets over his coughing.*)

TCHEHOV. What were we saying? Oh, yes, German taste . . . What do they pay that band?

OLGA. How should *I* know, dear? More than they ever pay *us* at the Moscow Art—

TCHEHOV (*interrupting her, with a sudden change of tone*). The Moscow Art theatre . . . Pigeon, we must go back to Russia!

OLGA. Later, Antosha, later.

TCHEHOV. No, Olga. At once! First we'll go to Trieste and then a steamer for Odessa and then—

OLGA. Dr. Schwörer says—

TCHEHOV. I don't give a damn what Dr. Schwörer says. These German doctors have stood me on my head. Doctors? I'm one myself. What's the date, my goldfish?

OLGA. Second of July.

TCHEHOV. July already? High time I was cured. (*facetiously*) In fact, now I think of it . . . I *am* cured.

OLGA. Now, Antosha, Dr. Schwörer—

TCHEHOV. Dr. Schwörer can drown himself in the Rhine! Doctor Tchehov says Anton Tchehov is cured. But he won't stay cured much longer if he has to listen to this band—seven o'clock every morning, seven o'clock every evening . . . .

(*The band comes into the foreground.*)

OLGA. Shall I close the windows?

TCHEHOV. No, no, don't close the windows. I must have air.

(*Short fit of coughing; during the following speeches the band fades away.*)

TCHEHOV. I wish I could do with this band what one does with the rhythm of a train. You know, poppet, how one sits in a train and the train goes chuggity-chug, chuggity-chug, chuggity-chug, with infinite monotony, but as you listen, you can change it into any rhythm you like—the poems of Pushkin or . . . or . . .

OLGA. Or the Serenade for Strings by Tchaikovsky—

TCHEHOV. Yes, or the hymns in church when I was a little boy and father made us sing in the choir.

In Taganrog, that was.

(*coughing*)

I don't like churches but I *did* like those hymns.

Sunbeams in his Hat

(His voice grows distant.)

The ikons were pretty too. Father was determined we should all grow up Christians—

(Out of the distance comes an Orthodox Greek Church Choir.)

TCHEHOV'S FATHER *(roughish voice)*. Anton, you must believe in God.

CHILD'S VOICE. Yes, father.

FATHER. Alexander, Nikolay, Anton, Ivan—You must all believe in God.

CHILD'S VOICE. Yes, father.

(The choir in the background stops singing.)

FATHER. Put your trust in God and everything will go well. Think of what Grandfather did.

CHILD'S VOICE. What did Grandfather do?

FATHER. You know that your grandfather used to be a serf. In the bad old days before serfdom was abolished. To be a serf—that was a terrible thing, but your grandfather trusted in God. He saved up his money, penny by penny, until he had saved—how much? How much do you think?

CHILD'S VOICE. How much?

FATHER. Three thousand five hundred roubles.

CHILD'S VOICE. My!

FATHER. He bought his family freedom at seven hundred roubles per head. The good God smiled on his labours. Are you listening, Anton?

CHILD'S VOICE. Yes, father.

FATHER. Fear God and you cannot go wrong. You see this shop of mine—'Colonial Produce: P. E. Tchehov'? I didn't always have this shop—

CHILD'S VOICE. Didn't you?

FATHER. No, my children. For a long, long time I worked as a clerk; the hours were long and hard and the money was very little. But I trusted in God and I put my pennies in a box. So at last the day came, I stopped being a clerk, I bought a

76

business of my own. I bought this business and God made it prosper—'Colonial Produce: P. E. Tchehov'. So you see, my children: fear God and you cannot go wrong. Alexander, Nikolay, Anton, Ivan, fear God and you cannot go wrong . . . .

(*His voice thins outwards like a ripple, overlaps back into the present.*)

TCHEHOV. 'Fear God and you cannot go wrong . . .'. When I was in my 'teens my father's shop went bankrupt. He had to move to Moscow. In Moscow he again became a clerk. They paid him a starvation wage.

(*Knocking on the door—but he disregards it. He has probably told her all this before, but is reminiscing for his own sake.*)

TCHEHOV. The rest of the family went to Moscow too; they all starved together. That's why my brother Nikolay later became consumptive. Moscow was the beginning—

(*Repeated knocking.*)

OLGA. That will be the masseur. Herein! Herein!

(*Pause.*)

OLGA. Good morning, Monsieur Legrand.

MASSEUR. Good morning, Madame. Good morning, Monsieur. And how are we today?

TCHEHOV (*switching at once to his 'funny' manner*). We have just found out we are cured. We are chock full of butter and porridge. That is one thing these Germans can do—they make the most beautiful porridge.

MASSEUR. Monsieur has such a sense of humour . . . . Well, we had better start work. First, please, will you lie on your front? So. Now please, Madame, where is the basin of water?

TCHEHOV. Having massage is really a treat. It makes me think of my mongoose.

MASSEUR. Of your *what*?

TCHEHOV. He liked being stroked so much.

MASSEUR. Who did, Monsieur?

OLGA. His mongoose, Monsieur Legrand.

TCHEHOV. I brought him back from Sahalin.

MASSEUR. From where, Monsieur?

OLGA. Please, Monsieur Legrand, don't ask so many questions.

TCHEHOV. From Sahalin. Otherwise called Hell. (*He groans.*)

MASSEUR. Am I hurting you? Then turn a little more on your side . . . . That's right.

TCHEHOV. If you ever want to go to Hell . . . .

MASSEUR. Monsieur has such a sense of—

TCHEHOV (*suddenly serious again, though 'throwing it away'*). A sense of reality, my friend. Sahalin is one of our penal settlements. If you want to see humanity at its worst—

MASSEUR. But I do *not*, Monsieur.

TCHEHOV. You are mistaken then. If you like humanity you have to see the dregs of it. You know where Sahalin is? An island south of Kamchatka and north of Japan. The dreariest, dirtiest outpost of Holy Russia. To get there—

MASSEUR. A moment, Monsieur. Still more over on your side. . . . Good.

TCHEHOV. First you take a steamer down the Volga, then you take a steamer up the Kama. A river that looks like coffee slops. Then you tackle Siberia . . . .

OLGA. I can never think, Anton, why you went there.

TCHEHOV. Nobody could. They all thought I was mad.

MASSEUR. I imagine, Madame, your husband was looking for copy.

TCHEHOV (*bursting out*). Copy! Copy! . . .

MASSEUR. Be careful, Monsieur, you will hurt yourself.

TCHEHOV. What do you mean by talking to me about copy?

MASSEUR. But surely, Monsieur, as a writer—

TCHEHOV. A writer! Don't you know I'm a doctor?

MASSEUR. Yes, of course, but—

TCHEHOV (*bitterly*). Well, forget I'm a writer. That's why I went to Sahalin. To get away from the people who called me a writer. I got the Pushkin Prize, so they thought they must ask me to dinner. And while I was eating their dinners my brother died of consumption. So I went to Sahalin. That was in 1890.

(*A steamer is heard hooting in the distance. The next speech, delivered quietly and rhythmically, is really a soliloquy.*)

TCHEHOV (*dreamily*). Down the Volga and up the Kama. Days of rain and days of snow. First there was mud and then there was snow and then there was dust. First there was killing cold and then there was killing heat . . . . Innumerable muddy rivers . . . . Endless plains where the wind sings in the stunted birch trees. Further and further from civilisation. Miles and miles of snow and desert—Russian snow and Russian desert. Russia? Poverty . . . distance . . . disease. Tomsk and Irkutsk . . . further and further.

(*Siberian music creeps in.*)

TCHEHOV. Further and further on the road to Sahalin. Further and further on the road to Hell.

(*The music swells up to place Tchehov in the past—and in Sahalin.*)

GENERAL (*a hearty type of Philistine*). Now that you're here, Anton Pavlovitch, what can we do for you? Why you've come here I can't for the life of me imagine, but—

TCHEHOV. I've come here to study the convicts.

GENERAL. God bless me, what an idea! Well, if you *really* want to study the convicts, just tell me what you require and I'll give you every facility. Now if you'd like to see a flogging—

TCHEHOV. Thank you, General. My idea is to make a kind of census.

GENERAL. A kind of what?

TCHEHOV. A census. I want to make a census of the whole population of Sahalin.

GENERAL. My very dear doctor! Do you know that the convicts alone run into thousands and thousands?

TCHEHOV. So much the better. My object—

GENERAL. I suppose you want to write a novel or something?

TCHEHOV. A novel, General? What do you think I am? I want to contribute something to medical science.

GENERAL. Very well, Doctor, it strikes me as rather eccentric, but I'll see what I can do for you. I'll give you a competent nurse to show you around the settlement.

(*Music to register an interval.*)

TCHEHOV. Who lives in there, nurse?

NURSE (*brutalised*). Don't know his name but the place is filthy.

(*Tchehov knocks on the door of a hovel.*)

NURSE. Don't go in there. You'll catch something.

TCHEHOV. I tell you I'm making a census.

NURSE. Digging your grave, you mean.

(*He knocks again.*)

NURSE. Leave this lot out. They're scum.

TCHEHOV (*quietly*). Scum? So are we all.

(*He knocks again.*)

NURSE. Thank goodness for that. No one at home.

TCHEHOV. Well, I'll just peep inside.

NURSE (*muttering*). Crazy! Plumb crazy . . . .

(*Pause while Tchehov enters the hovel. Inside his voice sounds different.*)

TCHEHOV. Terribly dark in here. Anyone in?

NURSE. Ach, the stink, the stink!

TCHEHOV. Anyone here? Anyone at home?

(*He is answered, as if from a corner, by a little boy's voice, very hostile.*)

BOY. *I'm* here.

TCHEHOV. Who are you, sonny? Come over here and talk to me.

BOY. Get out of my house.

TCHEHOV. Now, now . . . I'm not going to hurt you . . . . Have a sugar-stick.

NURSE. Doctor, I'll wait for you outside.

TCHEHOV. Nice, isn't it? . . . Now, sonny, what's your name?

BOY (*chewing*). Alyoshka . . . . What's yours?

TCHEHOV. Anton Pavlovitch . . . . How old are you?

BOY (*still not 'giving' anything*). Ten. How old are *you*?

Sunbeams in his Hat

TCHEHOV. Thirty. Isn't it old? (*Pause*) Do you live here with your father?

BOY. Yes.

TCHEHOV. What's your father's surname?

BOY. Don't know.

TCHEHOV. Don't know? You live with your father and you don't know his name!

BOY (*'dead-pan'*). He *isn't* my father.

TCHEHOV. But you said . . . . Now look here, Alyoshka, is he your father or isn't he?

BOY. Oh, *he* just lives with mother.

TCHEHOV. Your mother? Is she married or a widow?

BOY. Widow. Came down here with her husband.

TCHEHOV. Then what became of her husband?

BOY (*'dead-pan'*). Mother killed him.

TCHEHOV. What did you say?

BOY. Mother got tired. She killed him.

(*The Siberian music creeps in again. Tchehov makes a last effort.*)

TCHEHOV. Do you remember your father? Your real father?

BOY. Give me another sugar-stick.

TCHEHOV. But please tell me, Alyoshka—

BOY. Give me another sugar-stick.

(*The music comes up by itself to round off that fiasco, then gives place to the German band—and to Badenweiler.*)

TCHEHOV. So you *see*, Monsieur Legrand . . . ? That was a long time ago—fourteen years—but they still send convicts to Siberia, they still send convicts to Sahalin. Millions of lost souls, millions of broken bodies . . . I brought back a lot of statistics. Also a mongoose.

MASSEUR. And what did you do with your statistics?

TCHEHOV. Handed them over to our rotten bureaucracy. Tell me, Monsieur Legrand, you do not know our Russia?

MASSEUR. No, Monsieur, I have not that privilege, alas.

TCHEHOV. Then let me tell you. Russia is a huge . . . beautiful

. . . *monster*. A monster sunk in lethargy . . . destroying its children . . . destroying itself. Some day perhaps it will wake—

OLGA. Now, Antosha, don't go talking like Gorki . . . Monsieur Legrand will think you are dying of social consciousness.

TCHEHOV (*dryly*). I'm dying anyway, Olga.

(*An embarrassed pause while he picks up the thread he has broken; beginning again with precise emphasis.*)

TCHEHOV. There is one thing that's the ruin of Russia—

(*A short fit of coughing interrupts him.*)

MASSEUR. What is that, Monsieur?

TCHEHOV. *Ignorance*. Gross abysmal ignorance. The mother of all evils . . . from the Baltic to Vladivostock . . . Sahalin was a bottomless pit of ignorance. When I got back to Moscow—

MASSEUR (*still suave*). A happy day, I take it?

TCHEHOV. I found it was worse than Sahalin. All the nonsense began all over again. Literary salons . . . dinner parties . . . .

OLGA (*with forced cheerfulness, hoping to stop him moralising*). So you know what he did? He got together with his old friend Souvorin—

TCHEHOV. And we went to Monte Carlo.

MASSEUR. But why?

OLGA. They went to Monte Carlo and played roulette. They came back bankrupt.

MASSEUR. But I would not have thought . . . .

OLGA (*at last losing her patience*). You would not have thought what?

MASSEUR. Excuse me, but I do not understand. If Monsieur was worried with social problems—

OLGA. You wouldn't have thought he would flit to Monte Carlo. Well, he *did*. It seems quite natural to me.

MASSEUR. Natural, yes, but *logical* . . . ?

OLGA. Logic! A man goes round making censuses—writing reports about cholera—collecting subscriptions for hospitals

—in his off moments he writes short stories and plays—he becomes a master of literature—social conditions give him a nightmare—he shakes off the dust of Moscow—he takes the boat for Monte Carlo. You, Monsieur, are a Frenchman. You think this is all illogical. You think, if a man is appalled by his country's poverty, it's silly to go and play roulette—

TCHEHOV. It was silly, but it did me a world of good . . . . It cleaned out my pockets and it cleaned out my soul. Life recovered its tang. Souvorin—

OLGA. Poor old Souvorin! You led him a dance.

TCHEHOV (*gaily, almost boyishly*). He didn't need leading. How well I remember him standing there over the tables . . . . You know Monsieur Legrand, the Casino is marvellous. A really exquisite vulgarity—gilt and plush—crowds of bourgeois faces, all of them eau-de-nil in the light reflected from the tables. Even Souvorin had a green face. How well I remember it all. Just as if it were yesterday . . . yesterday . . . yesterday . . . .

(*A slight discreet babble drowns his reminiscing voice and brings to life his reminiscence.*)

CROUPIER. Faites vos jeux, messieurs et mesdames.

ENGLISHWOMAN. But can't you see, George—

TCHEHOV. Souvorin, watch the angry Englishwoman.

CROUPIER. Faites vos jeux, messieurs et mesdames.

ENGLISHWOMAN. Can't you *see*, George? You must let me put a louis on a *number*. What's the good of betting on a red. I *knew* 27 would turn up . . . .

HUSBAND. Emily, you make me sick. I didn't want to bring you here at all—

CROUPIER. Faites vox jeux, messieurs et mesdames.

ENGLISHWOMAN. I'm going to put this—all of it—on Number . . . Number . . . Number Eighteen.

HUSBAND. You're going to do nothing of the sort. You'll put it on Impair. An even chance, Emily, an even chance . . . .

Sunbeams in his Hat

(The camera, as it were, pans round the Casino; different voices emerge and disappear.)

VOICES. Numéro cinq . . . Rouge . . . Impair . . . Numéro Quatorze . . . Noir . . . etc.

SOUVORIN. Well, Antosha, had enough?

TCHEHOV (*in high spirits*). Enough? Certainly not. Look how angry the Englishwoman is; her husband won't let her bet on a number. What was the number she wanted?

SOUVORIN. Eighteen.

TCHEHOV. Right.

(We hear the clicking of the ball.)

CROUPIER. *Dix-huit.*

ENGLISHWOMAN (*furious*). George!

TCHEHOV. You see. She picked a winner.

SOUVORIN. But not for herself, poor thing.

ENGLISHWOMAN. George, those Russians! They betted on eighteen.

TCHEHOV. Souvorin, old man, my pockets are bulging.

SOUVORIN. Looks as if this is our day.

TCHEHOV (*lightly*). Boring if we win too much.

(From this point the scene is highly stylised; excited music begins here, faint at first but ever increasing in volume, while the dialogue gets faster and faster.)

1ST CROUPIER. Faites vos jeux, messieurs et mesdames.

2ND CROUPIER. Les jeux sont faits.

TCHEHOV. Two gold pieces on Number Seven.

2ND CROUPIER. Cinq.

1ST CROUPIER. Faites vos jeux, messieurs et mesdames.

TCHEHOV. On 19.

2ND CROUPIER. Quatorze.

SOUVORIN. There go another ten louis.

1ST CROUPIER. Les jeux sont faits.

2ND CROUPIER. Faites vos jeux.

TCHEHOV. Nine.

1ST CROUPIER. Vingt-et-un.

TCHEHOV. Twenty-three.

2ND CROUPIER. Cinq.

TCHEHOV. Five again. All right—cinq.

1ST CROUPIER. Les jeux sont faits.

2ND CROUPIER. Zéro.

TCHEHOV. Nineteen.

1ST CROUPIER. Quinze.

2ND CROUPIER. Faites vos jeux.

TCHEHOV. Seven.

1ST CROUPIER. Vingt-cinq.

2ND CROUPIER. Rien ne va plus.

TCHEHOV. Damn it. Impair.

1ST CROUPIER. Huit: Rouge: Pair.

2ND CROUPIER. Rien ne va plus.

TCHEHOV. Very well. Rouge.

1ST CROUPIER. Noir.

2ND CROUPIER. Rien ne va plus.

TCHEHOV. Noir.

1ST CROUPIER. Rouge.

2ND CROUPIER. Rien ne va plus.

TCHEHOV. Twenty.

1ST CROUPIER. Onze.

2ND CROUPIER. Rien ne va plus.

TCHEHOV. Seven.

1ST CROUPIER. Cinq.

2ND CROUPIER. Rien ne va plus.

(*The music here reaches its peak, then cuts out abruptly; a pause before Souvorin speaks in a dead silence.*)

SOUVORIN. What have you left, Antosha?

TCHEHOV (*with a laugh in his voice*). My return ticket to Nice.

BOTH CROUPIERS (*together and with unrealistic emphasis*). Rien ne va plus.

(*A pause—enough to return us to the present.*)

TCHEHOV. The band seems to have stopped, Olga.

OLGA. No more brass till seven this evening.

TCHEHOV. Thank God for that.

OLGA. Time for you to get up, Antosha. How do you feel now?

TCHEHOV. My massage did me good but Heavens . . . !

OLGA. Heavens what?

TCHEHOV. If I stay any longer among all this German peace and order!

OLGA. Longing for Russia?

TCHEHOV. Yes, and *you*? Longing for the Moscow Art Theatre?

OLGA. A little, Antosha, just a little.

TCHEHOV. Stanislavsky and Nemirovich-Danchenko and Artem and—

OLGA. Don't make me homesick.

TCHEHOV. You love the stage, don't you, my little beetle?

OLGA. Of course I do. It's my life.

TCHEHOV. A frightening invention . . . the stage. I never meant to get mixed up in it. No sensible man would be a playwright.

OLGA. How nice that you're not sensible!

TCHEHOV. The degradation, the prostitution, the fret and the flutter, the frightful disappointments—

OLGA. Disappointments?

TCHEHOV. Remember 'The Seagull'?

OLGA. Oh, the production in St. Petersburg? Once Stanislavsky produced it—

TCHEHOV. And you were its leading lady—well, that of course was different. But when they did it in St. Petersburg . . . and the bath-chair broke on the stage . . . .

(*His voice gives place to the catcalls and laughs of a crowd. A hubbub continues through the following conversation in the wings.*)

STAGE MANAGER. There goes the bath-chair, Anton Pavlovitch.

TCHEHOV. Never again! Never again!

STAGE MANAGER. Never again what?

Sunbeams in his Hat

TCHEHOV. You are a Stage Manager. Never again will I write for your medium.

STAGE MANAGER. You won't, eh? Well, Anton Pavlovitch, judging by the reactions of the house—

(*A fresh outburst from the audience interrupts him.*)

STAGE MANAGER. Judging, I said, by the reactions of the populace, I think your decision is correct. You *can't* write for the stage.

(*The hubbub recedes, vanishes into the past.*)

OLGA (*teasingly*). Never again, eh?

TCHEHOV. I meant it, too. If it hadn't been for Nemirovich-Danchenko—and Stanislavsky—and the whole Moscow Art—

OLGA. *We* did the 'Seagull' rather better. Didn't we, Anton darling? But, Lord, wasn't I frightened? And as for Stanislavsky . . . !

TCHEHOV. He felt that his life depended on it.

OLGA. *Your* life, Antosha, *your* life. It was just after all those haemorrhages. We were scared right to the end. To the scene where they bring in the beer and I'm centre stage behind the table and Trigorin's looking at that awful stuffed gull and then there's the shot in the wings and—

(*She is cut off by a loud pistol shot. After a pause she speaks again, now 'throwing her voice' as on the stage.*)

OLGA (*as Madame Arkadin*). What's that?

'DORN'. That's nothing. Must be something gone off in my medicine-chest. Don't be anxious . . . .

(*A door opens—and after a pause, closes.*)

'DORN'. That's what it is. A bottle of ether exploded.

(*He begins to hum.*)

OLGA (*as Madam Arkadin*). 'Ough, how frightened I was . . . . It reminded me of how . . . . It made me quite dizzy.

'DORN'. Seen this magazine, Trigorin? There's an article here . . . from America . . . I wanted to ask you, among other things . . . as I'm very much interested in the question . . . .

87

(*intimate*) Get Irina Nikolayevna away somehow. The fact is, Konstantin Gavrilitch has shot himself.'

(*A slight pause—and applause breaks out from the audience; then fades away slowly, bringing Olga back to the present.*)

OLGA. Yes, indeed, we did it a great deal better. And then Uncle Vanya. Remember that speech of mine in the second Act? When my husband's gone off to have his lime-flower tea and Vanya is complaining that he's had no sleep and I just despair about the whole household. 'It's dreadful—' how does it begin—'It's dreadful . . .'?

TCHEHOV (*feeling for the lines*). 'It's dreadful in this house. Your mother hates everything except her pamphlets and the Professor—'

OLGA (*as Yelena*). 'The Professor is irritated, he does not trust me, and is afraid of you; Sonya is angry with her father, angry with me and hasn't spoken to me for a fortnight; you hate my husband and show open contempt for your mother; I am overwrought and have been nearly crying twenty times today . . . . It's dreadful in this house . . .'.

TOLSTOY (*on echo, with angry emphasis*). It certainly is but what *is* the point of writing like this? What is the point, what is the point . . .?

OLGA. Everyone loved it. And the flowers I got!

TCHEHOV. Tolstoy didn't love it.

OLGA. Oh well, Tolstoy! Just shook his head and—

TOLSTOY (*on echo*). 'What is the point? What is the point?'

TCHEHOV. Tolstoy wanted a moral.

OLGA. He would. Dreary old thing!

TCHEHOV. No, no, my poppet. Not dreary.

OLGA. Well, look at Gorki. Gorki—

TCHEHOV. Gorki has a different view of art.

OLGA. He certainly has. Remember that row in Yalta? We were all sitting out on the terrace and someone was playing a guitar behind the big eucalyptus tree—

Sunbeams in his Hat

TCHEHOV. Yalta? Yes. That wasn't life, that was raspberries and cream.

OLGA. The cream had turned a bit *that* day. If it hadn't been for the guitar . . . going on in spite of those two . . . .

(*A guitar steals in, adjusting the focus to Yalta.*)

TOLSTOY. Gorki, you're utterly wrong . . . . What do *you* think, Anton Pavlovitch?

TCHEHOV (*humorously deprecating*). Me? I don't know about Art. I don't know what the word means.

GORKI. Well, you can't agree with Tolstoy!

TOLSTOY. Anton Pavlovitch, don't be so feeble. You *must* have views on the subject. The problem of Art—

TCHEHOV. *Is* there a 'problem of Art'? A writer—

GORKI. A writer must be true to his inspiration.

TCHEHOV. Nonsense, Maxim. A writer should have eyes in his head and a knowledge of life. A writer is just like a chemist, he's got to be objective. As objective as a chemist—

TOLSTOY. The writer's function is to better the world.

GORKI. Better it in what way? Encourage people to lie down under oppression? Encourage the masses to starve and—

TOLSTOY. Encourage people to put their hopes upon God.

GORKI. And by that you mean give up their hopes of humanity.

TOLSTOY (*Thumping on the table*). Humanity! Maxim Gorki, you are nothing but a . . . a sentimental would-be revolutionary.

GORKI. Sentimental! What do you call yourself? *You*, Leo Nikolaevitch Tolstoy—a white-gloved landlord posing as a peasant.

TOLSTOY. And you are just a young peasant who can't digest his ideas.

GORKI. There is only *one* idea—

TOLSTOY. One idea is more than *you* can manage, Maxim. When you are ten years older—

GORKI. Perhaps I will give up trying? You want me to give up trying. You want—

Sunbeams in his Hat

TOLSTOY. What do *you* think, Anton Pavlovitch?

GORKI. Yes, what do *you* think?

OLGA. Anton doesn't think anything. He's busy.

TOLSTOY. Anton Pavlovitch! What on earth are you doing with your hat?

(The guitar begins again.)

TCHEHOV *(would-be naïve)*. I'm trying to catch a sunbeam.

GORKI. What?

TCHEHOV. If I can catch a sunbeam, catch it in my hat, then I can put it on my head and . . . .

(They drown him in peals of laughter—their argument forgotten. As the laughter thins out, the guitar shows through it. Then Tolstoy speaks, half choking.)

TOLSTOY. Anton Pavlovitch, you are incorrigible.

(They all laugh again—with and at Tolstoy. The guitar takes over the foreground, then breaks off.)

OLGA. Lord, how I laughed. And Tolstoy—I thought his beard would come off. That was the way to deal with him. Sunbeams . . . sunbeams in your hat!

TCHEHOV *(quietly)*. Maybe he was right all the same.

OLGA. Who was right? Tolstoy?

TCHEHOV. Yes. Or maybe Gorki.

OLGA. They can't both have been right.

TCHEHOV. They can both have been right in contrast to me. The artist must grind an axe: Tolstoy thinks so, Gorki thinks so —of course they are different axes. But poor Anton Pavlovitch—he just hasn't got an axe to grind. Even Souvorin used to rebuke me for it. He said I was indifferent to good and evil.

OLGA. What nonsense, Antosha.

TCHEHOV. Gorki, now—he thinks that Art is the handmaid of Progress. And progress of course means Revolution. According to Gorki, the writer must have a political platform. Politics—

OLGA. Damn his politics. If Gorki wants to go in for propaganda, he's welcome. You and I, Antosha, we know what Art really means.

TCHEHOV. Oh no, we don't.

OLGA. Nonsense, Antosha. These people like Gorki who want you to write propaganda—they don't understand that you're not a political hack. You're first and foremost a playwright.

TCHEHOV. I am first and foremost an ordinary person. Secondly I'm a doctor. Thirdly I'm a writer of short stories—but not so good as Maupassant. Fourth—and a very poor fourth it is —I am a writer of Vaudeville.

OLGA. Antosha, you're maddening. Vaudeville indeed! When the crowning point of your career was . . . .

TCHEHOV (*coldly*). Was what?

OLGA. The first performance of 'The Cherry Orchard'.

TCHEHOV. Oh, *that*? That's Ancient History anyway.

OLGA. Ancient History? January of this year!

TCHEHOV (*genuinely forgetful*). Was it?

OLGA. Your Jubilee, my sweet!

TCHEHOV. Oh yes, yes, my Jubilee. As if I was a politician or a Grand Duke or a sanitary inspector or someone. If only I could have got out of going to the theatre!

OLGA. And missed your wife as Madame Ranevsky?

TCHEHOV (*slowly with feeling*). No . . . I wouldn't have missed that!

(*An actress is heard playing her part in the distance. Her voice comes nearer and nearer. It is Olga.*)

OLGA (*as Madame Ranevsky*). 'Oh, my childhood, my innocence! It was in this nursery I used to sleep, from here I looked out into the orchard, happiness waked with me every morning, and in those days the orchard was just the same, nothing has changed. (*Laughs with delight.*) All, all white! Oh, my orchard! After the dark, gloomy autumn and the cold winter; you are young again and full of happiness, the heavenly angels have never left you . . . . If I could cast off the burden that weighs on my heart, if I could forget the past!'

91

Sunbeams in his Hat

(*Pause*)

TCHEHOV. No, my goldfish, I wouldn't have missed that.

OLGA. 'If I could forget the past . . .'. When you wrote those lines, Anton, how far . . . how far was that yourself?

TCHEHOV. Myself? Not at all, silly. *I'm* not a Tchehov character. Except, in so far as the Cherry Orchard's concerned . . . .

OLGA. Except what?

TCHEHOV. Well, the curtain, you know. Everyone must have a curtain. In a cherry orchard or . . . Badenweiler. Old age in one case, T.B. in another. Artem was good in that last speech.

OLGA. Yes, wasn't he good? I watched him from the wings. Shambling in in those slippers—I wonder they didn't come off—and trying the handles of the doors and then coming forwards towards the audience.

ARTEM (*as Firs*). 'They have gone. . . . They have forgotten me. . . . Never mind . . . I'll sit here a bit. . . . I'll be bound Leonid Andreyevitch hasn't put his fur coat on and has gone off in his thin overcoat. (*Sighs anxiously.*) I didn't see after him. These young people . . . (*mutters unintelligibly*). Life has slipped by as though I hadn't lived. . . . I'll lie down a bit. . . . There's no strength in you, nothing left at all. Oh, you good-for-nothing!

(*Stage sound as of breaking harp-strings: silence: ovation.*)

STANISLAVSKY (*from stage*). Ladies and gentlemen,

(*Cheering*)

Ladies and gentlemen, will you please remain in your seats.

MALE VOICE. That's Stanislavsky.

FEMALE VOICE. Who's that in the middle?

MALE VOICE. The other director—Nemirovich-Danchenko. The empty chair is for the author.

FEMALE VOICE. Where *is* the author?

VOICES. Author! Author! Where is Anton Pavlovitch?

MALE VOICE. There he comes—

(*Terrific cheering.*)

Sunbeams in his Hat

FEMALE VOICE. Doesn't he look ill? Quite transparent! And what a shabby grey suit! Of course they say that it's both lungs now. I'd have thought all the same . . . .   .

MALE VOICE. Hush! Danchenko's going to make a speech.

DANCHENKO. Ladies and gentlemen—

> (*Clapping and cheering.*)

DANCHENKO (*rather pompously*). Ladies and gentlemen, on behalf of the Moscow Art Theatre and my co-director, Konstantin Sergeievitch Stanislavsky—

> (*Still louder clapping and cheering.*)

DANCHENKO (*emotionally*). I wish to thank you all. . . . I have not words to express it. . . . I wish to thank you all for your wonderful reception of this play.

Secondly . . . on behalf of the whole company . . . and also of you, the audience, I wish to say a few words in homage to the author of this play, Anton Pavlovitch Tchehov—

> (*Enormous cheering.*)

DANCHENKO. This, my friends, is a special occasion. It is Anton Pavlovitch's birthday. It is also the Jubilee of his literary career. Anton Pavlovitch, I address you on behalf of the Moscow Art Theatre. Without you our theatre would be nowhere. The debt that we owe you is beyond all words. Your heaven-sent talent, your generous heart, your *soul*. . . . My friends, the Moscow Art Theatre is *Tchehov's* theatre, Tchehov is the main-spring of our art. Tchehov is the sun that has ripened our endeavours. Tchehov is—

> (*Wild cheering.*)

DANCHENKO. Anton Pavlovitch, I wish to ask you . . . perhaps you will speak to us yourself?

> (*Pause.*)

OLGA (*in low voice*). He *won't* speak. He's exhausted.

STANISLAVSKY (*in low voice*). He can't speak. He mustn't.

DANCHENKO. Will you do us the great honour, Anton Pavlovitch—?

Sunbeams in his Hat

STANISLAVSKY (*aside to Olga*). Why can't they leave him alone?

OLGA. Danchenko mustn't make him speak.

(*Pause.*)

DANCHENKO. My friends, Anton Pavlovitch regrets that he cannot address you himself—he is feeling too tired—but he thanks you all from his heart—

VOICE FROM AUDIENCE. *We* thank *him!*

DANCHENKO. Anton Pavlovitch thanks you all for everything and now that he is saying goodbye—

VOICE FROM AUDIENCE. Goodbye? Why goodbye?

DANCHENKO. Anton Pavlovitch is going abroad for his health. He is going to spend some time in—(*he feels for the name*) Badenweiler.

(*Slight pause; then the German band, fading up, materialises Badenweiler.*)

OLGA. It must be seven o'clock, Dr. Schwörer. There's that band.

DR. SCHWÖRER. Seven o'clock, Madame Tchehov? Time for your husband's supper. . . . Seven o'clock indeed! I must be toddling home.

OLGA. And you really think Anton is better?

DR. SCHWÖRER. Better, Madame? You must understand me. When I say 'better', the term is merely relative. His condition yesterday made me very anxious. Today—

OLGA. Today he's as gay as a schoolboy. He's been telling stories and roaring with laughter. If only he could get a proper sleep—

DR. SCHWÖRER. Well, remember what I told you. Before he goes to bed, a cup of strawberry tea.

OLGA. I give him it, Herr Doktor, but it doesn't seem to help much . . . and he's kept awake by the clock in his bedroom.

DR. SCHWÖRER. Clock? Take the clock away.

OLGA. It's a grandfather clock, a fixture . . . and the landlady won't let me stop it, she says it's bad for the works.

Sunbeams in his Hat

DR. SCHWÖRER. Well, give him his cup of strawberry tea, and you have my telephone number if anything happens. Goodnight, Madame Tchehov, goodnight. I'll be round at the usual time tomorrow.

(*The German band soars to a peak of banality, then cuts out; in the gap which it leaves there emerges the heavy tick-tocking of a clock.*)

OLGA. Now, Antosha, here's your strawberry tea.

TCHEHOV. Thank you, poppet.

OLGA. Sleepy?

TCHEHOV. I *am* rather.

OLGA. Tonight I have a feeling you're going to sleep *well*.

TCHEHOV. If I don't have dreams.

OLGA. You might have nice ones.

TCHEHOV. Nice dreams, Olga? No. My dreams these days are frightening. Pictures and voices from the past. And then there's that deep river.

OLGA. What deep river?

TCHEHOV. I told you, Olga, I told you. I've dreamt about it for years. It's like those rivers in Siberia. Great grey slippery stones on the bank; cold autumnal water; mist . . . mist over everything. It's all incredibly dismal and damp and I know that I have to cross it. Then I hear hooters in the mist. There are little tugs going up and down the river—

OLGA. You only dream that when your blanket falls off. Tonight I shall tuck you in *well*. . . . There! How's that?

TCHEHOV. Marvellous.

OLGA. Good. Now you're all fixed. Goodnight, Antosha darling. There's your little bell on the table. . . . Goodnight.

TCHEHOV. Goodnight, my practical wife.

(*A pause, then the hooter of a steamer.*)

TCHEHOV (*in his sleep*). The water looks so cold . . . and I can't see the other bank. . . .

(*The hooter again—forlornly. The voices which he now hears, have a strange—a dream—quality.*)

1ST CROUPIER. Faites vos jeux, messieurs et mesdames.

TCHEHOV. But who are the people in the boat?

FATHER. Fear God and you cannot go wrong.

2ND CROUPIER. Faites vos jeux, messieurs et mesdames.

(*Hooter.*)

TCHEHOV. The water looks so cold. . . . That's Nikolay in the boat, I fear he's getting consumption.

1ST CROUPIER. Les jeux sont faits. Rien ne va plus.

TCHEHOV. And that old man looks like Artem——Artem, my favourite actor.

ARTEM. 'They have gone . . . they have forgotten me. Never mind . . . I'll sit here a bit. . . . I'll be bound Leonid Andreyevitch hasn't put his fur coat on—'

TCHEHOV. He'll need his fur coat. It's cold on the water. . . . Isn't that Tolstoy sitting in the stern?

TOLSTOY. Anton Pavlovitch, don't be so feeble. You *must* have views on this subject.

(*Hooter.*)

TCHEHOV. Which subject?

1ST CROUPIER. Faites vos jeux, messieurs et mesdames.

FATHER. Fear God and you cannot go wrong.

BOY. Mother killed him. Give me another sugar-stick.

(*Hooter.*)

TCHEHOV. Which is the steamer for Odessa?

1ST CROUPIER. Les jeux sont faits. Rien ne va plus.

TCHEHOV. Which is the steamer for Odessa?

BOY. Mother killed him. Give me—

TCHEHOV (*urgently*). Which is the steamer for Odessa?

(*Long blast on the hooter: and it fades away as he wakes.*)

TCHEHOV (*crying out*). Olga!

(*He rings the hand-bell; she comes in.*)

OLGA. What is it, Antosha?

TCHEHOV. Which is the steamer for Odessa?

OLGA. What?

Sunbeams in his Hat

TCHEHOV. Nothing; I'm dreaming . . . .

OLGA. Do you feel all right?

TCHEHOV. Yes, I think so.

OLGA. You musn't dream like that. Was it the river again?

TCHEHOV. The river? Yes. The river. (*Pause.*) Olga!

OLGA. Yes?

TCHEHOV. I don't feel all right. I think I'd better have the doctor.

OLGA. The doctor!

TCHEHOV (*trying to laugh it off*). First time in my life I've asked for such a person. Being a doctor myself . . . .

OLGA. I'll ring him at once.

TCHEHOV. Don't go away, Olga.

OLGA. I'm just going down to the phone. Back in a second.

(*The clock fills in an interval.*)

OLGA (*in the foreground, but hushed*). But Dr. *Schwörer*—!

DR. SCHWÖRER. No, I'm afraid not . . . I saw this coming . . . but I didn't think that *tonight*—

OLGA. Are you *absolutely certain*?

DR. SCHWÖRER. Absolutely, Madame.

TCHEHOV (*from the background*). I know what you're saying over there—

OLGA (*switching on brightness*). Look, Antosha, look what the doctor's brought . . . Champagne!

TCHEHOV (*with sly seriousness*). Champagne! I know what that's for. (*With attempted jollity.*) Pour me a glass at once. . . . That's right; up to the brim.

DR. SCHWÖRER. Here you are, Dr. Tchehov.

TCHEHOV. Thank you, Herr Doktor, you're too kind, much too kind. . . . I know what you mean, you know; I am a doctor too. . . . Ich sterbe, Herr Doktor—that's good German, isn't it? Give me the glass. . . . Thank you . . . Olga, poppet, your health!

OLGA. Carefully, Antosha—

DR. SCHWÖRER. No, no, let him drink it to the bottom. . . .

Sunbeams in his Hat

That's the way I like to see a man drink.

(*The glass tinkles as it is put down.*)

TCHEHOV (*very feebly*). Good! . . . I hadn't tasted champagne for a long time.

DR. SCHWÖRER. Now, Madame, let him lie on his side . . . .

(*The clock, which we had forgotten, reasserts itself; dominating the death-bed.*)

DR. SCHWÖRER. No, do not speak to him now . . . . (*He drops his voice.*) What a wonderful smile!

(*The clock continues.*)

DR. SCHWÖRER. Wait, Madame, wait.

(*The clock continues, then suddenly breaks off and there is a gap of silence.*)

DR. SCHWÖRER. It is over, Madame.

OLGA. It is . . . over?

DR. SCHWÖRER. He died gently.

(*A slight pause and she speaks—contemplatively but decisively.*)

OLGA. Anton, doctor, did everything gently.

(*Silence and then the hooter of a steamer. Tchehov's voice is heard, speaking slowly in a great space.*)

TCHEHOV. Which is the steamer for Odessa? . . .

Where do we book our passage? Your passage and mine. For a future which *should* be happy.

THE NOSEBAG

a Russian folk story

TO

FRANCIS DILLON

CAST

The Nosebag was first broadcast in the B.B.C. Home Service on March 13th, 1944. The main parts were played as follows:

SOLDIER	ROY EMERTON
THIRD BEGGAR	BRYAN POWLEY*
LANDLORD	IVOR BARNARD
MARYA	MOLLY RANKIN*
CHAMBERLAIN	MALCOLM GRAEME
TSAR	PETER USTINOV
DEVIL CAPTAIN	HOWARD MARION-CRAWFORD
LITTLE DEVIL	JOHN GILPIN
DEATH	GLADYS YOUNG*

Production by the author.

NOTE : The square brackets on pages 111, 114, and 120 denote cuts in the broadcast (see also page 200).

INTRODUCTORY NOTE

The Nosebag is a direct and very simple dramatisation of a traditional Russian folk story which is usually entitled *The Soldier and Death*. Such programmes go well on the air, and, unlike satirical fantasies (see my two March Hare programmes), are usually popular with the listening public. It is surprising that more folk stories and fairy stories have not been dramatised for radio—outside the Children's Hour. There is, however, one notable pioneer in this field, Mr. Francis Dillon, whose wit, imagination, and sympathy with his original, have enabled him to make excellent radio plays out of Hans Andersen. These latter are more topical in feeling than *The Nosebag* and rightly so, as Hans Andersen was not of the folk; thus when Mr. Dillon in his version of *The Snow Queen* made the wicked Magicians atom-bomb scientists, he was simply developing Andersen's intention. But a folk-story proper, being timeless, cannot be so feasibly brought up to date *if* it is intended to retain its original flavour. In the characters of the Tsar and the Chamberlain (the latter my own interpolation) I hinted at modern types—with a touch of satire—but I did not tinker with the hero, and carefully avoided throughout both the temptation to cod and the shown-to-the-children manner. The 'folk' who made these stories were after all adults.

This broadcast suffered from not having special music (as I realised even more when in dramatising at a later date Apuleius' story of *The Golden Ass* I had the great advantage of special music by Mr. Antony Hopkins). As it was, I relied entirely both for linking and effects music on gramophone records, drawing on Liadow, Rimsky-Korsakov, Moussorgsky, Stravinsky *et al.* The mixture naturally failed to be a blend and the snippets of effects music failed to be duly functional.

The part of the Soldier was magnificently embodied by Roy

The Nosebag

Emerton whose death during the last year deprived his profession of a very rare personality. Having a deep, very powerful voice which was naturally rough but without any 'accent', he was peculiarly suited to a part which had to be so genuinely earthy.

THE NOSEBAG

ANNOUNCER. The Nosebag! The programme that follows is a traditional Russian folk-tale. The story itself is fantastic but the hero is a true Russian peasant. We hope you will all find something in: The Nosebag.

(*Introductory music.*)

SOLDIER. Damn the sergeant! Damn the officer! Damn the Colonel! Damn the General! Who do they think they are to do such a thing to me? After twenty-five years of service. Out on my neck and the wind is cold and the steppes are wide and the years are empty. A discharged soldier that nobody wants. Twenty-five years of service to God and the Great Tsar. And now discharged . . . discharged! And nothing to show for it all but three dry biscuits. Three . . . dry . . . biscuits. Well. It's a long road; I'd best be moving. Left—left—left right left; left—left—

1ST BEGGAR. Soldier! Soldier! Stop!

SOLDIER. What's up, father?

(*Pause.*)

No, I've got no money.

1ST BEGGAR. No money, soldier. Food! I have sixty years of age and little breath in my body. Hunger is always with me and—

SOLDIER. Hunger? Take him away. And take this biscuit too.

1ST BEGGAR. May the good God bless you, soldier.

SOLDIER. Aye, may the good God bless me. Two . . . dry . . . biscuits. Left—left—left right—

2ND BEGGAR. Soldier!

SOLDIER. What do *you* want?

2ND BEGGAR. Food, soldier, for the love of God. I have seventy years of age and—

SOLDIER. No flesh on your bones, eh. This won't help you much but—

2ND BEGGAR. A biscuit! A biscuit! May the good God reward you.

The Nosebag

SOLDIER. In the next life maybe. One . . . dry . . . biscuit. Well, well, a Russian soldier cannot drown in water or burn in fire. This is a long road but who knows whether—

3RD BEGGAR. Soldier!

(*The Third Beggar speaks with a serenity lacking in his predecessors.*)

SOLDIER. A third old rag-and-bones!

3RD BEGGAR. Soldier, forgive me for stopping you. I am an old man—older than you can guess—I have not eaten today, yesterday I dined on birch-bark—

SOLDIER. I've done that in my time. I know what you'd like. See this?
Not so fast, greybeard. Suppose we break it in two?

3RD BEGGAR. Just as you will, soldier.

SOLDIER. Seems more sense to halve it. All the same . . . .

3RD BEGGAR. All the same?

SOLDIER. Your brother beggars got a biscuit each; it don't seem fair that—Here!

3RD BEGGAR. All for me?

SOLDIER. Aye, beggar. I never liked biscuits anyway.

3RD BEGGAR. I thank you, soldier. Now it is my turn. Tell me how I can help you.

SOLDIER. You! Help me! God bless you, beggar, you couldn't help a fly.

3RD BEGGAR. You think not? Have faith. What would you like?

SOLDIER. Nothing, old fellow, nothing. Leastways, maybe, for a keepsake—you haven't a pack of cards, have you?

3RD BEGGAR. Cards? Here.

SOLDIER. Upon my soul, brand-new!

3RD BEGGAR. Whomsoever you play with, using these cards you will win.

SOLDIER. Eh?

3RD BEGGAR. And here . . . is something else.

SOLDIER. What's that? A nosebag!

3RD BEGGAR. A nosebag.

The Nosebag

SOLDIER. A nosebag! What in the name of—

3RD BEGGAR. Soldier, mark what I say. You have been good to me, I will be good to you.

SOLDIER. Aye, but a nosebag without a horse—

3RD BEGGAR. You can have horses and all if you want. As you go on by this road, whatever you see that you fancy, be it beast, bird or fish—just you hold out this bag and open the mouth of it so and call out 'Beast or bird! Jump in here in my nosebag.' And mark my words, they will.

SOLDIER. Ha! Ha! Ha! Ha! Ha! That's a good story if ever I—

3RD BEGGAR. A good story is a true story. You do not know who I am, soldier—

SOLDIER. Who *are* you?

3RD BEGGAR. I leave you to guess, soldier. But make a good use of my gifts. Farewell now. God bless you.

(*A balalaika fades up; introducing an Inn crowded with noisy peasants.*)

1ST PEASANT. Come on, landlord. Vodka on credit.

LANDLORD. Nothing on credit, friend. Not in these days.

1ST PEASANT. Stingy old cheese-paring—

MARYA. No, he's right. In these days a body has got to—

1ST PEASANT. A body has got to have vodka.

2ND PEASANT. Aye, that's right. Folks won't come to no good unless—

LANDLORD. Folks won't come to no good unless they work, I tell you.

2ND PEASANT. A body can't work without drink. And food too, o'course. When I remember the old days—

ALL. A-a-ah!

1ST PEASANT. Rivers of brown beer!

2ND PEASANT. Armies of roast geese!

SOLDIER (*entering*). Who wants roast geese?

LANDLORD. Come in, soldier. Sit down. But, if you want drink, you must pay.

SOLDIER. I said: Who wants roast goose?

The Nosebag

MARYA. Who wants it! Hark ye, soldier, you look like a stranger here and a joke's a joke but—

SOLDIER. See what I've got in my hand?

MARYA. A nosebag. What about it?

SOLDIER. Well, it looks full, don't it? Guess what I've got inside.

2ND PEASANT. *I* know . . . Hay!

VOICES. That's right. Hay.

SOLDIER. Well, look here.

One!

Two!!

Three!!!

LANDLORDS. The saints preserve us! Geese!

ALL. Geese! Geese! Geese!

SOLDIER. Three wild geese. Landlord, take 'em. The first you can roast for my supper, the second you can change for vodka—

2ND PEASANT. Ooh, won't he be drunk!

SOLDIER. And the third you can keep as payment.

LANDLORD. Upon my soul—

SOLDIER. Is that fair or isn't it?

LANDLORD. Fair? Of course it's fair, sir. Now, sir, if you'd like to sit here, sir—

SOLDIER. You needn't sir me and I won't sit here. Give me that big table and lay a place for all.

MARYA. What do you mean?

SOLDIER. When I have luck I share it. Sit you down, folks.

1ST PEASANT. Me?

2ND PEASANT. Me?

SOLDIER. All of you.

(*Cheers.*)

2ND PEASANT. All of us except Marya. She has to do the cooking.

MARYA. Aye and it'll take time.

2ND PEASANT. All the more time for drinking.

SOLDIER. Aye, and for music. Landlord!

The Nosebag

LANDLORD. Yes, sir?

SOLDIER. Give us some music, can't you?

LANDLORD. Music, sir, but—

SOLDIER (*authoritatively*). Music!

(*The balalaika strikes up.*)

SOLDIER. That's more like it.

(*A pause; then he puts an idle question.*)

SOLDIER. What's that big house yonder out of the window?

(*The balalaika breaks off abruptly; the peasants whisper.*)

SOLDIER. Why has the music stopped?

LANDLORD. Because of what you said, sir.

MARYA. The music always stops when a body mentions that.

SOLDIER. Mentions what?

2ND PEASANT. The house outside the window.

SOLDIER. Why! A man can mention a house.

LANDLORD. Aye, sir, but that is the Tsar's palace.

SOLDIER. Pah! A man can mention a palace.

LANDLORD. Aye, sir, but this is a haunted palace.

(*The peasants murmur endorsement.*)

SOLDIER. Haunted?

LANDLORD. Aye, soldier, by devils.

1ST PEASANT. Aye, a regular pack of 'em. Every shape and size and—

MARYA. See them windows, soldier? Bain't a whole pane of glass in 'em.

1ST PEASANT. They meets there every night. Horrible goings-on.

SOLDIER. They do?

LANDLORD. They do indeed, sir. Every night at midnight in they comes a-growling and screeching—you can hear 'em from over here.

MARYA. Playing cards and dicing and—

SOLDIER. What does the Tsar do?

LANDLORD. Tsar? He ain't put his foot in there for over a dozen years.

The Nosebag

2ND PEASANT. That's right. No one can spend a night in that there palace and live.

SOLDIER. Is that so? Where can I find this Tsar?

(*The peasants express alarm.*)

LANDLORD. He lives in the next parish but what do you—

SOLDIER. Never you mind. Fill up your glasses, friends. (*decisively*) I shall call on your Tsar tomorrow.

(*Court music leads to the Court—and to Tomorrow.*)

CHAMBERLAIN (*approaching*). Your most Imperial Majesty.

TSAR. Yes, yes, what the deuce is it now?

CHAMBERLAIN. A discharged soldier is waiting without at the gate.

TSAR. A discharged soldier? Go and discharge him again.

CHAMBERLAIN. But your Imperial—

TSAR. I will *not* have my mornings disturbed by men of the people. There *is* such a thing as autocracy. Why, in my father's time—

SOLDIER (*entering*). Good morning. Are you the Tsar?

TSAR. What!

CHAMBERLAIN. Who let that man in here?

SOLDIER. I let myself in, master. I've got business with—

TSAR. Call in the guard and clap this fellow in gaol.

SOLDIER. In gaol, eh? (*Slyly*) Why not the haunted palace?

TSAR. The haunted—What do you want, you scum, with the haunted palace?

SOLDIER (*dead-pan*). I want to see them devils.

TSAR. Why? They'd tear you to pieces, man.

SOLDIER. You think so?

TSAR. I know so. Other people have tried this game before. And not just trash like you. Well set-up young fellows with blue blood in their veins but it was all the same. When we sent round in the morning all we found was their bones. (*With gusto.*) And the ivory floors were red with their blood.

SOLDIER. Red? Why not blue?

The Nosebag

TSAR. I believe it *was* blue. But as I was saying—

SOLDIER. What will you give me if I get rid of them devils?

TSAR. Give you? What did we offer 'em last time?

CHAMBERLAIN. I do not remember, Your Majesty. It was a large sum.

SOLDIER. Well, give me a large sum. Now where's the key?

CHAMBERLAIN. What do you mean, boor? His Majesty has not as yet consented to—

TSAR. Give him the key, give him the key. There you are, soldier. Let yourself in tonight and we'll fetch you out tomorrow.

CHAMBERLAIN (*smoothly*). His Majesty means your bones.

(*Ghost music creeps up and continues while the Soldier walks round inspecting.*)

SOLDIER. So this is the haunted palace. Fancy carvings. Ivory. Marble. Must have cost a bit. Draughty though—and don't it smell? That'll be all this muck on the floors. Devils done that, I reckon. Bones, feathers—(*he laughs but not happily*) might be a barnyard. Lucky the moon shines in, I can find me a place to sit. (*He speaks slowly, settling himself.*) Time for a nice smoke before it comes on to midnight.

(*Music and Wind. A clock begins striking midnight, then is drowned in jabbering and screeching.*)

DEVIL CAPTAIN. Devils! You all here?

VOICES. Aye, aye, Captain.

DEVIL CAPTAIN. Good. Orders for tonight are simple. Palace to be haunted from end to end as usual. Every devil to be on his worst behaviour. Is that in disorder?

VOICES. Aye, sir.

DEVIL CAPTAIN. Right. In you go!

(*Music swells up, as the Devils cheer.*)

1ST DEVIL. Hugger and mugger, pell and mell,
Here we come the devils from Hell.

2ND DEVIL. Fire and brimstone, bug and nit,
Here we come from the burning pit.

3RD DEVIL. Horn and dewclaw, blood and malice,
Here we come to the Tsar's palace.

4TH DEVIL. Cloven hoof and burning bill,
This big devil is out to kill.

LITTLE DEVIL. Shining tusk and twining tail,
This little devil is . . .

is . . .

is . . .

Oh, I do want a rhyme!

DEVIL CAPTAIN. Devils! Halt! (*The music ends.*) This is no time for rhymes. What do I see at the far end of the hall?

1ST DEVIL. A man!

2ND DEVIL. A man!

3RD DEVIL. A man!

4TH DEVIL. A man!

LITTLE DEVIL. A live one!

DEVIL CAPTAIN. Ahoy there, man!

SOLDIER (*distant*). Ahoy there, devils!

DEVIL CAPTAIN. Come up here.

SOLDIER (*distant*). Com-ing.

4TH DEVIL. Ph-e-ew! Now for some fun.

2ND DEVIL. Not seen one of these in a twelvemonth.

LITTLE DEVIL. Aw, why did I leave my pitchfork at home?
(*The devils growl in anticipation.*)

DEVIL CAPTAIN. Silence there. I'll handle this business. No one to act till I give the order. I want no biting, scratching, pronging, eating-up or other molestation, until such time as—

SOLDIER (*joining them*). Hullo there, Scaly.

DEVIL CAPTAIN. Welcome, soldier, to our little party. What can we do to amuse you?

SOLDIER. I'm amused already. Ha! Ha! Ha! Such a funny-looking bunch I never in my life—Ha! Ha! Ha!—
(*The devils hiss at him.*)

The Nosebag

DEVIL CAPTAIN. I beg your pardon. I merely wanted to know what are your favourite pastimes. Dancing? Skittles? Knucklebones? Cards?

SOLDIER. Cards.

DEVIL CAPTAIN. Excellent. Now take a seat here at this table and—Who's got a pack?

SOLDIER. I have.

DEVIL CAPTAIN. A new pack, eh?

SOLDIER. Somebody gave it me. Want me to deal?

DEVIL CAPTAIN. Go ahead.

(The devils scratch on the table and jabber.)

DEVILS. Yub-a-yub-a-yub-a-yub-a-yub-a-yub-a-yub . . . .

SOLDIER. Now then. Turn 'em up.

1ST DEVIL. [Seven of Hearts.

2ND DEVIL. Four of Clubs.

3RD DEVIL. Knave of Clubs.

4TH DEVIL. Ten of Diamonds.

DEVIL CAPTAIN. Queen of Spades.

SOLDIER. Ace of Diamonds.

DEVILS. Urrr-urrr-urrr-urrr-urrr . . . .

SOLDIER (*very calmly*). Your gold, please. Your deal, Scaly.

DEVIL CAPTAIN. Thank you.

LITTLE DEVIL. Hee-hee-hee. Now we'll see some play.]

(Short passage of music to cover another round.)

SOLDIER. Your gold please.

(Ditto.)

SOLDIER. Your gold please.

(Ditto.)

SOLDIER. Your gold please.

(The music ends. The devils are very angry.)

DEVILS. Urrr-urrr-urrr-urrr-urrr . . . .

DEVIL CAPTAIN. Extraordinary, quite extraordinary. Skraglitch!

LITTLE DEVIL. Here, sir.

DEVIL CAPTAIN. Run back to Hell and fetch some more money·

The Nosebag

LITTLE DEVIL. Yes, sir. How much, sir?

DEVIL CAPTAIN. Every ounce you can carry. And don't go dropping it in space.

LITTLE DEVIL. No, sir; I won't, sir.

DEVIL CAPTAIN. Well, soldier, your luck's been quite phenomenal. (*The devils growl.*) But, as I always say, he who laughs last—Ah, Skraglitch! Put it down here.

LITTLE DEVIL. Pretty good time, eh, captain? I didn't drop none either.

DEVIL CAPTAIN. Put the money down and stop talking. Now then, friends, whose deal is it?

(*The devils scratch the table and jabber as before. Short passage of music.*)

SOLDIER. Your gold, please.

(*The music ends abruptly. This is too much.*)

SOLDIER. What, are you all cleaned out? Looks as if the game is over.

DEVIL CAPTAIN. On the contrary, soldier, the game is about to begin. Devils! Where are your pitchforks?

(*Hubbub.*)

LITTLE DEVIL. Aw, why did I leave mine at home!

DEVIL CAPTAIN. Now then, before we destroy him—Aren't you afraid, soldier?

SOLDIER. Afraid? What of? A Russian soldier cannot drown in—

DEVIL CAPTAIN. Yes, yes, yes, I know that proverb: A Russian soldier can't burn in water. (*The devils laugh.*) But, Russian soldier or no Russian soldier, you've cheated at cards and you're going to pay for it.

(*The devils growl, warming up.*)

SOLDIER. Stand back devils. See this?

DEVILS. A nosebag?

LITTLE DEVIL. A dirty old, empty old nosebag.

SOLDIER. Dirty. Maybe. Empty? We'll see about that.

(*More growling.*)

The Nosebag

SOLDIER (*with sudden authority*). Devils—in the name of God—in with you into my nosebag!

(*Screams. Music.*)

SOLDIER. That's right. One—two—three—four—five—six— seven—eight—nine—ten—eleven—twelve—thirteen . . . .

(*His voice is drowned in music—which passes away like the night.*)

CHAMBERLAIN. Your Imperial Majesty. Your morning vodka.

TSAR. Morning already! What's going on in the world?

CHAMBERLAIN. Nothing new, Your Majesty. Except the soldier, of course.

TSAR. Soldier?

CHAMBERLAIN. The one that slept last night in the haunted palace.

TSAR. Oh, yes, yes—Have they fetched his bones yet?

CHAMBERLAIN. No, Your Imperial—

TSAR. If not, why not?

CHAMBERLAIN. The Captain of the Guards reports that he called at the palace at dawn but there were no bones to be found.

TSAR. Not even bones. Poor fellow!

CHAMBERLAIN. The odd thing is, Your Majesty, a report has just been received that a soldier of similar appearance was seen an hour or two back calling on the village blacksmith.

TSAR. On the village blacksmith? Why?

CHAMBERLAIN. He is said to have been carrying a nosebag.

TSAR. A what?

CHAMBERLAIN. A nosebag, Your Majesty. Rather a common object.

TSAR. Hmph. What are the other facts in the case?

CHAMBERLAIN. No other facts, Your Majesty. Merely a soldier, a nosebag, a blacksmith.

(*A pause.*)

SOLDIER. Now then, smith. You and your mate get hold of this bag and lay it there on the anvil.

1ST SMITH. Right.

The Nosebag

2ND SMITH. Right.

1ST SMITH. Oh, heavy!

2ND SMITH. Heavy. Aye. What you got in her, soldier?

SOLDIER. Never you mind. Just lay that bag on the anvil and beat it hard the pair of you—in the ancient manner of smiths.

1ST SMITH. [Right, let me get my breath. I'm sweating already with the weight of her.

2ND SMITH. The devil must be in that nosebag.

LITTLE DEVIL (*muffled*). You're right, father. We are!

1ST SMITH. What's that?

2ND SMITH. The saints preserve us!

SOLDIER. The saints will preserve you. Get on with the job. Lay to.]

      (*A rhythmical clanging; the devils shriek.*)

SOLDIER. This is music, this is. Bling, blong, bling, blong. Harder, my friends. harder!

(*The clanging rises to a peak, then slowly fades away. The devils are back in Hell—but very tired.*)

4TH DEVIL. Ooh—I never thought we'd see this place again.

2ND DEVIL. Smell the good old pitch and—How are your bones, brothers?

1ST DEVIL. Broken every one of 'em. If he hadn't let us out when he did, I think I'd have—

LITTLE DEVIL. Where's the Captain?

3RD DEVIL. That's right. Where's the Captain?

2ND DEVIL. Don't say he's still back there.

4TH DEVIL. He may be, you know. He was at the bottom of the bag.

LITTLE DEVIL. Poor old Captain! He was a bit strict sometimes but—

1ST DEVIL. Talk of the devil! Here he comes now.

ALL. Welcome, Captain. Welcome back to Hell.

DEVIL CAPTAIN (*breathless*). Give me a chair, someone.

4TH DEVIL. What happened, Captain, what happened?

DEVIL CAPTAIN. Keep this under your horns. That blest soldier
—when he unbuckled the bag—I was the last, you know—
well, it's really all too humiliating—

LITTLE DEVIL. Go on, Captain, tell us.

DEVIL CAPTAIN. The fellow caught me by the tail and before he
would let me go—a strong fellow, that soldier—he got me to
sign a contract.

DEVILS. A contract!

DEVIL CAPTAIN. Yes, I know, it's unheard of. But what could I
do? I—

4TH DEVIL. You didn't promise nothing, did you?

DEVIL CAPTAIN. I'm afraid I did. I—

LITTLE DEVIL. Well, you can break it, Captain.

DEVIL CAPTAIN. That's enough from you. A devil's promise is a
gentleman's promise. ('*That's right*' *say the adult devils.*) I
have undertaken to serve that soldier whenever he chooses
to call on me.

2ND DEVIL. Umph! That's hard.

DEVIL CAPTAIN. Hard, my good man? It's degrading. But I'll
get my own back. If ever that soldier fellow fancies a billet
in hell—Sergeant!

4TH DEVIL. Here, sir.

DEVIL CAPTAIN. From this day forward double the guard. Have
all the gates reinforced. Lookouts on every turret.

4TH DEVIL. Yes, sir.

DEVIL CAPTAIN. On the first report of a soldier with a nosebag,
ring the tocsin and man the ramparts.

4TH DEVIL. Yes, sir.

DEVIL CAPTAIN. He laughs longest who laughs last. That soldier
may think himself clever, he may have the entrée to all the
kingdoms of earth, but he won't have an entrée here.

LITTLE DEVIL. What's an entrée, Captain?

DEVIL CAPTAIN. No, he won't; not in a billion years.

2ND DEVIL. That'll learn him. Maybe now he's saying to him-

The Nosebag

self he's happy. What a mistake! Happy! Happy!

(Idyllic music flowers up, covering a passage of time.)

SOLDIER. Oh how happy I am. All in the world that I want except a wife.

(Music.)

SOLDIER. My dear wife! What joy it is to be married. All in the world that I want—except a son.

(Music.)

SOLDIER. More vodka there! More vodka! Raise your glasses, brothers. We will drink to the health of my son who was born today.

(The music comes to a happy close.)

TSAR. Chamberlain, what's the news?

CHAMBERLAIN. No news, Your Imperial Majesty.

TSAR. How is my good friend, the discharged soldier?

CHAMBERLAIN. Nothing new about him. He's just happy, as usual.

TSAR. Rich as ever?

CHAMBERLAIN. Yes, Your Im—

TSAR. Wife as lovely as ever?

CHAMBERLAIN. So they say, Your Majesty.

TSAR. And how is his little boy?

CHAMBERLAIN. According to the Court News he is five years old tomorrow. And never yet, Your Majesty, never yet had a cold.

TSAR. Never had a cold! Bah! I don't believe it. Why, I was swaddled in velvet and I had a cold in the cradle—

(sneezes)

Yes—and I've got one now.

CHAMBERLAIN. I am more than grieved to hear it.

(sneezes)

Your Majesty will perceive that I have a cold myself.

TSAR *(snaps at him)*. Then don't come near me. Yours might be something worse.

The Nosebag

CHAMBERLAIN. Something worse, Your Majesty? I can assure you it's—

TSAR. My German doctor tells me there's plague about.

CHAMBERLAIN. Yes, Your Majesty. Two or three-thousand cases. But that begins with boils.

TSAR. You got any boils?

CHAMBERLAIN. Your Majesty!

TSAR. All right, all right. One can't be too careful though. The doctor tells me these boils spring up overnight. And once that appears, you're done for.

(*The Soldier's Wife is heard—calling out as she approaches.*)

WIFE. Husband! . . . Husband! . . . Husband!

SOLDIER. What is it now, wife of my heart? Have you lost your pearls again?

WIFE. No. It's little Ivan. I've found a boil on his neck.

SOLDIER. A boil? . . . A boil. . . . Not the . . . the plague?

WIFE. I have sent for the Tsar's doctor. He is looking him over now.

SOLDIER (*slowly; unprecedentedly serious*). If it was to be the plague . . . .

DOCTOR (*approaching*). Gnädige Frau. Be so good as to send for some water.

WIFE. Water? He needs water?

DOCTOR. No, it is I who need it. To wash my hands, verstehen. In contact with fatal diseases I make it my practice to—

SOLDIER. What do you mean—fatal diseases?

DOCTOR. Your son has the plague. (*The Wife exclaims in agony.*) I give him twenty-four hours. Will you please send for that water? So. And a towel.

(*Music punctuates the following.*)

SOLDIER. Dead within twenty-four hours.

. . . .

Within twelve hours.

. . . .

The Nosebag

Within six hours.

.   .   .   .

Dead within three hours.

. .   .   .

Within two hours.

.   .   .   .

Within ONE hour.

.   .   .   .

(*The music wilts away.*)

WIFE (*broken*). Husband! Can you do nothing?

SOLDIER. I'm not a doctor. What the devil can I—Eh! 'What the *devil*'? Where's that contract gone to?

WIFE. What contract? Why are you searching in the mattress?

SOLDIER. Here it is, here it is! Leave me alone, my love, time is short.

WIFE. But, husband—

SOLDIER. Leave me alone, I say.

WIFE. But I must nurse Ivan.

SOLDIER. I will see to Ivan. Go. Go out of the room.

WIFE (*submitting to a forlorn hope*). Very well then.

(*The door closes.*)

SOLDIER. Now then. Quickly. Where's that cheat of a devil?

DEVIL CAPTAIN (*popping up*). Cheat! . . . Who says that I am a cheat?

SOLDIER. All right. You prove you're not. See this contract?

DEVIL CAPTAIN (*ungraciously*). What do you want me to do?

SOLDIER. Look over there. In the cot.

(*Pause while the devil moves over. His voice sounds further off.*)

DEVIL CAPTAIN (*matter-of-fact*). Hm! Your son looks ill.

SOLDIER. The plague, devil, the plague!

DEVIL CAPTAIN. Want me to cure him?

SOLDIER. Can you?

DEVIL CAPTAIN. That remains to be seen. I have something here in my pocket. This glass. Fill it with water.

The Nosebag

(*A sound of bubbling water.*)

DEVIL CAPTAIN. Thank you.

Now then; we hold this glass over the patient's bed. Come here and stand by me. Look in this glass and tell me what you can see.

SOLDIER. See, devil? . . . Nothing. Nothing but bubbles, that is.

DEVIL CAPTAIN. Those bubbles will soon settle. Keep on looking. Well?

SOLDIER. Bubbles; only bubbles.

DEVIL CAPTAIN. Go on. Go on looking.

SOLDIER. Ah!

DEVIL CAPTAIN. Yes?

SOLDIER. I see . . . I see . . . I see my son in his cot.

DEVIL CAPTAIN. Yes?

SOLDIER. And I see the figure of a woman standing beside him.

DEVIL CAPTAIN. Know who that is, soldier? That is Death.

SOLDIER. Death!

DEVIL CAPTAIN. Of course. Where is she standing?

SOLDIER. Where?

DEVIL CAPTAIN. At his head or his feet?

SOLDIER. His feet.

DEVIL CAPTAIN. That's all we need to know. If Death stands at his feet your boy will survive.

SOLDIER. Thank God!

DEVIL CAPTAIN. Now if she were at his head—ha! ha!—nothing could save him, soldier.

Here, take this water and pour it over the child.

CHILD. Ouch!

DEVIL CAPTAIN. You see? He has come to.

SOLDIER. Ah, God be praised for this—

DEVIL CAPTAIN. *God* be praised, eh? Well, anything else you want?

SOLDIER. No, devil. Unless . . . .

DEVIL CAPTAIN. Unless what?

The Nosebag

SOLDIER. Would you give me that glass of yours?

DEVIL CAPTAIN. Oh no! Oh no you don't.

SOLDIER. Go on, devil. If you give me that glass, I'll release you from this here contract.

DEVIL CAPTAIN. Ah, that's different. Hand me the contract and I'll—Thank you.

(*A noise of tearing parchment.*)

DEVIL CAPTAIN. Goodbye, soldier. You know how to use the glass?

SOLDIER. Aye. From this day on *I'm* setting up for a doctor.

(*Funereal music creeps in, leads to the Chamberlain's sickbed.*)

CHAMBERLAIN. [Where's that doctor? Where's that doctor? Didn't you take him my message?

MAIDSERVANT. I'm sorry, master. He says, if you've got the plague, he's attending no more cases.

CHAMBERLAIN. The damned German! Isn't there—

MAIDSERVANT. He says, master, that all that remains for you is to say your prayers and die. But if you was to ask *me* . . . .

CHAMBERLAIN. What? Go on, I'm asking you.

MAIDSERVANT. I'd say my prayers and send for that discharged soldier.

CHAMBERLAIN (*with distaste*). The discharged soldier? Why?

MAIDSERVANT. Folks do say that he has a cure for the plague. He's cured a few already. Boyars, generals and that. Does it all with a glass.

SOLDIER (*entering*). Aye. With a glass. Like this.

MAIDSERVANT. Well! Talk of the devil!

SOLDIER. No, you don't; don't talk of the devil to me. (*cheerily*) Now then, Chamberlain, want to be cured?

CHAMBERLAIN. What's that medicine?

SOLDIER. Water, only water. And I hold it above you so. Now come here you and tell me what you can see.

MAIDSERVANT. See? . . . I can see bubbles.

SOLDIER. Go on looking. Now?

The Nosebag

MAIDSERVANT. I see the master lying on his bed.

CHAMBERLAIN. Hmph! You don't have to look in a glass to—

SOLDIER. Hsh! Anything else?

MAIDSERVANT. Aye. A kind of a woman—

SOLDIER. That's not a woman; that's Death.

(The Chamberlain moans with horror.)

MAIDSERVANT. Death?

SOLDIER. At his head or his feet?

MAIDSERVANT. At his, er—now, now, now, I can't see if you joggle the glass—She's standing right at his feet.

SOLDIER. Here's a cold douche for you, Chamberlain.

CHAMBERLAIN. Ow! What do you mean by—

SOLDIER. I'll send you the bill in the morning.

(Funereal music, as before.)

DOCTOR. A boil! So? The plague! Call the lawyers and I'll make my will.

SOLDIER *(entering).* Your will will keep, Herr Doktor. Want to be cured?

DOCTOR. Who let *you* in, quack?

SOLDIER. 'Want to be cured?', I said.

DOCTOR. No one can cure this plague. I am a doctor, I know.

SOLDIER *(sardonically, moving off).* Well, if you know . . . .

DOCTOR. Where are you going?

SOLDIER. Well, I thought as I'm not welcome—

DOCTOR. What is this cure of yours?

SOLDIER. It's simple, Herr Doktor, but it's costly.

DOCTOR. What is your fee?

SOLDIER. If I cure you, as I can, you must resign to me—*(he pauses to get his effect)* your post as the Tsar's physician.

DOCTOR. As the Tsar's—but no, no, no! I will not give up my post. Besides it is ridiculous. You as the Tsar's physician! No, no, no! A million times no. A thousand times no. A hundred times no. Ten times no . . .].

(Funereal music as before.)

The Nosebag

CHAMBERLAIN. Send for the Tsar's physician. The Tsar is ill unto death.

SOLDIER. You need not send, Chamberlain. News travels fast these days; I travel faster. Just fill me this glass with water and—

TSAR. Who's that? The discharged soldier?

SOLDIER. The Tsar's physician, Your Imperial Majesty.

TSAR. Thank God you are here. You can cure me?

CHAMBERLAIN. He cured *me*, Your Majesty.

TSAR. That's nothing to do with it.

CHAMBERLAIN. He has also cured hundreds of boyars, dozens of generals and—

TSAR. Hold your tongue. Have you filled his glass with water?

CHAMBERLAIN. Yes, Your Imperial—

TSAR. Well, then, let him get on with it.

SOLDIER. Chamberlain, stand by me. Look in this glass and look very carefully. What do you see?

CHAMBERLAIN. Bubbles.

SOLDIER (*smugly echoing him*). Bubbles.

CHAMBERLAIN. A figure.

SOLDIER. A figure.

CHAMBERLAIN. The Tsar in his bed.

SOLDIER. The Tsar in his bed.

CHAMBERLAIN. And another figure.

SOLDIER. Death.

CHAMBERLAIN. Death! Dear me, is that—

SOLDIER. Death standing at his feet.

CHAMBERLAIN. But no, soldier, no.

SOLDIER (*shocked*). What!

CHAMBERLAIN. Look in your own glass. It's Death standing at his head.

SOLDIER. At his what? . . . What! . . . (*resigning himself*) Aye. Death standing at his head.

(*Pause.*)

The Nosebag

TSAR. Come on, come on; I'm not cured yet.

SOLDIER (*quietly*). You never will be, Your Imperial Majesty.

TSAR. What's that? What do you mean, man?

SOLDIER. You have three hours left to live.

TSAR. You liar!

SOLDIER. No, your Imperial—

TSAR. Did you not cure the boyars?

SOLDIER. Aye.

TSAR. And the generals?

SOLDIER. Aye.

TSAR. And my Chamberlain here?

CHAMBERLAIN. Aye—Yes, I mean.

TSAR. And you refuse to cure me!

SOLDIER. I do not refuse, I—

TSAR. You are a traitor. I'll have you beheaded at once.

CHAMBERLAIN. Shall I pass on the order, Your Majesty?

TSAR. Yes. Behead him at once and—

(*A female voice cuts in—very rarefied and formal.*)

DEATH. I only bargained for one. Now it seems there'll be two.

TSAR. What's that? Who's talking?

DEATH. One by the plague and one by the block.

CHAMBERLAIN. Cherchez la femme, Your Majesty, cherchez la—

SOLDIER. Hsh, you! Look in this glass, can't you? There's the
one that's doing the talking. Death! Hi, Death! That you?

DEATH. Aye, soldier. Greetings.

SOLDIER. You are waiting to take the Tsar?

DEATH. I am, soldier.

SOLDIER. Supposing now . . . supposing . . . .

DEATH. Supposing what?

SOLDIER. You are a person of honour. You only bargained for
one. Well now . . . .

DEATH. Yes?

SOLDIER (*taking the plunge*). Instead of the Tsar, why don't you
take me?

The Nosebag

DEATH. You, soldier?

SOLDIER. What's the odds? He's going to behead me anyway. Give the old pig his life and take me instead.

DEATH. Do you want it that way?

TSAR. We do!

SOLDIER. Nobody asked you. Aye. I want it that way. But give me just three hours more. Then I'll have time to get home and say farewell to my family.

DEATH. So be it, soldier. I release my claims on the Tsar and you shall have three hours more. I shall be there at your bedside.

(Music punctuates the following.)

SOLDIER. Farewell, my friends.

Farewell, Ivan my son.

Farewell, my beloved wife.

DEATH. Your time is up, soldier.

(The music ends; the Soldier's time is up.)

SOLDIER (*feebly*). That you, Death? Where are you?

DEATH. Your eyes are dim. You have only three minutes left to live in the bright world. So hurry, soldier, I'm waiting. What are you doing, rummaging under the pillow?

SOLDIER. Looking for something. A locket.

DEATH. A locket? Hm. Always the same story. Well, find it quickly and—

SOLDIER. Here she is.

DEATH. That's not a locket.

SOLDIER. What is it then?

DEATH. Why that thing's a . . . .

SOLDIER. What?

DEATH. Why, that's just an old nosebag.

SOLDIER. You sure about that?

The Nosebag

DEATH. Of course I am. Enough of this nonsense; I've got other
engagements—

SOLDIER. One thing at a time, Mistress Death. If this is a nosebag
—jump into it.

(Musical effect, representing the Nosebag Trick.)

PEASANT. Hey, soldier. What have you got in that nosebag.

SOLDIER. Never you mind. Is this the way to the forest?

PEASANT. Yonder's the forest ahead of you. That bag of yours
looks heavy.

SOLDIER. It *is* heavy, my brother.

PEASANT. It's cold in that forest, soldier.

SOLDIER. Cold? *(gleefully)* The colder the better.

(Music and wind. Here is the forest.)

SOLDIER *(grunting from his efforts)*. Now then—the bitter aspen—
the very top of it—the topmost twig—fasten her well.
(triumphantly) Goodbye, nosebag. Goodbye, Death. Looks as
if from now on folks won't die any more.

(The forest music recedes slowly into Ancient History.)

TSAR. Extraordinary thing, Chamberlain. Nobody's died here
lately. Noticed that in your rounds?

CHAMBERLAIN. How could I not, Your Majesty? The bishop says
it's a scandal.

TSAR. No more burial fees, eh?

CHAMBERLAIN. No, Your Majesty; it's serious.

(Passage of music: the Non-Dying Era progresses.)

CHAMBERLAIN. Your Majesty, this really is serious.

TSAR. What's it now, Chamberlain?

CHAMBERLAIN. The census has just come in.

TSAR. Yes? What of it?

CHAMBERLAIN. It proves beyond a doubt that your kingdom is
over-populated.

TSAR. Is it? Why?

CHAMBERLAIN. Because, Your Majesty, none of us ever die.

TSAR. When was the last death?

The Nosebag

CHAMBERLAIN. Oh years ago, Your Majesty.

TSAR. Years? You mean decades!

CHAMBERLAIN. Your Majesty is always right. I ought to have said decades.

(*Another passage of music*).

SOLDIER. Well, well, well, lovely weather today! Just the right day to have taken this trip to the city. Beautiful blue sky, everyone ought to be happy. But they're not, you know, they're not. Look at that old woman blowing about in the wind—and there's hardly a wind to speak of—just like she was a straw. My word, that's an old woman. It's almost time she died.

OLD WOMAN (*croaking with age and misery*). You took the words out of my mouth, discharged soldier. Almost time I died! That time has come and gone. Long, long years ago. And ever since then my life—if you call it life—is an agony. And you know whose fault that is. The day that you put Death in the nosebag, I had no more than an hour to live in the white world. All I want is rest and it's you who's kept it from me.

SOLDIER. I'm sorry, mother.

OLD WOMAN. Sorry! Do you know what you've done, soldier? You've committed an unforgivable sin. And there's other folk like me. Have you ever thought about that?

SOLDIER. No, I can't say I—

OLD WOMAN. Then you'd better think now. And if you can undo what you've done—maybe you can't—

(*Suddenly converted, he interrupts her.*)

SOLDIER. No? . . . Maybe I can.

(*Back to the Forest. Wind and music.*)

SOLDIER (*shouting*). Death! Death! . . . Where's that bitter aspen? Ah, here we are.

Death! Hey, Death, are you alive?

DEATH (*distant and very feeble*). Aye, soldier; just.

The Nosebag

SOLDIER (*shouting up to the aspen top*). Good. I've come to take you home with me.

(*The Forest slowly recedes again.*)

WIFE. Husband! Husband! Why are you going to bed? The sun's still up and——

SOLDIER. I've got business to do.

WIFE. Business? In bed?

SOLDIER. That's what I said. Give me a kiss and go.

WIFE. Oh very well. Here's your kiss. I'll bring your supper in later.

(*The door closes.*)

SOLDIER. Supper? Ha! Ha! Now then, where's that nosebag? Patience, Death; I'm just about to unbuckle it.

DEATH (*muffled*). Thank you, soldier, thank you.

SOLDIER. But only on one condition.

DEATH (*muffled*). What's that?

SOLDIER. That, before you take anyone else, you take me.

DEATH (*muffled*). Why?

SOLDIER. I have had a sinful life and a long one. I reckon death will be best for me.

(*Pause.*)

Is that understood?

DEATH (*muffled*). Yes.

SOLDIER. Good. Then I'll let you out.

(*Musical Effect: the Nosebag Trick in reverse.*)

SOLDIER. Hey! Where are you off to?

DEATH. Catch me if you can.

SOLDIER. But you promised——

DEATH. I promised nothing. Do you think that I want to have any more truck with *you*?

SOLDIER (*pleadingly*). But Death, Death——

DEATH. It's no good begging my pardon. If people play tricks on me I can play tricks on them. You'll never see me again. Goodbye now and ill-luck to you.

The Nosebag

(The door bangs.)

SOLDIER. Never see her again? That means I can never die. The beasts will die and the trees and everyone else but me. And I am a sinful man . . . sinful . . . sinful . . . . But there's an idea. They have a place for sin. I know what I'll do; I'll take me off to Hell. Just as I am. I'll pay for my sins alive. And I only hope it will be warm.

(A tocsin is heard in the far, far distance. It grows louder. Hell is in a state of alarm.)

DEVIL CAPTAIN. Sergeant!

4TH DEVIL. Sir?

DEVIL CAPTAIN. Who gave orders for that?

4TH DEVIL. For what, sir?

DEVIL CAPTAIN. For the tocsin.

4TH DEVIL. You did, sir.

DEVIL CAPTAIN. *I* did?

4TH DEVIL. Yes, sir. Two and twenty years ago. Remember, sir? The soldier with the nosebag.

DEVIL CAPTAIN. *That* fellow! You don't say *he* is—

4TH DEVIL. Yes, sir. He was seen at oo. hours approaching the West Gate. He ought to be there by now.

DEVIL CAPTAIN. The sentries got their instructions?

4TH DEVIL. Yes, sir. But if I was you, sir—

DEVIL CAPTAIN. You're quite right, Sergeant. I'll go along myself.

(The tocsin reaches a peak, then fades away.)

SOLDIER. But I tell you, devil, I'm guilty. I'm a guilty soul to be tortured.

SENTRY. Can't help that. You're alive.

SOLDIER. Alive? Maybe, but—

SENTRY. We don't take in no live 'uns. Besides, *you've* got a nosebag.

SOLDIER. What's that got to do with it?

SENTRY. It's a standing order of ours. Any soldiers with nosebags—

The Nosebag

DEVIL CAPTAIN (*arriving*). What's the trouble here, sentry?

SENTRY. *He* is, Captain.

SOLDIER. Scaly! We meet again.

DEVIL CAPTAIN. Oh no, we don't. Get away there from the gates. Off with you into space. We've got no room for you here.

SOLDIER. But, Scaly, I've come to be tortured.

DEVIL CAPTAIN. Tortured? Ha! Ha! Ha! You'll be a lot more tortured drifting around in space. Rents are high in hell. Think that we'd let a practical joker like you—

SOLDIER. Any little corner—I'm not particular—

DEVIL CAPTAIN. You go away somewhere else. And in double quick time, do you hear?

SOLDIER. Somewhere else? Where?

DEVIL CAPTAIN. They say there's a place called Heaven—

SOLDIER. Heaven? They wouldn't look at me. Unless . . . unless . . . Scaly, do me a favour. And then I'll leave you in peace.

DEVIL CAPTAIN. What is it?

SOLDIER. Give me two hundred souls. Black ones out of the Pit. To take with me up to the gates of Paradise. Then perhaps they'll forgive me my sins and—

SENTRY. Well, of all the nerve!

DEVIL CAPTAIN. Shut up, sentry. Anything to get rid of him. Two hundred souls did you say. If you'll take yourself off at once—and promise not to come back—I'll throw in an extra fifty.

SOLDIER. That a deal?

DEVIL CAPTAIN. Two hundred and fifty souls from the Pit. Take 'em away and be blessed to you!

(*Ethereal music mounts with the souls through space.*)

ROBBER SOUL. Well, well, well, ain't it cool up here? Anyone got a spare sheepskin?

FEMALE SOUL. What I want to know is: how much higher are we going?

The Nosebag

CROOK SOUL. Soldier, hey, soldier! The lady here—

ROBBER SOUL. Lady? Ha! Ha! Ha!

CROOK SOUL. The lady here would like to know where you're taking us.

SOLDIER. Why! Didn't the devils tell you? I'm taking you all to Paradise.

(The Bad Souls murmur in astonishment.)

ROBBER SOUL. Paradise!

FEMALE SOUL. Wings, you mean? And harps? What luck that I've kept my complexion.

ROBBER SOUL. Kept your complexion? Where?

(The Bad Souls break into coarse laughter.)

SOLDIER. Stop laughing, you fools. Look yonder.

CROOK SOUL. Hm! What's that? The sun's so bright in my eyes I can't exactly—

SOLDIER. The sun's below you, brother. That's the Gate.

THE SOULS. The Gate! . . . The Gate of Paradise!

SOLDIER. That it is, so you'd better behave decent.

CROOK SOUL. Decent? And why not? When in Rome, as I said when I cheated the Grand Tartar—But one point, soldier, do we have to pass through the Customs?

SOLDIER. Why do you ask that?

CROOK SOUL. Well, they're only trifles of course but as I was leaving Hell—

FEMALE SOUL. Look, darlings, look! I can see the pearly ramparts.

ROBBER SOUL. Yus, and I can see some fellows up there with spears. Watching us too, they are. Don't look too good to me.

(A pause while we switch to Paradise.)

OFFICER. Gatesman.

GATESMAN. Yes, sir.

OFFICER. What's that crowd down there? They on their way here?

The Nosebag

GATESMAN. Yes, sir. Two hundred and fifty guilty souls from Hell and one live soldier with nosebag from—er—Earth.

OFFICER. Oh, indeed?

GATESMAN. What shall I do, sir? Give 'em the rightabout turn?

OFFICER. No. Let 'em come in. Two hundred and fifty's a nice round number.

GATESMAN. Two hundred and fifty-one, sir.

OFFICER. Two hundred and fifty I said. Can't have that soldier in here.

GATESMAN. Right, sir. I understand. They're coming up now, sir.

OFFICER. Good. Give the order to the Gates.

GATESMAN. Yes, sir.

(He turns and shouts out the formula.)

Gates!

Gates of Paradise!

Stand by to admit two hundred and fifty souls.

Gates! Unbolt! Swing on your hinges! Open!

(Music opens the gates.)

SOLDIER. Here, you.

ROBBER SOUL. Me?

SOLDIER. Quick. Take hold of this nosebag. As you go in, say to me—get this right—Say to me 'Soldier, jump into the nosebag'.

ROBBER SOUL. All right, all right, let go of it.

SOLDIER. But don't forget—this is my only chance—so don't forget, promise me, don't forget . . . .

(The Gatesman's voice rings out.)

GATESMAN. Gates!

Gates of Paradise!

Stand by to close!

Swing on your hinges. Close!

(Music closes the gates. Silence. The Soldier is alone.)

SOLDIER. So he forgot, the pig! And took my nosebag with him.

131

The Nosebag

Well, that's the way things are. These gates will never open again for me. And Hell's out of it too and Death she won't come near me. Nothing for it, I reckon. Can't stay hanging round here; it's cold in space tonight. I can fancy a worse thing now than a place on a Russian stove and music maybe and a pipe of tobacco. I think I'll go back to earth.

(*A balalaika steals in; then peasant chatter. He has been here before.*)

MARYA. Landlord! Remember that soldier many years gone come in here once with three wild geese in a nosebag?

LANDLORD. The one that drove the devils out of the Tsar's palace?

MARYA. That's him, landlord. He's here again.

(*Incredulous exclamations all round.*)

LANDLORD. What! I heard he'd died.

SOLDIER (*himself again*). No, landlord; no such luck. Here's my last rouble; bring me some vodka.

LANDLORD. Marya, a bottle of vodka.

SOLDIER. Well, what's the news round here since I've been gone?

LANDLORD. News! Where've you been? The country's gone to war.

SOLDIER. War?

LANDLORD. Aye. They'll soon be calling on you.

SOLDIER. Not on me. I am a man of sin.

LANDLORD. Sin? Don't make me laugh. You're a soldier, ain't you?

SOLDIER. I was a soldier once. Then they discharged me.

LANDLORD. How much service did you have?

SOLDIER. Twenty-five years.

LANDLORD. Not much.

MARYA. The vodka, masters.

LANDLORD. Thank you. Fill up the soldier's double.

MARYA. He looks as if he can do with it.

SOLDIER. You're right, woman. Here's to—

LANDLORD. Not yet, soldier, not yet. *I'm* going to give you a

The Nosebag

toast. You've had twenty-five years of service? Well; you're going to have more. Campaigns like you never dreamed of. You had a magic nosebag, I see you've lost it. Well, that don't matter, you've got something better. You've got a—

SOLDIER. I've got a terrible thirst. Give me your toast.

LANDLORD. You've got a fighting heart and a fighting arm. Well, now you're going to fight with 'em. That's what you're going to do, all through the centuries, you are. Tartars, Swedes, French, Teutons—

SOLDIER. That will all come when it comes. Give me your toast.

LANDLORD. All right, soldier. Here's to Mother Russia.

SOLDIER. Here's . . . to Mother . . . Russia!

THE MARCH HARE SAGA

(1) *The March Hare Resigns*
(2) *Salute to All Fools*

TO

ESMÉ PERCY

INTRODUCTORY NOTE

The two March Hare programmes, written on the principle of a-little-bit-of-mud-for-everyone, both managed to outrage a large number of listeners. Partly because these listeners could not adjust themselves to what was happening (a *serial* crazy like *Itma* makes such an adjustment less drastic), partly because of their mistaken assumption that satire must be partisan, and partly because of their instinctive desire to pigeonhole everything—fun must be pure fun, satire must be pure satire, you can't be serious and frivolous simultaneously. Thus *The March Hare Resigns* made one listener complain that, *as a satire on planning*, it was pulling its punches (I leave it to the readers of the text to decide whether this listener's premise was correct). Still more surprisingly, *Salute to All Fools* provided the Social Credit Party with a sermon, based on a comparison of this programme with *Itma*: The *Itma* team 'feel with unthinking gusto. But you cannot THINK yourself into feeling with unthinking gusto'. Unthinking gusto, I must confess, is something I have never aimed at. And the Social Creditors' slogan of 'Feeling first'—whether or not it will solve, as they promise, the world's problems—has not normally been a guiding principle of writers of satirical fantasy. See Aristophanes.

The first object of both these programmes was, I must admit, entertainment. I am fond of nonsense literature. But even Lewis Carroll, in passing, throws light on his own times, gives a 'criticism of life'. I am publishing both these scripts because, though they often cover the same ground, and include indeed some of the same gags, they use a different emphasis. *The March Hare Resigns* is the more lyrical, its basic theme being the clash between the poetic (and sympathetic) madness of the Hare and the pedestrian (and repellent) madness of everyone else. *Salute to All Fools* rubs in much more salt; compare the Gael with the Smuggler, the Colonel with the Squire, the Marxist and the Scientist with the Planner and the Utopian. The latter, I think, was the better programme, not only because it has more bite but because the dialogue is crisper and the whole construction tighter; in *The March Hare Resigns* the characters are less significant and the transitions are often quite arbitrary.

Salute to All Fools was also better produced, as I made a point of getting speed in it; this was the easier thanks to the substitution of Nonesuch for Fitzpotter as second lead. As the March Hare must often fall into a grand and measured manner, the elementary radio principle of contrast requires that his feed should be quick; the Travelogue style, which Fitzpotter had to use, precluded this. In both programmes the March Hare goes on a tour; here Mr. Hopkins' music was invaluable. Any tour being an identity in difference, we used in each case a stock theme (*Over the Hills and Far Away* in the first programme and *Alleluia, I'm a Bum* in the second) which could be varied according to its context. Talking of identities in difference, I should add that the two broadcasts, though a year apart, were more closely related to each other (so forming what I have called a Saga) by the presence in both of Mr. Esmé Percy. Without him either of them might well have been a frost. I know of no other actor who could so convincingly and sympathetically be-hare himself. In the last minutes of *The March Hare Resigns* he achieved—what I wanted but what was almost too much to ask—a perfect transition from brittle fantasy to lyrical warmth. Both those who missed and those who resented this sudden intrusion of feeling I must class among the pigeon-holers. The fact that I think every institution and dogma—and nearly every person—need mocking has not made me a cynic.

CAST

The *March Hare Resigns* was first broadcast in the B.B.C. Home Service on March 29th, 1945. The main parts were played as follows:

THE MARCH HARE	ESMÉ PERCY
MINISTRY OFFICIAL	ALAN HOWLAND
FITZPOTTER	MACDONALD PARKE
YES-MAN	ARCHIE HARRADINE
DON	PETER USTINOV
HANSARD	BASIL JONES*
M.P.	ALEXANDER SARNER*
BUILDER	ROGER SNOWDON*
PLANNER	CYRIL GARDINER*
SQUIRE	BRYAN POWLEY*
MAGNATE	FRANK PARTINGTON*
MINER	BASIL JONES*
SMUGGLER	HARRY HUTCHINSON*
GENERAL DEBILITY	PETER USTINOV
LOVER	PETER NOBLE*
BELOVED	DOROTHY SMITH
THE FOUR LADIES	MOLLY RANKIN,*
	GRISELDA HERVEY,*
	ANN CODRINGTON,*
	MARJORIE WESTBURY*

Special music by Antony Hopkins.
The lyrics were sung by Archie Harradine.
Production by the author.

THE MARCH HARE RESIGNS

(Musical Overture.)

COMMENTATOR. The programme which follows was intended for All Fools' Day but, though it is not yet All Fools' Day, we hope this will find you as it leaves us. We present now: Salute to—

(Crackling of script.)

COMMENTATOR. I'm sorry—the wrong script; the right one has some mud on it. As this—er—precludes my reading the rest of the announcement, I leave you now in the paws of the March Hare.

(Fanfare.)

MARCH HARE. Ladies and gentlemen—Just a moment while I hang some daffodils over the microphone . . . There! What an exquisite pink. Now what was I saying? . . . Oh yes, ladies and gentlemen . . . But you aren't, you know; far from it. If you were you wouldn't be listening to *me*; you can't touch pitch, my dears. I got some pitch on my paws as I came up Portland Place. I was dancing as always—I have to dance by my nature—and having my eyes closed in a vernal ecstasy I bumped into a prefabricated non-existent bungalow. So the pitch was sticky of course—but I did a leg-glide and here I am in the studio. Hare Marches On! But not for ever, alas!

You've heard the terrible news? Parliament met today in secret session and they've decided that this year March is to end on the 31st—and be succeeded by April. So sudden, isn't it? And you see how that affects *me*? Being a March Hare I am a mad hare, but, *if* March comes to an end, why, then I lose my status; I become sane—like you; I cease to be myself! And what could be worse than that? Why, I'd rather be jugged.

WAITRESS'S VOICE. One jugged hare coming up! One jugged hare coming up!—Look out though; he'll bite.

HARE. Yes, of course I'll bite; I've bought a new denture at
Christie's. But as I was saying—

There is a tide in the affairs of hares
Where March gives way to April. There's the rub:
To be or not be mad. Which not to be
Is not to be myself. And, not himself,
Why should the March Hare live?

A FLAT VOICE (*near*). Yes, why indeed?

HARE. It seems then I am doomed. Big Ben moves on;
The month of March which came in like a lion
Will go out like a lamb—mint-sauce and all—
And I shall then be sane. Could I but halt
The spiteful calendar—

AN IRISH VOICE. Why don't ye try? Ring up one o' them
Ministries; they'll fix it for ye surely.

HARE (*matter-of-factly*). Thank you, my friend; that's a most unreasonable suggestion. I'll ring up the Ministry of . . . of . . .

A GOLDEN VOICE. Information?

HARE. No, no, no; they might give me some. I'll ring up the
Ministry of Flops and Stoppages.

(*A telephone rings—orchestrally—till stopped by a Ministry
Official, who, tired and hedging, speaks as if he had a cigarette
in his mouth. In the pauses in the following speech the Hare is
heard jibber-jabbering distortedly at the far end of the line.*)

MINISTRY OFFICIAL. Hullo? Hullo? . . . Yes, this is the
Ministry of Flops and Stoppages . . . . Oh is that the March
Hare? Well, what can we do for you, sir? . . . Have the
calendar stopped, did you say? And the current month
indefinitely extended? Well, I'm not quite sure that—
. . . Oh yes, we *do* but this is a biggish order. No pre-
cedent for it since *I've* been here. I'm afraid that in face of
public opinion—what did you say? . . . An unknown quantity? You really think so? Well, in that case, if you could do
a galloping survey or something—if you can discover a

quorum of persons throughout this country to agree to your scheme for the prolongation of March—well then, having weighed the evidence, we *might* see our way to— What's that? . . . You'd like to start on your galloping survey at once? . . . No, there's nothing against it but you realise of course that the Ministry can't at this stage commit itself—

(*He falls back on false heartiness.*)

Look, old boy—old hare, I mean—why not call around here before you start on your tour and we'll give you someone to cook it for you? Yes, yes, a kind of a guide. O.K., Hare, I'll expect you.

(*The telephone clicks off.*)

HARE. There! A ray of hope! Open that studio door—I'm off on my dancing survey!

A PUBLIC ADDRESS VOICE. Change here for Bedlam and Widdershins! Change here for Bedlam and Widdershins! First stop—Whitehall. Whitehall!

(*Tour music.*)

COMMISSIONAIRE. Sorry. You can't enter this building without a pass.

HARE. Oh! Can I enter with a somersault?

(*A violent crash.*)

MINISTRY OFFICIAL. Somebody's falling upstairs; that must be the March Hare.

HARE. It is! It is I myself! Now where is that impresario?

MINISTRY OFFICIAL. Impres—You mean the guide. I'm assigning you Mr. Fitzpotter here. He knows this country backwards—and forwards—*and* in technicolour.

FITZPOTTER. I sure do. Glad to meet you, Mr. Hare. I'll be delighted to conduct you round wonderful Britain, one of the most famous and unspoiled of all the North Sea Islands. Just come with me down this corridor.

(*Tour music.*)

The March Hare Resigns

HARE. Here I go—down the long corridors
    Dancing and rollicking, chasing the impossible,
    Drinking in the ozone, thinking the unspeakable
    Until we come to—
                (*The music stops.*)

FITZPOTTER. We come now to an old-world department in the
    Ministry of Flops and Stoppages, with its quaint colourless
    inhabitants—folk who from time immemorial—

(*He is interrupted by a moaning and wheezing in the background.*)

HARE. What's that, Mr. Fitzpotter?

FITZPOTTER. Some guy dying, I guess. Do you want a look-see?

                (*A door opens. A pause.*)

FITZPOTTER. Yeah, he's dying all right. Do you want to ask him
    anything?

HARE. I do.

FITZPOTTER. Then make it snappy. The way he looks right now
    he—

HARE. My dying friend!

YES-MAN. Eh?

HARE. Would you consent to the year being stopped at March?

YES-MAN. Which year?

HARE. This year.

YES-MAN. *This* year! I haven't yet reached it. Last year's still
    priority. Isn't that so, Miss Stencil?

MISS STENCIL. Yes, Mr. Triplick. The files for 1945 are still in
    the decontamination room.

YES-MAN. I'm sorry, sir. Now go away and let me die. I've just
    been composing my owl-song.

MISS STENCIL. Swan-song, Mr. Triplick, swan-song.

YES-MAN. Quite so, Miss Stencil, owl-song.

      (*He sings to the tune of The Tarpaulin Jacket :*)
  A Ministry yes-man sat dying
    At his desk in the midst of a mess;
  When the Minister came to him sighing

The March Hare Resigns

He sighed back repeatedly: YES—
   Yes, I must make another nice blue-print
(*Chorus*)   blue-print
   While my mood and my pencil are blue,
(*Chorus*)   are blue
   And I must write another white paper
(*Chorus*)   papah
   To prove we've done all we can do.
(*Chorus*)   can do.

   I know that I'm crossing the bar, sir—
      I'll leave you my change of address—
   But I trust that I shan't be too far, sir,
      To cry through the stratosphere: YES—
   Yes, I'll make you another nice blue-print
(*Chorus*)   blue-print
      I'll draft it up here in the blue—
(*Chorus*)   the blue—
   And I'll write you another white paper
(*Chorus*)   papah
   To prove we've done all we can do.
(*Chorus*)   can do.

   Now hear my last words as I'm dying:
      Beware of Free Speech and the Press
   And if anyone asks if you're trying
      Be sure that you answer them YES—
   Yes, we're making another nice blue-print—
(*Chorus*)   blue-print—
      Since the mood of the country is blue,
(*Chorus*)   is blue,
   And we're writing another white paper
(*Chorus*)   papah
   To prove we've done all we can do.

The March Hare Resigns

(*Chorus*)   can do.

(*As the orchestra ends, a new voice enters the room—briskly.*)

DON (*approaching*). Miss Stencil! Regarding that memo—

MISS STENCIL. Hsh, sir. Look yonder.

DON. Dear me, dear me, another of my colleagues gone. And to look at him you wouldn't see the difference.

FITZPOTTER. You've said it, Prof. But to turn from the dead to the mad, have you met my friend the March Hare?

DON. Delighted! Delighted! So *you've* joined the Civil Service too? Then may I ask you a question—

HARE. May I ask *you* a question? I want to have the year stopped at March and—

DON. Stopped at March! You mean no more April?

HARE. No more April, no more May, no more June, no more—

DON. Yes, yes, I get your point. Personally, I'm opposed to it.

HARE. But—

DON. You see—this is off the record—in peace-time I'm a don. At All Fools' College, Oxford—you've heard of it of course? Our chef makes a very fine crème brûlé. Well, my work here in the Ministry's extremely interesting—interesting— but the truth of it is the pace is a bit too fast for me—fast. So, believe it or not, I'm looking forward to victory. And I can't have the year stopped in March because my friend old Moore—and *he* has very long ears—

HARE. So have I, so have I.

DON. So you have, sir, but please don't flick them at me. As I was saying, from my point of view, the year must move on and I must move back. Back to the Senior Common Room. And crème brûlé—brûlé!

FITZPOTTER. Come on, Hare. You haven't made first base yet. I know a place—a kind of a private house—where the residents like staying put.

HARE. They *like*—

FITZPOTTER. Yes, sir. Those old-timers, they've been sitting there now for nine and a half years, so I guess they must kind of enjoy it. So I propose we visit them. (*Slyly*) And we might find a couple of parties going on there.

HARE. Ah! Fun and games?

FITZPOTTER. Yes, sir. Musical chairs.

HARE. Come on. Let's go to this House!

(*Tour music.*)

FITZPOTTER. And so we come to happy Westminster with its dreaming towers and its innocent childish chatter—

HANSARD. Mr. Fitzpotter? Mr. M. Hare?

FITZPOTTER. That's right. How did you know?

HANSARD. I know everything. My name's Hansard. What can I do for you?

HARE. Find me a Member of Parliament—even one tiny back-bencher—to agree to the suspension of the calendar.

HANSARD. Suspension of the calendar? Hm. What you want is one of the members of the 1713 Committee.

FITZPOTTER. Why 1713?

HANSARD. Because Queen Anne wasn't dead then. Look! Here's one of them now. The honourable member for Oldways. Put him your question, Mr. Hare.

HARE. Sir, may I ask you—

M.P. I must have notice of this question.

HANSARD. It's about the reform of the calendar.

HARE. Yes, it's—

M.P. I would refer my honourable and furry friend to the state-ment made by Julius Caesar—

HARE. You mean *the* Julius Caesar?

M.P. Yes, sir, I'm a Preservative. When I once put my foot down—

HARE. Ow! . . . Ow!

M.P. I must ask you to withdraw that remark.

HARE. But you're standing on my paw, sir.

M.P. Possibly. In pursuance of Standing Order Number One—

The March Hare Resigns

One—One—One—One Mr. Speaker nominated me Chairman of Standing Committee XXXXX. It is therefore, sir, my duty to stand on people's paws.

HARE. Is it? Then take that, sir!

(*Sound of a slap.*)

HARE. In pursuance of Dancing Order Number 022-022-0 I nominate myself Chairman of Dancing Committee YYOY Not. And I hope that I'll dance on your grave, sir. Goodbye.

M.P. Unheard of! Unheard of!

Mr. Hansard, ask that hare why he doesn't carry a rear light.

HANSARD. I'm sorry, sir. He's adjourned, sir.

M.P. I'll be hanged.

HANSARD. Yes, sir. I'll be bound.

(*Tour music.*)

HARE. What have we here, Fitzpotter?

FITZPOTTER. Here we have one of the forgotten arts.

(*The orchestra drops bricks.*)

FITZPOTTER. An old-world builder dropping his bricks on the new world.

HARE (*calling up*). Builder! May I—

BUILDER. My name's Jerry. Heads below!

(*A single brick-drop.*)

HARE. Well now, Jerry, if you can spare the time—

BUILDER. I know what you want and I can't. I heard about you on the wireless and me answer's No, Mr. Hare. Get stuck in March! What next!

HARE. Nothing next.

BUILDER. Quite so! And what about all me prospects? See this here road? This is a wicked waste. Arterial road this is and it ain't got hardly no houses on it. Well, let me tell you this: once we gets victory over I reckon to line this here road with houses as far as Scotland. Look out, Guv'nor! Heads!

(*A brick drops.*)

146

HARE. My good man, is it part of your plan to brain your possible clients?

BUILDER. Plan! I ain't got no plan. I hates the sound of that word —and as for them nosey planners! (*He spits*) Why, there's a bloke up there—see where I'm pointing—that house on top of the hill what looks like it's made of glass—

(*A brick drops; Fitzpotter yells.*)

HARE. There, there, Fitzpotter; don't say it. Let's move on to the Planner's. People who live in glass houses won't, at least, drop bricks.

FITZPOTTER. No, but they'll drop suggestions. I don't like all this Brave New World stuff. I'd rather be in Tahiti.

HARE. Don't be so craven, Fitzpotter. Come! Let us mount the hill.

(*Brave New World music.*)

PLANNER. No, no, no, Mr. Hare, I'm afraid you are a reactionary. (*The Hare tries to protest.*) Have the year stopped! I won't have anything stopped. Perpetual progress, that's my watchword. Elsie, wind up the dialectic.

ELSIE. Yes, sir—and what about your beverage?

PLANNER. I'd like it hotter today—and while you're about it, Elsie, go to the refrigerator and bring me my model of the Future.

ELSIE. Yes, sir.

HARE. Why do you keep it in a refrigerator?

PLANNER. It walked in here with snow on its boots; if I keep it outside it goes bad. But that's our insular climate. As soon as I get the weather subjected to proper controls—it will need a big staff of course—

ELSIE (*returning, agitated*). Oh, sir! Oh sir!

PLANNER. What's wrong?

ELSIE. Those runner beans you planted—they're all turning into red tape.

PLANNER. Are they? Excellent. I'm very short of tape. You see, gentlemen, in the immediate future everyone—absolutely everyone—will be an employee of the State. Even you, Mr. Hare.

HARE (*alarmed*). Oh no, no, please not. The State and I—well, really, we're hardly on speaking terms. Ever since that day we oiled the watch with butter—it should have been margarine but—

PLANNER (*scandalised*). You oiled a watch with butter!

HARE. Yes. I did.

PLANNER. In that case . . . you must be liquidated. Elsie!

ELSIE. The rabbit-trap? Here, sir.

PLANNER. Right. You see this trap, Mr. Hare? For your own good I direct you now to walk into it. It is, as you see, stream-lined and air-conditioned—

(*A crash of breaking glass.*)

ELSIE. Oh sir! They've jumped right out through the wall. I told you that glass was breakable.

(*Tour music which segues into 'John Peel'.*)

SQUIRE. Upon my soul! If it isn't that lunatic hare! Well—and what've you been up to?

HARE. Dancin' and jumpin', Squire. But I've come to ask you a favour.

SQUIRE. Well, if you'd like a run with the beagles—

HARE. No, Squire, not today. This is a larger question. What lovely weather it is and how very well you're looking. You look very happy, Squire. Wouldn't you like to remain just as you are for ever?

SQUIRE. I *shall* remain just as I am for ever.

HARE. Oh well . . . what I really mean . . . .

SQUIRE. Come on! Come on!

HARE. Wouldn't you like this month to persist for ever? An eternity—an infinity—of March?

SQUIRE. March? Eternity? Don't talk rubbish. If there was only March in the year, think of what we should lose! April the

The March Hare Resigns

Second—Double Summer Time; Twelfth of August—
grouse; First of September—partridge; First of October—
pheasant—

HARE. But, Squire—

FITZPOTTER. It's no good, Hare. He certainly knows his mind.

SQUIRE. I should by now; I've had it for fifty years. You listen
to me, my good animal. There may be chaps in the industrial
cities who don't know one month from another, but—

HARE. May there? Come on, Fitzpotter!

(Tour music.)

FITZPOTTER. And so we come to the midmost parts of England,
the workshop of Queen Victoria, home of forgotten
exports and factory hooters, where the simple big-hearted
magnates take care of their excess profits and, as if to remind
us of—

MAGNATE (*Lancashire accent*). Come in, gentlemen. I understand
you have a proposition.

FITZPOTTER. He has.

HARE. I have. I want the year stopped. Now!

MAGNATE. Eh? Then what about victory?

HARE. Victory?

MAGNATE. Aye. We shan't get victory this month, and, if we
don't get victory, then we shan't have our boom, y'know.

HARE. What boom?

MAGNATE. What boom? Don't be daft. Haven't you heard of
trade cycles?

HARE. No, I—I always keep off the roads.

MAGNATE. Eh? Look here; what's your profession?

HARE. Lunacy.

MAGNATE. Umph. Writer?

HARE. No, I—

MAGNATE. That's funny. Most lunatics *I* know are writers. Why
do you wear that suit?

HARE. Suit? This is my skin!

149

MAGNATE. Utility fur, eh? Purchase tax on that. You don't belong to Common Health, do you?

HARE. Certainly not; I—

MAGNATE. Then you believe in private enterprise?

HARE. What's private enterprise, Fitzpotter?

FITZPOTTER (*unctuously*). It's a beautiful old world custom that—

MAGNATE. Excuse me, gentlemen, time's up. But remember what I said about the boom. Now then, where's my cycle?

(*Boom music; then workshop noises and workers' chatter.*)

HARE. So this is a factory. What is the odour?

FITZPOTTER. I don't know. Better ask the Drains Trust.

(*Through the tapping of hammers a Scots worker is singing slowly to the tune of 'Annie Laurie'.*)

1ST WORKER. 'There was a crooked man . . .'.

HARE. What's that man doing?

1ST WORKER. 'And he went a crooked mile . . .'.

FITZPOTTER. He's singing while he works.

1ST WORKER. 'He found a crooked contract . . .'.

HARE. Does that mean he's happy?

1ST WORKER. 'And he made a crooked pile—'
Happy? Ach! I'm doing overtime.

FITZPOTTER. He gets paid extra for that.

1ST WORKER. Aye and I've nothing to spend it on.

HARE. What about when the boom comes?

1ST WORKER. Och! What about when the slump comes? But it's all one to me. I'll be out of a job by then.

HARE. No more overtime?

1ST WORKER. No more any time. I'm just here because of the shortage of man-power. I'm unskilled, you see. They drafted me into this job. When peace comes back they'll throw me out on my ear.

HARE. And you won't like that?

1ST WORKER. Who says I won't like that? My heart's in the Highlands, my heart is not here, My heart's in the—

The March Hare Resigns

HARE. Which is your favourite month?

1ST WORKER. December.

HARE. Oh, not March?

1ST WORKER. Don't be foolish. Where does March get you?

HARE. Where does December get you?

1ST WORKER. It gets you to Hogmanay.

(*The workers laugh.*)

2ND WORKER (*Midland woman*). That's one for you, Mister.

HARE. Fitzpotter, this is desperate. I will speak to these people. Ladies and gentlemen—

(*Laughter and whistles.*)

FITZPOTTER. No, no, comrades.

HARE. Ladies and comrades, I have come to your factory with a simple proposal which will, I believe, confer great benefits on you all. All of you here have for five years or so enjoyed comparative security. You are so badly needed that nobody dares to sack you. But that may change, my friends. The time may come when you have to tighten your conveyor belts, to queue up once more at the doors of the Labour Exchanges and—if you are women—to be cooped up again in your homes—

2ND WORKER. I'd *like* to be cooped up in me home!

(*Cheers from the women.*)

HARE. Ladies and—

FITZPOTTER (*aside*). Comrades!

HARE. Comrades and comrades! The future is wrapped in clouds. 'Forty years on, getting colder and colder—'

3RD WORKER (*Northern girl*). Now laddie! No Jarrow school songs here, please!

HARE. I repeat; colder and colder. But here, in this factory, it's warm. And your present position is stable.

4TH WORKER. Stable? He's right! Like horses.

HARE. Please! You can clock in here each day that you want to—

5TH WORKER (*woman*). We don't want to clock in at all!

(*Cheers.*)

1ST WORKER. That's right. We want to go home.

4TH WORKER. We're sick of being transferred; we'd like to transfer ourselves.

(*Hear! Hear!*)

2ND WORKER. We've had our fill of E.W.O.; what we want is Tea for Two.

6TH WORKER. What we want is fags for fourpence.

4TH WORKER. What we want is beer that's beer.

1ST WORKER. And that's all still to come.

ALL. Hear! Hear!

HARE. It's no good, Fitzpotter. Take me somewhere else.

FITZPOTTER. Anywhere else?

HARE. Anywhere that you choose.

FITZPOTTER. O.K. I guess I know where that is.

(*A chord.*)

COMPÈRE. Hullo everyone. By special request we have pleasure in opening this afternoon's programme of Light Music with that popular number: 'Dream Soup'.

(*'Dream Soup' and chattering ladies.*)

1ST LADY (*gruff*). My dear, this band gets better every day. They're really almost good enough to broadcast.

2ND LADY (*cracked-sweet*). Yes, dear, they should—but then, the leader's profile—

1ST LADY. Wouldn't come out? I know!—but they say television's coming back soon.

2ND LADY. And those silly people in London lost my set in the Blitz! My dear! Just look who's come in. How unusual!

1ST LADY. You mean that hare?

2ND LADY. No, no, I mean the American.

(*'Dream Soup' continues to flow.*)

FITZPOTTER. And here we come, Mr. Hare, to an old-world five-star hotel, renowned for its cuisine and its distance from enemy action. The five stars are considered in popular lore to represent the following ancient British virtues: Self-Importance, Self-Repetition, Kindness to Pekes, Unearned Increment, and Indigestion.

(*'Dream Soup' ends; desultory clapping.*)

HARE (*aside to Fitzpotter*). Perhaps, now the band's stopped—shall I make my plea now?

FITZPOTTER. O.K. Go ahead. Shoot.

HARE. Comrades—

(*Gasps of indignation.*)

FITZPOTTER. Hsh!

1ST LADY. Who is this impertinent animal?

FITZPOTTER. Make it more formal, you sap.

HARE. Ladies of England, pillars and columns of society, I come before you today with a sword hanging over my head—

2ND LADY. *I* don't see any sword.

1ST LADY. It's a metaphorical sword, dear.

HARE. It's not, it's an infra-red sword. And that being so, I must beg you—

WAITER. Sorry, sir; no begging allowed in here.

HARE. Oh very well, I'll demand. Here and now in the name of the Hounds of Spring—of whom I'm the M.F.H.—

1ST LADY. Oh so he hunts; that's different.

HARE. In the name of the flowers of this month—forsythia and almond, oxlip and coaltip, crocus and pocus, in the name of the Emergency Flowers Act itself, in the name of your own antecedents—your altruistic activities, your welfare work in the County, your endless successes at bridge—

3RD LADY (*hard and high*). Don't flatter us, my dear beast. We did lose that rubber in Malaya.

(*Hsh! Hsh!*)

HARE. Oh let foregones be foregones. In the name of—

1ST LADY. In the name of goodness what are you driving at, sir?

HARE. I want to stop the calendar.

LADIES. To what?

The March Hare Resigns

HARE. I wish the year to stay where it is and never move forward
again.

(*The ladies gasp.*)

3RD LADY. Never . . . move . . . ? . . . !

HARE. Does anyone here second me?

1ST LADY. Second you! It's my belief, sir, you're mad. Stop the
year where it is!

(*The band strikes up a 'Continental' theme.*)

1ST LADY. When we've just made our plans for the summer!

LADIES. So have we all! So have we all!

4TH LADY (*bubbling*). You see, Mr. Hare, as soon as this war's
over, we're going to revisit the Continent.

On the road to Biarritz
Which no debutante omits
And the dawn comes up like Pernod—and you might be in
the Ritz.

1ST LADY.

On the road to Ancient Rome
Underneath Bramante's dome
And the dawn comes up like Verdi and it's such a home
from home.

3RD LADY.

On the road to the Tyrol
Where one feels one has a soul
And the dawn is wunderschoener and the hats are—oh, so
droll.

2ND LADY.

On the road to Bukarest
Where the men were all well-dressed
And the dawn came up too early and—er—perhaps you
know the rest.

1ST LADY. On the road to Carcassome—

HARE. Well, I really must be gone.

When you land in Europe wire me (*he turns away*)—tell me

how you're getting on.

(*The door bangs; the band and the Safe Hotel recede.*)

FITZPOTTER. Hey there, Hare! Don't go so fast. Watch your step now.

HARE. I must get out, I must get out, I must get out.

FITZPOTTER. Well, that's the umbrella stand on your right—and that's a bed of pinks on your left—and right there in front of you, that's the lily pond.

UTOPIAN (*very slow*). If you want to reach Utopia, walk on the dotted line.

HARE. And who are you, sir?

UTOPIAN (*slower still*). I am a man whose ideas outpace the clock.

HARE. And the calendar?

UTOPIAN. *And* the calendar.

HARE. Oh!

UTOPIAN. I am a Front Room Boy. Things can't ever move fast enough for me. You come into my lab and I'll show you what I'm working on. Know what it is? The Mill . . . enn . . . i . . . um!

Yes, *I* know where I'm going.

(*splash as he falls into the water.*)

FITZPOTTER. And so we leave our long-sighted friend in the lily pond, and, turning our backs upon Safe Hotels and Utopias, we go on our way once more, passing a mobile canteen—

HARE. Don't let's pass. I'm hungry.

CANTEEN WAITRESS. Hungry, Mister? Here you are.

(*A plate is slapped down on a counter.*)

CANTEEN WAITRESS. Cut off the joint and two veg.

HARE. Ah, two veg! But where's the—er—

CANTEEN WAITRESS. Cut off the ration? You've had it.

(*A plate is snapped away again.*)

FITZPOTTER. And so we go on our way, leaving a cold plate and looking for a warm answer. But who will give us this answer?

HARE (*with sudden intuition*). I know! The Average Man.

FITZPOTTER (*slyly*). Yeah—and the Average Woman.

(*Tour music.*)

HARE. Are you the Average Man?

MEN (*in unison*). We are the Average Man.

HARE. Are you the Average Woman?

WOMEN (*in unison*). We are the Average Girl.

HARE. Then—to begin with the ladies—You, madam, are *not*, I take it, planning to spend your summer upon the Continent?

(*The answer is given by a chain of voices.*)

WOMEN. Nay lad don't talk daft what do 'ee think us is dinna ye ken ye fule we ain't got no time for the Continent.

(*All together.*) Not *this* summer! No!

HARE. Excellent. Now you, sir? You aren't, I assume, banking on any Utopia?

MEN. 'OO? Me! Banking! Blimey! That's proper nonsense y'know ee if you was to ask me lad if you ask me chum ye'd steer clear of Utopias *and* myopias *and* cornucopias—and keep your money in a tea-pot.

(*All together.*) Utopias for *us*? No!

HARE. Fitzpotter! At last! Here are two types at least who are after my own heart. This couple want to stay put.

MEN AND WOMEN. Eh! Just a moment!

Stay . . . put . . . *where*?

HARE. In the month of March. For ever!

GIRL. Oh no you don't.

WOMEN. No you don't!

HARE. But why, if—

GIRL. Stay put in March! With the Spring Fashions to come! And me that's saved me coupons!

WOMEN. That's right.

HARE. Then I turn to you, sir. Will you, as a man of reason—

MEN. Stay put in March? No!

1ST MAN. Miss our Easter Monday!

The March Hare Resigns

WOMAN. We may not want summer on the Continent—

2ND MAN. But we do want our next Bank Holiday—

(*They all cheer and set the mood for a lyric.*)

TENOR. Easter Monday's just around the cor-ner,
    I'm orf to find the World that Never Was,
I missed the bus before but I feel no longer sore
    For I'm going to make the grade today because . . .
I 'opes to take a nip in The Case is Al-tered,
    I 'opes to play me fiddle while Robbie burns,
And then look in on the Goat and the Tote and the Eagle
    And *then* I'll sink a pint in The Dog Returns.

CHORUS. Oh the Bank
    Holiday, holiday, holiday!
The Bank
    Holiday, holiday, hic!
The Bank
    Holiday, holiday, holiday!
The Bank, Bank
    Holiday, holiday hic!

TENOR. The only Girl in the World is on the car-pet,
    We're orf to 'ave a spree as never was;
She slapped my face before but it feels no longer sore
    And today she'll be quite diff-e-rent because . . .
We're orf to 'it it 'igh in The Case is Al-tered—
    We're orf to spend a spot of what we earns—
We're orf to drink in the Bell and the Smell and the
    Benbow
    And one for the road in The Dog Returns.

CHORUS. Oh the Bank
    Holiday, holiday, holiday!
The Bank
    Holiday, holiday, hic!
The Bank
    Holiday, holiday, holiday!

The March Hare Resigns

The Bank, Bank
Holiday, holiday, hic!

(*As the orchestra ends, a cheer-leader gives three cheers—Hic! Hic! Hooray!*)

HARE. The dog returns—but *I* move on. Oh this England! Let's try Wales.

(*Tour music—turning Welsh.*)

FITZPOTTER. And so we come to the picturesque old mining village of Cymric-ap-pliss-don't-come-agen.

MINER. That is not the way to pronounce it.

HARE. Excuse me. Are you a Bevin Boy?

MINER. I am not. I am a professional.

HARE. Would you like the calendar stopped?

MINER. I would not. If the calendar is stopped my wages is stopped. Besides the war will end soon and then we may open new seams. In a new pit, you know. In my present pit the coal-face runs away from me.

HARE. I sympathise. My face does that too. If I weren't so quick with my paws it would soar up—oh, so high—

MINER. How high? Top C?

FITZPOTTER. No, his face is a bass.

Gosh, it's beginning to rain.

MINER. Yes, how wet is my business.

HARE. Rain? Rain? What can we do about this?

MINER. Will you come down in the mine?

HARE. No, no, no; we'll go to Ireland.

(*Tour music—turning Irish.*)

HARE. My friend! You've dropped a parcel. Just over there on the Border.

SMUGGLER. Thank ye, sir. I know I have.

HARE. But why—

SMUGGLER. Whisht! I'm a smuggler.

FITZPOTTER (*beginning to gush*). Ah! The historic custom of smuggling—

SMUGGLER. Yes, but it's fallin' off, sir. That's why I'm lookin' forward now to the summer.

HARE. So *you're* looking forward too?

SMUGGLER. Indeed I am. I'm expectin' a General Election. It's as certain as grass is green and lilies is orange. I'm afraid I've missed the Dail but Stormont will do just as well.

FITZPOTTER. Gee! You don't mean that *you*—

SMUGGLER. I mean that I want a seat. I'm sick an' tired of clamberin' over these fences; I want somewhere to park meself. They tell me that houses of Parliament always has easy chairs.

HARE. But do you think you'll get in?

SMUGGLER. Get in, is it? Haven't I took a large-sized herd of cattle and—

(He is cut off by an angry shout.)

GENERAL. Contact! Contact!

SMUGGLER. Look out. That'll be the general. Mind the air-screw now. He's just takin' off for England.

HARE. Then perhaps he'll give us a lift. What is his name?

SMUGGLER. Ach, I wouldn't know. He's a fine old English gentleman.

(The General's fanfare.)

FITZPOTTER. Beg pardon, General; could we bum a ride on your airplane?

GENERAL. What's that, sir? I'm deaf.

HARE. We hope you won't deem us cavalier but—

GENERAL. No good that rabbit talking. I never could hear what they say.

HARE. Rabbit! May I inform you I'm not a—

GENERAL. Not in the habit? Quite so. Cooked but not heard's the motto.

Come on there! Contact! Contact!

Where are those blank effects? Where's that gramophone girl?

GRAMS GIRL (*cooingly*). I'm sorry, General. The censor sat on the disc.

GENERAL. Oh all right; take it as played . . . .

(*Pause.*)

Gentlemen, we are now air-borne.

FITZPOTTER. Then I guess we'd better introduce ourselves. My name is—

GENERAL. My name is General er—General er—Dammit, I've forgotten again . . . My name is General Debility.

FITZPOTTER. My name is—

GENERAL. You look to me like a journalist. Tell me: has Mafeking been relieved yet?

FITZPOTTER. Yes, sir.

GENERAL. Good. I had a bet with a fellow—he was a bit of a bore —that before I died—That's what I'm up to now, you know.

HARE. What, sir?

GENERAL. Dying. I die on the First of April.

HARE. But why on the—

GENERAL. Can't die in March. Too cold.

HARE. Well, in *that* case—As long as March remains, *you* must remain. So if you don't want to die—

GENERAL. Who said I don't want to die?

Effects there! Effects!. . . All right; take 'em as played. Very nice landing that. And here, all ready to meet us, is my great friend, Major er—Major er . . . .

(*The Major's fanfare.*)

GENERAL. Ah yes, my friend Major Drawback. Anything you want to know; just ask him and he'll sink it.

MAJOR. What *do* you want to know, gentlemen?

HARE. We want to know if you'd agree—

MAJOR. I never agree to anything. Next question. Don't keep me waiting.

HARE. Well, regarding the months of the year, what do you think—

The March Hare Resigns

MAJOR. I never think.

HARE. Well, um, well . . . in that case . . . .

MAJOR. When you've any more to say, if you have, you'll find me over there in the club-house. Good day to you, gentlemen.

HARE. Oh dear! . . . Shall we follow him?

FITZPOTTER. Shall we follow him! Come, Hare; walk with me in the steps—size twelve—of an old English major and while on our way to the club-house—

(*His attention is distracted by the murmur of two voices. At the same time the orchestra has crept in with a love-theme.*)

FITZPOTTER. What have we here on the fairway?

(*The Hare and the listeners eavesdrop.*)

HARE. 'In the spring a leveret's fancy—' I don't think we should disturb them.

(*The music ends and the young couple turn towards him.*)

LOVER (*slightly cockney*). You can't disturb us. We're happy!

BELOVED (*Scots*). We're so happy we want to share it with everyone.

LOVER. Yes, because, you see, we'll never be so happy again.

HARE. What's that?

BELOVED. Och, what Jim means is it'll be sort of different.

HARE. Then in *that* case—

BELOVED. And the weather's so lovely now. I think this is just the loveliest time of the year.

HARE. Then listen to me; I—

BELOVED. Of course we do look forward to getting married.

LOVER. Yes, we've seen just the house we want but somebody else has got it.

BELOVED. Besides, we couldn't afford it—not when the war's over. I'll be out of my job and Jim, poor lamb, he'll be—

HARE. But, my dear children! You're just the people I've been looking for. You say you couldn't be happier than you are at this moment?

BELOVED. That's right.

HARE. And you say your future is doubtful?

LOVER. That's right.

HARE. Then why not stop the clock—nay, stop the calendar? Stay for ever here in the fairway of the Present. In the kindly winds of March which flutter the flags on the greens and—

LOVER. Oh we couldn't do that. (*With a blush in his voice.*) The wedding's in June.

HARE. But you may not have anything to live on.

BELOVED. That's right. Still we do want a house of our own and—

HARE. Endless housework, bills choking the letter-box, tea-leaves choking the sink—Goodbye to the neiges d'antan, the perquisites of passion. And then middle age. And old age.

BELOVED. Och, that's a long way off. Jim and I—we're young still.

HARE. Yes. You're *terribly* young.

(*Pause.*)

Come, Fitzpotter. I give up. Nobody cares about March, nobody cares for the poor March Hare, nobody wants to stay put. The calendar must go on—three hundred and sixty-five days and all the routine as usual. I'm returning to base. Back to that studio in Broadcasting House. My positively last appearance. For after this I resign.

And you—you two children—goodbye. I hope you'll never regret . . . what was a very good offer.

(*Tour music—slow. When it ends he is back in the studio.*)

HARE. Ladies and gentlemen, I return to this microphone defeated. I have toured your country without finding any support. You have let down your March Hare. It seems that madness—of my kind—is vieux jeu. And March is now running out—like precious sugar from a leaking bag. There is little more sweetness left. The day after the day after tomorrow I shall be no longer myself. As a common hare I shall feel uncommonly dull. But you—what do you care?

The March Hare Resigns

Pursuing the course of your sanity, you will stand in queues as ever, fighting for places on elevators and escalators, on band-wagons and non-stop wagons-lits. But let me not be ungenerous. The moment my doom is sounded and March turns into April, I wish you all many happy returns of the day—and on April the First may you all fool each other. I shall be fooled no more. A winged shadow is coming up from the South. It is the first cuckoo. 'In April come he will.' Summer is i-cumen in—Hare he is a-dancin' out. For I cannot go down fighting but I shall go out dancing. I snap my fingers at you and your stupid calendar. And here and now— you've been waiting for this—I resign!

(*A cuckoo calls; then musical finale: 'Summer Is I-Cummen In'.*)

CAST

Salute to All Fools was first broadcast in the B.B.C. Home Service on April 1st, 1946. The main parts were played as follows:

THE MARCH HARE	ESMÉ PERCY
NONESUCH	HOWARD MARION-CRAWFORD
LITTLE BIT OF PAPER	MARJORIE WESTBURY*
PHOTOGRAPHER	STANLEY GROOME*
JOE	TOMMY DUGGAN
THE JOURNALISTS' TRUTH	GWEN DAY BURROUGHS
POET	BASIL JONES*
POETIC TRUTH	CHERRY COTTRELL
NEO-YOGI	LAIDMAN BROWNE*
COLONEL	CYRIL GARDINER*
TORY TRUTH	GLADYS YOUNG*
MARXIST	CHARLES LENO*
PSYCHO-ANALYST	RUDOLPH OFFENBACH
GAEL	HARRY HUTCHINSON*
SCIENTIST	RICHARD GOOLDEN

Special music by Antony Hopkins.

The lyrics were sung by Martin Boddy and Marjorie Westbury.

Production by the author.

SALUTE TO ALL FOOLS

ANNOUNCER. Salute to All Fools! No one has asked for this programme but here it is. Our subject tonight is Truth. Today being April the First, we consider this theme appropriate. Listeners will have the privilege of hearing a number of experts on Truth, all of them equally infallible; our question-master is the March Hare. For those who are still switched on, we now present:
Salute to—Salute to—Salute to—Salute to—etc. . . .

1ST VOICE (*rough*). Come on, come on, come on; get unstuck.

ANNOUNCER. Salute to—Salute to—Salute to—

2ND VOICE (*high and sweet*). All fools?

ANNOUNCER. Yes.

(*The programme proper now starts with a lyric to the tune of 'Alleluia, I'm a Bum'.*)

TENOR.   Oh April the First
      Is the feast of All Fools
   Without any chairman,
     Without any rules—
       Howpeculiah! You're a fool,
       Howpeculiah! Don't be sore.
       Howpeculiah—begging your pardon
       We must fool you once more.
       (*The chorus repeats these four lines.*)

TENOR.   No doubt you all think
      You are perfectly sane
   But on A-per-il Fool's Day
      You'd best think again . . . .
        (*A figure on the trumpet.*)

TENOR.   Now salute to you all
      From the depth of my heart;

CHORUS. If you'll keep on that wireless,
      We're ready to start!

Salute to All Fools

(The orchestra stops. A 'common' voice steps patly into the silence.)

NONESUCH. No, no, ducky. 'If the hat fits', my father used to say—

MOLLY. Yes, dear—but he was a hatter.

NONESUCH *(snobbishly)*. One of the Mad Hatters, Molly. But his never did of course. The first fit he had, he died.

MOLLY. So that's why you gave up the business?

NONESUCH. That's it, ducky; wanted to better myself. Selling ideas? Yes. Selling passes? Yes. Selling pups? Yes. But selling hats? No!

MOLLY. And today you've become an Agent! But, Nonesuch dear, what are you an agent for?

NONESUCH. Oh um.... Theatre, television, test-matches, tiger-shooting—Everything that starts with T.

MOLLY. T?

NONESUCH. Yes, Molly; no black market—one-and-six the packet. *(He reels off the items at breakneck speed.)* Trumpet-players, trombone-players, trout-fishing; tennis-royal, tennis-table, tennis-lawn; tattoos-military, tattoos on the chest or back; taffeta, theology, thaumaturgy, titbits. Tossing the pancake, throwing the weight. Tin-mining, typing, terrorisation. And a few less important side-lines—things, you know, of one syllable: tips, tops, tiles, tubs, toques, tykes, times, tides, tar, tripe, tosh, trash—and, er, truth, of course.

MOLLY, Truth, Nonesuch?

NONESUCH. That's what I'm seeing this client about today. I wish it was something else. An old friend of my father's too. The March Hare. If he'd only come to me yesterday!

MOLLY. Why?

NONESUCH. Because it was March then. Then I could have sold him anything. But today—well, you see, he's not quite himself today and he's got this thing about truth.

MOLLY. The March Hare? Really?

NONESUCH. Yes, dear. Not what he used to be.

(*The chorus comes bang in:*)

The Old March Hare he ain't what he used to be,
   ain't what he used to be, ain't what he used to be,
The Old March Hare he ain't what he used to be
   only a day ago!
Only a day ago . . .etc.

(*The March Hare appears as the music ends.*)

MOLLY. Look, Nonesuch dear! What perfectly charming ears.

HARE. Ladies and gentlemen,—

VOICES. Hsh! The March Hare!

HARE. Ladies and gentlemen, you are quite right. A day ago I was officially mad. Throughout the month of March I was bound by the rules of my office to devote myself to fantasy. But today is the First of April, I am free to do what I like. The hares of Spring are on Winter's traces. I have decided to get married.

THE WOMEN. Married!

HARE. Yes, ladies, but not to you. The bride of my choice is Truth.

AN INCREDULOUS VOICE. Who?

HARE. Truth, I said. Today is the First of April. And that's why I've called on you, Mr. Nonesuch.

NONESUCH. At your service, Mr. Hare. Would you like her brunette or blonde?

HARE. Mr. Nonesuch! I am surprised at you. There is only one Truth in this world. You are my agent. Find her.

NONESUCH. Find her? Half a tick—Where did I put that address book?

(*A tiny voice pipes up.*)

LITTLE BIT OF PAPER. You don't need an address book.

NONESUCH AND HARE. Who's that?

LITTLE BIT OF PAPER. Only a little bit of paper.

NONESUCH. Only a—Where *are* you?

Salute to All Fools

LITTLE BIT OF PAPER (*very fast, in Yellow Dog Dingo rhythm*). Here am I, just a little bit of paper, lying in the bottom of the waste-paper basket—very poor company down in this basket—yesterday's newspapers, all unread—last year's bills, all unpaid—tomorrow's blueprints—

HARE. All very blue?

LITTLE BIT OF PAPER. No, sir; all very pink.
But if you would be so kind as to read me—

HARE. Read you? With pleasure. Hand me that basket, Nonesuch. Now! Away you bills, you tram-tickets, you trash—Ah, my little friend, how ragged, how crumpled you are—

LITTLE BIT OF PAPER. Read me, Mr. Hare, read me.

HARE. Why, she's just an address.

LITTLE BIT OF PAPER. The Focus-Pocus studios, a Likeness while you Wait; photographers ex cathedra, par excellence, and in excelsis—

NONESUCH. That's it. It was on the tip of my tongue. Taxi! Taxi! You'll see the Truth in a tick, sir.

PHOTOGRAPHER. Tick!
There you are, Mr. Hare. The Truth, the whole Truth and nothing but the Truth. Developed, printed and mounted—and only five guineas per copy.

HARE. The whole Truth? But this is a picture of me! And not, I may say, a good one.

PHOTOGRAPHER. Why not, Mr. Hare?

HARE. Well, for one thing, my fur. It looks so . . . so . . . so moth-eaten.

PHOTOGRAPHER. Your fur *is* moth-eaten. That is the truth, Mr. Hare.

HARE. And one of my ears looks longer than the other.

PHOTOGRAPHER. One of your ears *is* longer than the other. That is the—

HARE. No, it is not! Come, Nonesuch. Truth is not here; the camera always lies.

PHOTOGRAPHER. Now look, Mr. Hare, I could touch you up, you know—

HARE. Touch me up!

What is our next address?

LITTLE BIT OF PAPER. Follow *me*! Follow *me*!

HARE. What's that? The voice of an oracle?

LITTLE BIT OF PAPER. No, no, no, just a little bit of paper blown by the wind through the gutters of London;

(*The Alleluia theme on the orchestra gets them moving.*)

LITTLE BIT OF PAPER. All who are anxious to find the truth must follow me, follow me, follow me quickly, for I am on my way to the home of Truth—through Piccadilly Circus, don't look round—past the National Gallery, don't go in—and along the Strand—

HARE AND NONESUCH. Along the Strand—

LITTLE BIT OF PAPER. And here we are—in Fleet Street!

(*The music ends. Here they are.*)

JOE (*pseudo-American*). Will you look who's here! Nonesuch, old boy!

NONESUCH. Joe! Joe, meet my friend the March Hare. Joe, here's an ace newspaper man.

JOE. Pleased to meet you, Mr. Hare. Fag-end? What can I do for you?

HARE. Introduce me to Truth.

JOE. Sure. Come right up to my office.

HARE. The lady is in your office?

JOE. Not if she's a lady.

HARE. Oh but—

JOE. That's O.K. Lady, did you say?

HARE. Of course Truth is a lady.

JOE. Does she dance?

HARE. Of course she dances.

JOE. O.K. Follow me, boys. Taxi there! Taxi!

NONESUCH. Where are you taking us, Joe?

Salute to All Fools

JOE. Where do you think? The Charity Ball.

NONESUCH. The Char—

JOE. Bit of a zoo, I'm afraid. Driver, the Charity Ball.

HARE (*to himself, puzzled*). Bit of a zoo . . . a zoo? . . .

(*A kookaburra introduces other zoo voices which merge into a waltz and the chatter of human beings.*)

JOE. There she is now, old leveret. The one and only Truth, sir.

NONESUCH. Yes . . . the half-naked Truth. Nice bit of make-up though.

JOE. Sure. She knows her stuff. The one and only Truth—the Queen of Fleet Street.

JOURNALISTS' TRUTH. Talking about me, Joe?

(*Hsh! Hsh!*)

JOE. Yeah. Why not? I got you your entrée here.

JOURNALISTS' TRUTH. Lay off, brother. You Fleet Street boys seem to think you discovered me. Who's that animal with you?

JOE. Old Pussyfoot? He's your next boy-friend.

JOURNALISTS' TRUTH. Gee, another! Where's his credentials?

HARE. These are my credentials, madam. I am the March Hare and this is the First of April. I come of a noble, not to say nimble, family; my father won the high jump at the Olympic Games—my uncle won the boat-race—and in Ancient India an ancestor of mine was ambassador of the Moon. I can run in a circle, sleep with my eyes open, sing arias to the dawn and mend watches with butter. But now I search for Truth and if you, Madam, are she—

JOURNALISTS' TRUTH. Am I her! Say, Mr. Hare, if I wasn't a real lady, I would resent that. Am I Truth! Why don't you keep those long ears of yours to the ground?

HARE. Like this?

JOURNALISTS' TRUTH. Yeah. Like that. Now, brother, what do you hear?

HARE. I hear a million typewriters tapping out your praises, a hundred thousand rollers printing you new dresses—

NONESUCH. A new dress every day?

JOURNALISTS' TRUTH. A new dress every hour.

NONESUCH. Excuse me.

JOURNALISTS' TRUTH. You're welcome.

HARE. She *is* Truth, Nonesuch! She must be. Look at that mouth. The perfect Cupid's bow. Such a mouth could never tell a lie.

NONESUCH. 'Father, I cannot tell a lie. I did it with my little lipstick.'

HARE. She did not!

JOURNALISTS' TRUTH. I certainly did. You don't catch me leaving it all to Nature. Come on, big beast, why don't you ask me to dance?

HARE. But of course! When Truth and the March Hare meet what could be more to the point? To dance round cheek to cheek while the waltz goes on for ever—

(*The waltz ends.*)

HARE (*appalled*). Oh!

JOURNALISTS' TRUTH. That's too bad. Pardon me while I change my eyebrows.

POET. Leave your eyebrows alone! (*The crowd reacts.*) Madam, you are an impostress. I accuse you of false identity.

(*Exclamations.*)

JOURNALISTS' TRUTH. Really, young man? Who *are* you?

POET. I am a poet. Who are *you*?

JOURNALISTS' TRUTH. The name, brother, is Truth.

POET. Truth! *I* came here with Truth. She is my partner—from now till the end of the world.

JOURNALISTS' TRUTH. Is she? How come you weren't dancing?

POET. We have been sitting in the corner. That is she with her back to us.

NONESUCH. Pickled? Or just in a trance?

POET. In a trance, you common man. She is always entranced— and entrancing. Look, she is turning round.

Salute to All Fools

POETIC TRUTH. I . . . am Truth.

 (*This new and unreal voice sets the crowd whispering.*)

HARE. Was this the face that launched a thousand odes?

JOURNALISTS' TRUTH. If it was, it could do with some make-up.

POETIC TRUTH. Make way for me. I am Truth.

HARE (*aside*). Nonesuch, they can't both be!

NONESUCH. Hsh!

POETIC TRUTH. I am Truth, the partner of all poets.

JOURNALISTS' TRUTH. Then why don't you take the floor?

POETIC TRUTH. Because I take the sky. I beat in the void my
 ceaseless wings in vain. And only those can escort me who
 are also winged. Those who have inspiration.

POET. Which lets you all out but me.

HARE. Nonsense, sir. *I* have inspiration.

POETIC TRUTH. And who are *you*?

HARE. I am the March Hare.

POETIC TRUTH. Mad?

HARE. Yes.

POETIC TRUTH. Good.

 In love with me?

HARE. Yes.

POETIC TRUTH. Better.

 But do you know the answers?

 What is a poet?

HARE. A poet is the unacknowledged legislator of the world.

POETIC TRUTH. How does he legislate?

HARE. By sitting in a corner. And burning always with a hard
 gem-like flame.

POETIC TRUTH. What use is this legislation?

HARE. No use at all.

POETIC TRUTH. Full marks.

 What am I?

HARE. You are the plain Truth.

JOURNALISTS' TRUTH. Plain is the operative word.

Salute to All Fools

POETIC TRUTH. Madam!

JOURNALISTS' TRUTH. Madam yourself, wall-flower!

(*Poetic Truth screams, Journalists' Truth jeers; the onlookers join in with gusto.*)

NONESUCH. Now, now, now, girls; let me introduce you. Miss . . . er . . . Truth—Miss . . . er . . . Truth.

JOURNALISTS' TRUTH. Truth! Take that.

> (*A slap.*)

POETIC TRUTH. Truth! Take this.

> (*Another slap.*)

NONESUCH. Look out! The police!

POLICEMAN. Here, here, here; identity cards, please. You first, madam.

> (*Journalists' Truth groans.*)

HARE (*anxiously*). Is her name Truth?

POLICEMAN. No.

> (*The crowd laughs.*)

POLICEMAN. And you, Madam?

> (*Poetic Truth sighs.*)

HARE (*more anxiously*). Is *her* name Truth?

POLICEMAN. 'Course not.

> (*The crowd laughs louder.*)

POLICEMAN. And you, sir, why are you flattening your ears?

HARE. Because I'm frightened, officer.

POLICEMAN. Frightened, eh? Then you'd better be off home. Where do you live?

HARE. I live in a form.

POLICEMAN. In form? You mean in order?

HARE. No, not in order at all. It's made of bracken, you see, and the housemaid left last week—

POLICEMAN. I see, I see. Well, you'd better go back and fill it in. But not in pencil, mind.

HARE. Of course not, I always use earth.

POLICEMAN. The *good* earth?

HARE. Yes, the good earth. That's where I live.

POLICEMAN. Then off with you there at once. You can get a bus outside.

HARE. Bus? Far be it from me. I'll take the Joyful Plough. Ahoy there, Joyful Plough! Wait for us, we're coming.

(*A rustic piece on the orchestra takes him and Nonesuch to the country.*)

HARE. So here we are, back to the Good Earth. But oh, Nonesuch, look at the mud on my paws.

NONESUCH. Well, mud's better than paw-cuffs. That couple of females all but got us in jug.

HARE. One of my uncles was jugged once. He never came back. But where is my own little form? It's not such a very good form but—

COLONEL. Not good form at all, sir. Breaking my fence like that!

HARE. Oh excuse me, Colonel; I didn't see you.

NONESUCH. And we didn't know it was your fence.

COLONEL. Didn't you? Couldn't you see me sitting on top of it? I've a good mind to summons you both for poaching.

HARE. Oh but we weren't. I never have anything to do with poachers. One of my uncles—

NONESUCH. We're just here in search of Truth, sir.

COLONEL. Oh, Truth? That's quite another matter.

(*He turns away and shouts.*)

Truth! Come here, my dear lady.

TORY TRUTH. (*shouting back gruffly*). What is it, Colonel?

COLONEL. She's deaf—poor old dear. Tory old age, you know. Come here, Truth! These gentlemen want to meet you.

HARE. What a red face she has. And where did she get those tweeds?

NONESUCH. Hsh, Hare, hsh.

TORY TRUTH. Just a moment, gentlemen; this shooting-stick's a bit wonky. Jolly unfair, you know; Patience can sit on a monument but all I have—and I *am* Truth after all—

HARE. You *are* Truth after all?

Salute to All Fools

TORY TRUTH. Yes—and before all. I have my feet on the earth. The Good Earth, my friends.

NONESUCH (*sotto voce*). Yes—and the Large Feet.

TORY TRUTH. Well . . . what do you want to know?

HARE. We want to know all about you. Is it true that your motto is Back to the Land?

TORY TRUTH. Back to it? I've never left it! Ha! Ha! Ha! You don't catch me, my dear sir, going anywhere near a city. I just don't recognise cities.

HARE. But you must! A city's a fact.

TORY TRUTH. Nothing's a fact unless I choose to admit it. Why, you wouldn't pretend that the Industrial Revolution—

NONESUCH. That was a fact, surely?

TORY TRUTH. Fiddlesticks! As far as I am concerned, it never happened. Nor did Queen Anne's death. Nor did the present Government.

HARE AND NONESUCH. But . . . but . . . .

TORY TRUTH. No, I am Truth. I *know*. Nothing changes. This is the Good Earth. There will always be strapping squires like the Colonel here—

COLONEL. Thank you, madam.

TORY TRUTH. There will always be happy peasants like . . . like . . . Ahoy there, Hodge, come here! Now then, Hodge, show these people how happy you are.

HODGE (*quavering with misery*). Oh, ma'am, it be bitter cold today.

TORY TRUTH. He loves the cold, he loves it.

HODGE. Ah—if I could only get a bellyful of bread—and excuse me, Colonel, touching my forelock, sir, but if you could see your way to repair my roof—

COLONEL. For the thousandth time, Hodge, No! Haven't you heard I'm . . . er . . . bankrupt?

TORY TRUTH. You see. There will always be well set-up squires like the Colonel, there will always be laughing children of

Nature like Hodge, there will always be ten million wire-worms per acre, there will always be well-kept fences and (*glamorously*) shining boards saying Trespassers Prosecuted.

HODGE. Ah, that reminds me, that be what I come about. Begging your pardon, Colonel, it bain't my fault none of it, 'twas that there gap in fence . . . .

COLONEL. Well?

HODGE. There be trespassers got in.

COLONEL. Trespassers!

HODGE. Aye, sir. They be holding a party 'tother side of pheasant house.

COLONEL. A party, man?

HODGE. Ah, a party. And what be more, they be playin' about with red rags—I'm afeared old bull may see un.

COLONEL. Well, upon my soul—Where the devil's the game-keeper?

HODGE. They liquidated him, sir.

COLONEL. They what?

HODGE. He be liquidated, he be.

COLONEL. Oh drunk again, you mean? All right, shoulder guns.

TORY TRUTH. Shoulder shooting sticks. March!

HARE (*gaily*). Come on, Nonesuch. How I enjoy a party. I went to one once in summer under a tree. There was a dormouse there and a young lady whose name, I think, was Alicia . . . .

(*His voice dies away, giving place to a Marxist orchestra.*)

MARXIST. Silence, orchestral shock-troops!

(*The orchestra stops.*)

MARXIST. Comrades! What do I see advancing?

COMRADES. The enemy, comrade.

MARXIST. Correct. What do we do with them?

COMRADES. Shoot them.

MARXIST. Correct. Where is the wall?

1ST COMRADE. What wall, comrade?

MARXIST. The wall to put them up against

2ND COMRADE. There ain't no wall here, comrade.

MARXIST. In that case, comrades, build one.

3RD COMRADE. But they're almost on us, comrade.

MARXIST. Build one, I said. This is a Five Second Plan. One!

COMRADES. One!

MARXIST. Two!

COMRADES. Two!

MARXIST. Three!

COMRADES. Three!

MARXIST. Four!

COMRADES. Four!

MARXIST. Five!

COMRADES. Five!

COLONEL. Hey you! What are you all up to?

MARXIST. What right have you to ask?

COLONEL. I am the landlord.

(Grr! Grr!)

MARXIST. To the wall with him, comrades. Fire!

(Firing on percussion.)

MARXIST. And who are you?

HODGE. I be Hodge.

MARXIST. The Common Man?

HODGE. Oh *I* bain't common, I—

MARXIST. A kulak, eh?

(Grr! Grr!)

MARXIST. To the wall with him, comrades. Fire!

(Firing on percussion—bigger.)

MARXIST. Woman! Who are you?

TORY TRUTH. I am Truth.

(GRR! GRR!)

MARXIST. To the wall with her, comrades. Fire!

(Firing on percussion—biggest.)

MARXIST. And you?

Salute to All Fools

NONESUCH. As a matter of fact I'm—

MARXIST. No, you. The man with the long ears.

HARE. The hare with the long ears.

MARXIST. A hare?

HARE. Yes, comrade. A Marx hare.

MARXIST. Indeed? So you've come to join our party?

HARE. Exactly. Is there any vodka left?

MARXIST. Time enough for vodka. See this line?

HARE. Yes. Rather narrow, isn't it?

MARXIST. You walk along it, comrade. We'll soon see if you've got a sense of direction.

HARE. But why? I've not been drinking.

MARXIST. No—but you may have been thinking.

NONESUCH. No, no, old boy, he's not.

MARXIST. Nobody asked you. Get your paws on that line. Now then. Forward!

HARE. Cross your fingers, Nonesuch . . . .

(*Music takes him on his tortuous course; he pants and grunts in the effort to keep his balance.*)

HARE. Now . . . keep straight, keep straight, keep steady . . . . Left . . . left . . . . Oh, this is narrow . . . . There!

(*The music ends; he has walked the line.*)

MARXIST. You're not through yet. Now do the same thing backwards.

HARE. Cross your legs, Nonesuch . . . . Now.

(*Music as before.*)

HARE. Straight . . . straight . . . steady . . . Left . . . . Left . . . . There!

(*The music ends.*)

NONESUCH. Lucky he's got four left feet.

MARXIST. Very good, comrade. Sit down. Have a cup of tea.

HARE. No vodka?

MARXIST. Certainly not. You're not a commissar yet.

(*Bells are heard in the distance.*)

Salute to All Fools

NONESUCH. What's that?

MARXIST. That is the knell of private property.

HARE. At last! The expropriators are being expropriated.

MARXIST. That's right. Seems you're a well-read hare.

HARE. A well-*red* hare—Ha! Ha! Yes, *I* know the laws of historical necessity.

MARXIST. Good. Have some bread. Tell us more.

HARE. More? Let me see. It is not the consciousness of hares that determines their existence, but on the contrary their social existence determines their consciousness.

(*The comrades cheer.*)

MARXIST. Well done, comrade. Have some marge on it.

HARE. Thank you. Thank you very much.

MARXIST. Comrade; you are qualified now to behold the naked Truth.

HARE. The naked . . . ?

NONESUCH. He never bargained for that, old boy.

MARXIST. Truth is naked or nothing. Truth is ruthless. She can change the future—and she can change the past.

HARE. How can she change the past?

MARXIST. Don't talk like a bourgeois; how do you think? By tearing out pages from the history books.

A COMRADE. That's right.

MARXIST. Comrades, 'shun. She approaches.

(*The orchestra renders an advancing tank.*)

NONESUCH. In a tank, eh? Look out for your paws, Hare.

(*The music—the tank—stops. The comrades chant in unison :*)

COMRADES. We want Truth. We want Truth. We want Truth. T—R—U—T—H—TRUTH!

(*A rousing cheer. In the awkward gap which follows the Hare makes his faux pas.*)

HARE (*plaintively*). But she's not naked.

MARXIST. What's that you said?

HARE. Well maybe she is but I mean in that Marx Four tank—

only her head peeping out of the turret, you know—well, *I* wouldn't call that naked.

(*GRR! GRR!*)

MARXIST. Comrades! Take him to the wall. Liquidate this hare. He's a Trotskyist.

COMRADES. Aye, aye, comrade. Yah, you filthy beast!

(*Hubbub as they bundle him off. He has to raise his voice.*)

HARE. All right, all right; I'm not the first of my family to be shot. Put me against the wall; I have nothing to lose but my brains. And you, Truth, hail and Farewell—

COMRADES. Move along there, move along.

MARXIST. Flat against the wall with him. Haul him up by the ears. Now then, comrades. Slope Arms! . . . Standing Load! . . . Aim—

NONESUCH. Stop, comrades, stop!

MARXIST. What is it?

NONESUCH. Comrades, we all want a free, a classless—perhaps even a hareless—society.

(*Murmurs of approval.*)

NONESUCH. But before you liquidate my friend here, why not attempt a cure? Liquidation is fine but solidification is better.

MARXIST. And what is solidification?

NONESUCH. Comrade, I am surprised at you. (*Rattling it off.*) Solidification is a process of materialistic determinism which by the laws of the dialectic is bound to result in solidarity. And you all know what I mean by solidarity?

COMRADES (*absolutely synchronised*). We do, comrade, we do.

NONESUCH. There you are, you see.

MARXIST. But what sort of cure do you propose? How can you solidify this animal?

NONESUCH. Well, at the moment he's . . . er . . . volatile. We could cure that by sending him to an analyst.

MARXIST (*suspiciously*). You don't mean a psycho-analyst?

NONESUCH. Well, er, yes—why not?

Salute to All Fools

MARXIST. We do not believe in the psych.

NONESUCH. Quite right, old boy—But you know what day this is?

MARXIST. It is the Day of Proletarian Enlightenment—(*cheers*)—a flag in every fist and a tractor in every home.

(*Bigger cheers.*)

NONESUCH. Of course it is, but it's also—jump, Hare, jump—it's also the First of April.

(*The orchestra renders the jump and the race which follows; the angry cries of Stop are left behind; the music lands the Hare and Nonesuch in safety.*)

HARE (*breathless*). Oh what a race. Nonesuch! How did you keep up with me? After all I'm a hare.

NONESUCH (*breathless*). Well . . . after all I'm an agent. But you look as tired as I am. What about a spot of shut-eye?

HARE. Good idea.

(*He yawns; the orchestra takes over with a lullaby.*)

ANALYST (*with a Central European accent*). That is right. Close your eyes, Mr. Hare.

HARE (*starting*). Who're you?

ANALYST. I am your analyst.

HARE. But . . . but . . . but I—

NONESUCH. Excuse me, sir; I never meant that seriously.

ANALYST. Leave the meaning to me. We draw no distinction in psychology between what is called serious—

NONESUCH. Yes, sir, I see your point but I only said it as a ruse; the boys were going to shoot him. He doesn't need to be analysed.

ANALYST. Everyone needs to be analysed. Lie back, Mr. Hare; this will take several years.

HARE. I cannot spare several years. I am in search of Truth.

ANALYST (*archly*). Then you've come to the right shop. You know where Truth resides?

HARE. Not yet. I've been all over the country but—

ANALYST. Foolish Hare, foolish Hare. Truth resides in your own Unconscious.

Do you ever dream, my friend?

NONESUCH. Does he ever not?

ANALYST. Do not interrupt please. I will like it if you look the other way.

NONESUCH. I will like it too. Call me when you're through, Hare.

ANALYST. Now, Mr. Hare. By dreams we come at the truth. Now. What is it most you dream?

HARE. Ah, most I dream I am up in the moon—

ANALYST. Good, good.

HARE. With a butterfly net, you know—

ANALYST. I know. You catch the butterflies.

HARE. No, no, I catch the humming-birds. But that's not my strangest dream. Sometimes I dream I'm a man in the British Museum Reading Room.

ANALYST. You read the book?

HARE. Of course not; I have the bath. With lots of bath salts in it.

ANALYST. So? What kind of bath salts please?

HARE. Oh just the usual. Verbena, gardenia, amnesia, euthanasia—

ANALYST. So? Where do you buy these bath salts?

HARE. Black Market of course. Black Market.

ANALYST. Good. Give me the address please. Now where is my hat?

HARE. But—!

ANALYST. I have not for years bath salts. But make please haste. The address!

HARE. But there isn't any address. I told you this was a dream.

ANALYST. A dream! Damn all dreams! I was thinking you tell me the truth.

HARE. But you said that by dreams we come at the truth.

ANALYST. Ach! There is the door, Mr. Hare. You are not good for analysis.

NONESUCH. And it's not good for him. Come on, Hare, let's
hop it.

HARE. Goodbye, Mr. Analyst. Have a nice bath.

(*The door bangs.*)

ANALYST (*furious*). So? He leaves me holding the bath-tub. I shall
no more try this hare treatment. No more hares! No!

(*A pause; his tone changes to controlled malevolence.*)

He likes the bath? Good; let him go and get drowned. I
wish for him now to go to that place which in all the world
makes the hare most wet. Where is my atlas? So. Now where
does it tell me the rainfall?

(*'The Harp that Once' seeps in on an ocarina.*)

HARE. Nonesuch! What's that music?

NONESUCH. Sounds like the 'Harp that Once'.

HARE. The harp that once? Once what?

NONESUCH. The Harp that Once and never got over it. Tara's
Halls, sir, Tara's Halls.

HARE. I've never been to Tara's Halls. Might we find my Lady
Truth there?

NONESUCH. We might—but we won't find any halls.

HARE. No matter. Truth looks fairer in the open air.

NONESUCH. In the rain, you mean. O.K. Next stop, Tara.

(*The tune ends, giving place to heavy rain.*)

HARE. What a very wet place.

NONESUCH. What a very wet man.

HARE. Who?

NONESUCH. That chap there who's lost his trousers.

GAEL. Is it me has lost me trousers? The ignorance of yez! This is
me saffron kilt.

NONESUCH. But you're soaking, old man. You ought to go home
and change.

GAEL. Ach, I don't fancy the changes. And who minds soakin'
anyway?

HARE. But he's right. You ought to go home.

Salute to All Fools

GAEL. Sure this is me home—here on the sod of Tara. Me ancestors lie underneath it.

NONESUCH. You'll lie underneath it too if you stand out here in the rain.

GAEL. Rain? So ye call this rain!

(He sneezes violently.)

GAEL. I can see ye're English—the pair of yez.

HARE. English? Of course we're English.

GAEL. Ah poor fellows. There was nothing good ever come out of England. Sure *I* wouldn't use anything that was English.

NONESUCH. Except the language.

GAEL. Ah I only use that when I'm talkin' to black foreigners. When I'm here by meself I talk to meself in the Gaelic.

HARE. And do you understand yourself?

GAEL. I do. At times I do. There's great truth in the Gaelic.

HARE. Truth!

GAEL. Great and beautiful truth.

HARE. Nonesuch, we're on the track! Truth, sir, you say— Truth is a beautiful woman?

GAEL. She is, indeed she is. I know her well.

HARE. But she only speaks Gaelic, you say?

GAEL. What else would she speak? Isn't her proper name not Truth at all.

HARE. No? What *is* her name then?

GAEL. Cathleen ni Houlihan.

HARE. Cathleen ni—Nonesuch, make a note of that. And I must learn Gaelic. Buy me a grammar, Nonesuch.

GAEL. Why are ye wantin' a grammar?

HARE. Because I must speak with this lady. You're sure that she knows no English?

GAEL. Know English, is it? May the Round Towers turn square! Would she soil her delicate ears and be twistin' her beautiful mouth and pollutin' her pure green blood with a heathen language like that?

Salute to All Fools

Whisht—that's her now in the shawl. Takin' up her entrenched position over the graves of the kings. She'll be singin' now, so keep quiet . . . .

HARE. Singing in Gaelic?

GAEL. Amn't I after tellin' ye—

(*He is cut off by a soprano singing in a cockney accent.*)

SOPRANO. The blue moon is setting beyond the red pylon
    But south of the Border the whisky flows free

NONESUCH. Gaelic?

SOPRANO. With all the colleens wearing stockings of nylon
    And Father O'Flynn rolling down to the sea—

HARE. But surely she's singing in English?

SOPRANO. And ock! the dear mem'ries they still linger on
    Of Cuchullain and Guinness and Oscar and Conn.

GAEL (*outraged*). Stop! Stop! . . .

SOPRANO. With a carp on the harp and a salmon in the Shannon
    And the Poor Old Woman with the sorrows in her
        shawl

GAEL. Put on the other record! . . .

SOPRANO. An' meself on the shelf and King Billy on his filly—
    Oh hadn't we the sophistree on Tuesday in the House?

(*The orchestra alone while the Gael fumes.*)

GAEL. Change that record or I'll smash ye . . . I'm warnin' ye now; I'll smash ye.

SOPRANO. For Ock! the dear mem'ries—(*first smash but the song is obstinate*) they still linger on

(*The Gael does his second smash, shouting 'Take that!' The soprano's voice cracks on the word 'on'.*)

'ANNOUNCER.' Owing to a technical hitch we return you now to the studio. The March Hare will be with us in a moment. He is crossing from Ireland on the Home Service wavelength.

(*Whispering and crackling of scripts.*)

'ANNOUNCER.' I'm sorry; I'll read that again. The March Hare

185

will *not* be with us in a moment. He has boarded a very high frequency wave-length unobtainable on any wireless set. That is the end of the news.

(*Out of the violet distance comes a Yogi shanty-spiritual.*)

DISCIPLES. Om—Om—Yogi!

Om—Om—Swami!

Om—Om—Yogi!

Breathe, boys, breathe!

(*This is repeated till we have joined the congregation. It ends loud.*)

YOGI (*in a high, mystical quasi-oriental monotone*). Thank you, my children. We will now contemplate until April the First next year. I myself during this period shall not eat, speak or sleep—

NONESUCH (*calling from below*). Excuse me, sir!

YOGI (*from above*). Who are you?

HARE. Pilgrims in search of Truth. If you would kindly descend that rope—

YOGI. I may not descend to your level. You can speak to me from there.

HARE. Well, it's rather a strain on the voice but—Are you a Yogi, sir?

YOGI. I am a neo-Yogi. Whatever I am I am. Whatever I am not I am.

NONESUCH (*sotto voce*). Simple. Simple.

HARE. Why do you sit up there at the top of that rope?

YOGI. Why not?

HARE. Yes, quite—but what's the rope fastened to?

YOGI. Nothing.

HARE. Nothing!

YOGI. Which is the same as everything.

You two are in time, aren't you?

HARE. In time for what?

YOGI. I am above time. This is the higher level of existence.

HARE. And where is Truth?

YOGI. Truth is up here beside me.

186

Salute to All Fools

HARE. I can't see her.

YOGI. You wouldn't. You are blinded by your own personality.

HARE. But how can I reach her?

YOGI. By climbing up this rope.

HARE. I can't do that.

YOGI. No, you can't. Please go away. You smell.

HARE. I don't.

YOGI. You do. You smell of personality. *I* am above personality.

NONESUCH. You're above yourself, cock.

YOGI. Yes. I am above myself.

NONESUCH. Oh come on, Hare, let's go.

HARE. Go? I have been insulted. Also I have been challenged.
     Do you think I could climb that rope?

NONESUCH. No.

HARE. Nor do I. But never let it be said that the March Hare—I
     shall take a ten yards run.

NONESUCH. Make it twenty.

HARE. I'll make it twenty-five. Now then, One—Two—Three!
     (*The orchestra pulls; down comes rope, Yogi and all.*)

YOGI (*lapsing into cockney*). You little meddling rodent! You've
     pulled the whole thing down.

NONESUCH. Well, well, well—money for old rope.

HARE. A thousand apologies, sir. I hope you're not hurt?

YOGI. A neo-Yogi cannot be hurt.

NONESUCH. Then what are you rubbing your shin for?

YOGI. I am *not* rubbing my—

HARE. Of course you're not. Now let's put up this rope again.

YOGI. We can't.

HARE. Why not?

YOGI (*recovering his manner*). I decline to answer that question.

NONESUCH. He means the stage carpenter's gone.

YOGI. What I mean I mean. What I do not mean I mean.
     (*lapsing again.*) You might have known that rope wouldn't
     bear two of us.

HARE. But I thought you said—

(*The Yogi begins his comeback in cockney, then starts again at the beginning of the sentence.*)

YOGI. What I have said is the same as what I have not said.

Has either of you seen a paper parcel?

LITTLE BIT OF PAPER. Here am I, just a little bit of paper, wrapping up sandwiches, ham and spam—

NONESUCH. Aha!

YOGI (*snatching*). Give me those; they're mine.

NONESUCH. He's off. And never thanked me. Untidy chap, too, throwing that paper on the ground.

LITTLE BIT OF PAPER. Pick me up, pick me up; I can help you, I can help you; thank you very much—now read me, read me—

NONESUCH. Cover of a journal—'Science for All'—

LITTLE BIT OF PAPER. That's right—read me, read me— P.T.O. for all the gossip—M. & B. for colds and 'flu—

NONESUCH. The B.M.A. for L.S.D.—

LITTLE BIT OF PAPER. The Chemical Age, (*coyly*) a Note on Manure—The Plastic Age, a Hint on Housing—The Atomic Age, the Truth about Voltage—

HARE. The *Truth* about—

LITTLE BIT OF PAPER. Science owns the Door to the Future! Ring the Bell and the Door will Open!

HARE. Nonesuch! Ring the bell, please.

(*A cranky doorbell tinkles. A door opens. A maid.*)

MAID (*forbiddingly*). Yes?

NONESUCH. The Scientist in?

MAID. Yes—but he's not to be disturbed.

NONESUCH. Working?

MAID. He's splitting something. What he calls nuclear fission.

HARE. I don't care. I must see him.

(*He shouts past her.*)

Scientist! Scientist! Where are you?

SCIENTIST (*silkily; he is beside them*). Here I am.

188

Salute to All Fools

HARE. I'm afraid you're very busy—

SCIENTIST. I'm always very busy. Looking for Truth.

HARE. But that's what I've come about! I'm looking for her too.

SCIENTIST. *Her*? *It*, my dear sir. Metaphors are unsound.

HARE. But I'm going to marry it—her, I mean.

SCIENTIST. Tck! Tck! Tck! Metaphors are unsound. If you use them too much, you'll get into heavy water. Now, gentlemen, if you don't mind coming into my lab—

(*A door opens—cumbrously. When Nonesuch speaks his voice has a quite new resonance.*)

NONESUCH. Lab? This looks like the Albert Hall!

SCIENTIST (*gently*). It *is* the Albert Hall. I've hired it for my performance on the cyclotron.

HARE. And this is where you look for Truth?

SCIENTIST. This is where Truth will appear.

HARE. Out of these machines?

SCIENTIST. Out of these machines, as you call them.

NONESUCH. See your mistake, Hare? None of the other boys had a decent plant.

Do you know, sir? Mr. Hare here and I have spent this whole day consulting experts on Truth.

SCIENTIST. There *are* no experts. Except yours truly. You've heard of atomic energy?

NONESUCH. Well . . . we've heard it mentioned.

SCIENTIST. Only mentioned? Dear me, the public are slow in the uptake. Of course the uranium atom was only a modest beginning. But atomic energy is truth and I hope to get more and more of it. If now I were to split some other kind of atom—

HARE. A hare for example?

SCIENTIST. A hair!

HARE. Me.

SCIENTIST. Oh very good joke, sir; I always enjoy a pun.

HARE. It isn't a pun, sir; it is a proposition.

Salute to All Fools

SCIENTIST. Really? But have you any reason to suppose that *you* could release much energy?

HARE. I am the March Hare. Reason to suppose——! Watch me.

(The orchestra renders him jumping.)

NONESUCH. There he goes. Clean into the Upper Gallery.

SCIENTIST. Astonishing; quite astonishing.

NONESUCH. He comes of a family of athletes. They're all of them running at Aintree on Friday, you know.

SCIENTIST. Really? This interests me exceedingly. Supposing accepted your friend as a subject for nuclear fission——

NONESUCH. Nuclear what——

SCIENTIST. Ah, here he is, coming back again.

(The orchestra brings the Hare down.)

NONESUCH. Nice jumping, Hare, nice jumping.

HARE. I always land on my paws.

SCIENTIST. Mr. Hare, let me congratulate you. You *are* a source of energy. *(Wooingly)* I would very much like to try a small experiment on you.

HARE. An experiment?

SCIENTIST. Yes. For the sake of Truth.

HARE. For *her* sake I will do anything.

SCIENTIST. I should warn you, there is a very slight risk——

HARE. Only a slight risk? Why, for the sake of that beautiful lady——

NONESUCH. Look here, Hare, old leveret——

HARE. Electric hares we have heard of; *I* shall be the first Atomic Hare!

I have made up my mind. Let's go.

SCIENTIST. There is no need to go. Here is the cyclotron before you. Now please take your place in this pill-box. Now . . . we just screw you in . . . .

(The Hare grunts during this.)

So. Now when I've closed this lid we'll begin the bombardment.

NONESUCH *(startled)*. Bombardment?

Salute to All Fools

SCIENTIST (*gloatingly*). Ten million volts, my dear sir. Ready, Mr. Hare?

HARE. Close that lid. When this operation is over, may I see Truth face to face?

SCIENTIST. Truth has no face. Metaphors, as I said, are—

HARE. No face? Then let me out!

SCIENTIST. Oh no you don't.

(*Music closes the lid.*)

SCIENTIST. Atomic Energy Team! Stand by for action. Target for bombardment is the March Hare. Give him the works. Fission!

(*Music gives him the works.*)

SCIENTIST. Fine. Accelerate!... Accelerate!

(*The music accelerates and leads into the Chorus: 'The Old March Hare he ain't what he used to be, Only an hour ago!' The job is done.*)

SCIENTIST. You see? Now we open the lid.

(*As the lid opens, two snarling voices are heard.*)

NONESUCH. Good Lord, there are two of him now.

SCIENTIST. Nuclear fission, my friend. But they're both alive— and energetic, you'll find.

Come on, you two, climb out.

1ST HARE. No, you don't, you cad.

2ND HARE. I saw her first.

1ST HARE. Truth! She's mine.

2ND HARE. She's not, she's mine. My bride!

1ST HARE. Is she? We'll see about that.

2ND HARE. Take your paws off me.

(*They squeal and growl at each other.*)

NONESUCH. Hare! Hare, old boy.

SCIENTIST. Be accurate. They're plural.

NONESUCH. Hares, old boys. Stop it!

1ST HARE. Stop it, indeed!

2ND HARE. You keep out of this, Nonesuch.

Take that, you filthy rodent!

191

1ST HARE. Rodent yourself! Wait till I get my teeth in you.

2ND HARE. Ow!

Two can play at that game.

1ST HARE. Ow!

> (*Both Hares scream and scuffle.*)

SCIENTIST (*delighted*). What energy, what energy! But don't let's waste it. Help me to hold them apart.

Come, come, gentlemen . . . .

> (*Nonesuch seconds him. The animal noises stop.*)

SCIENTIST. There!

And have you seen Truth, my friends?

BOTH HARES. I have.

SCIENTIST. But she has no face?

BOTH HARES. She *has* a face.

1ST HARE. There! Can't you see it! Look up.

2ND HARE. It fills the Albert Hall.

NONESUCH (*sotto voce*). More than the Vigilantes could.

1ST HARE. Beautiful, Nonesuch, beautiful. My one and only bride!

2ND HARE. *Your* one and only? Beast!

1ST HARE. Beast? Put up your paws!

NONESUCH. Now, now, boys, don't start all that again. There's two of you and there's only one of Truth.

> (*This releases the echoes.*)

TORY TRUTH. But *I* am Truth.

JOURNALISTS' TRUTH. *I* am Truth.

POETIC TRUTH. *I* am Truth.

NONESUCH. Seem to be some ghosts around today.

SCIENTIST. Oh the Albert Hall is like that.

TORY TRUTH. It is. It never changes.

HARE. Silence! You're liquidated.

JOURNALISTS' TRUTH. Yeah—but what about me?

POETIC TRUTH. And me? You offered your paw to *me*.

ANALYST. Truth is in your Unconscious.

Salute to All Fools

MARXIST. Truth is what we decide at our next meeting.

YOGI. Truth is at the top of a rope.

GAEL. Where's that record they put on back to front?

PHOTOGRAPHER. Where's that photo? I think I'll touch it up now.

HARE. Where is this! Where is that! Silence, all of you. Where is the Face?

SCIENTIST (*smugly*). Has it gone?

HARE. It was here just now. Up here above us floating under the roof. But now it's vanished—And what's that thing in its place?

SCIENTIST. That? That's a diagram. One of my own.

HARE. So you have fooled me too.

SCIENTIST (*still cooing*). Well . . . it's April the First.

    (*The orchestra begins Alleluia.*)

HARE. One moment please!

    (*The orchestra obliges him and stops.*)

HARE. One moment please. Then you can have your finale.

    (*This releases a hive of ringing shouts.*)

GAEL. We don't want any finallies. Up the rebels!

ANALYST. Up the Oedipus Complex!

TORY TRUTH. Up the Upper Ten!

MARXIST. Up the Inevitability of History!

JOE. Up the Circulation of the Late Night Final!

YOGI. Up the Immanent and Transcendent Rope!

SCIENTIST. Up the New Era of Atomic Energy!

POETIC TRUTH. Up the Beautiful Ineffectual Angel who is older than the rocks on which she sits and—

HARE. Up the Garden Path! April Fools all of you.

    (*The Truths and the Experts hiss.*)

HARE. Why do you hiss? Don't you know what day this is? I, the March Hare, I also have been fooled. But I can survive. Can you?

Whatever I am, I am not so narrow as some; a hare may have

curious eyes but he wears no blinkers. I have not won my bride—but I have not married a stuffed one. And, if it is April the First, it is also Spring. The daffodils blow their trumpets, there is green fire in the hedge-rows, there is even a new note in the ring of the office telephone. It is your Spring—but it is also mine. Fetch me my springboard, Nonesuch.

Ladies and gentlemen, I am about to take off. Follow me if you dare. Hail and Farewell. I salute you!

(*The orchestra plays the finale on the Alleluia theme—When it has finished the Announcer speaks in the 'dead' studio.*)

ANNOUNCER. You have just heard Salute to—Salute to—Salute to—

SWEET VOICE. Salute to the Public?

ANNOUNCER. Quite so.

NOTES

NOTES

Page 23. *Roland as a boy* was, in the broadcast, brilliantly doubled by Cyril Cusack.

Page 28. *The tolling bell*, instead of being done by percussion alone, was reinforced and made ultra-suggestive by strings. Apart from percussion and one trumpet (reserved for the Challenge Call) Benjamin Britten confined himself in this programme to an orchestra of twenty-six strings from which he got the most varied and astonishing effects.

Page 29. *The Child of Stone* puzzled many listeners. The Mother in bearing so many children only to send them to their death, can be thought of as thereby bearing a series of deaths. So her logical last child is stone—her own death. This motif has an echo in the stone in the ring.

Page 30. *The Verbal Transition* from one scene to another is controlled from the panel and need not seem either abrupt or confusing. It not only makes a change from the musical transition but has certain positive advantages; e.g. as here, irony.

Page 38. *The Soak* I should have called Solipsist if that word were known to the public. His alcoholism is an effect rather than a cause. Robert Farquharson wonderfully achieved the right leer in the voice and the dream-like sinister undertones.

Page 41. '*I'm dreaming you*' is a famous stumper for reason. Compare *Alice Through the Looking Glass*, the episode of Tweedledee and the Red King:

' "And if he left off dreaming about you, where do you suppose you'd be?"

"Where I am now, of course," said Alice.

"Not you!" Tweedledee retorted contemptuously. "You'd be nowhere. Why, you're only a sort of thing in his dream!" '

Page 42. *The Stentorian Voice* butting in here changes the scene

Notes

with the speed of a dream. Radio, like dreams, having no set stage, can disregard spatial conventions.

Page 47. 'The sea today': this covers a number of days. The developing false idyl of Roland and Neaera is intercut with the voices of people playing tombola—always the same again. The idyl also is merely killing time.

Page 57. *The Mirage Sequence* needed a great deal of rehearsal but the stunt came off.

Page 63. *The Final Decision* may, I think, be too abrupt for a listener—though in life such a complex psychological conflict can, of course, resolve itself abruptly.

Page 64. *The Last Scene* is naturally the nearest to Browning. Compare:

> 'Not see? because of night perhaps?—why day
> Came back again for that! before it left,
> The dying sunset kindled through a cleft:
> The hills, like giants at a hunting, lay,
> Chin upon hand, to see the game at bay,—
> "Now stab and end the creature—to the heft!"
>
> Not hear? when noise was everywhere! it tolled
> Increasing like a bell. Names in my ears
> Of all the lost adventurers my peers . . .'.

SUNBEAMS IN HIS HAT

Acknowledgment is made to Constance Garnett from whose translations of Tchehov's plays I have quoted.

Page 73. *Tchehov died* of consumption at Badenweiler on July 2nd, 1904, at the age of forty-four; there is an account of this last day (the day which sets my programme) by his wife Olga Knipper. In his last letter to his sister, dated June 28th, he had complained both of the heat in Badenweiler and of the German lack of taste in dress, etc., and had played with the idea of escaping to Odessa by

198

Notes

steamer from Trieste. In earlier letters he had complained of German 'peace and order' and of the 'very expensive but talentless band' that played in the garden.

Page 78. *The visit to Sahalin* happened in 1890. Tchehov, who chose this island as a place 'where colonization by convicts can be studied', afterwards wrote a book about it which is said to have influenced the authorities to bring in some reforms. I stressed this Sahalin mission because it illustrates Tchehov's 'social consciousness'.

Page 80. *The incident of the Boy* is recorded in a letter to A. F. Koni.

Page 84. *Faites vos jeux*: I used Offenbach's can-can—inappropriate to the tempo of Monte Carlo, but right, I thought, for Tchehov's mood.

Page 86. *The Seagull* was first produced in 1896 in Petersburg, where it failed miserably. Tchehov wrote to his brother: 'The moral is: I must not write plays.'

Page 89. *Tolstoy and Gorki* often had such arguments in Tchehov's presence, as admitted by Gorki himself.

Page 91. '*Vaudeville*': Tchehov's own word for it.

Page 92. *Stanislavsky* I left uncharacterised on purpose. This was not the moment to introduce such a personality.

Page 95. *The Clock* is, I think now, rather a creaking device.

Page 95. *The River*: Tchehov wrote in a letter: 'When the quilt slides from my body during the night, I begin to dream of huge, slippery stones, cold autumn waters, naked banks,—all this vaguely, as in a fog, without a bit of blue sky showing; in melancholy and depression I gaze on the stones and feel, for some reason, the inevitability of crossing a deep river.'

THE NOSEBAG.

Page 101. *The best English version* of this story is *The Soldier and Death* by Arthur Ransome; I had not however come across it when I wrote my script.

Notes

Page 104. *The Third Beggar* is in some versions, though not in Mr. Ransome's, identified with Christ. Hence the line 'Do you not know who I am?' Without using a Narrator I could not be more explicit.

Page 104. *The nosebag* is by Mr. Ransome called a 'sack'—no doubt a more correct translation. But the word 'nosebag' sticks more.

Page 107. *The music stops* so aptly because it is an actor. Compare in *Salute to All Fools* the waltz at the Charity Ball.

Page 109. *The bestial noises* of the devils were achieved by a mixture of discs on the turn-tables and voices in the studio; my key disc was a recording of jabbering apes.

Page 111. *The square brackets*, here and later, denote cuts which I had to make in the broadcast merely for lack of time.

Page 113. *No bones in the palace*: in the narrative versions the Soldier is still in the palace when the Tsar sends round to investigate. This is one of several changes dictated by dramatic economy.

Page 114. *The clanging in the smithy* could have been rendered either by a spot effect in the studio or by a gramophone record. We had to decide whether to be realistic; these were corporeal devils and what the hammers would strike would be not the anvil but their bodies. In the end I disregarded realism and plumped for a ringing noise. The records of real smithies being too unpoetic, I used a recorded bell-bird.

Page 120. *The cut in the broadcast* here was very regrettable as the two earlier sickbeds were needed in order to 'build' to the Tsar's. The rigid time-limit of B.B.C. programmes has often undone things so.

Page 123. *The voice of Death* would be out of most actresses' compass. Miss Gladys Young attained it. While this programme was meant to be fun, I had no intention that 'Death' should be merely funny. She had to be frightening—and, in a way, pathetic.

Page 131. *The Gates of Paradise* more than anything else would have been strengthened by specially written music.

Notes

Page 132. *The War Theme* was my own interpolation; the traditional version ends less committally—'For all I know he may be living yet.' I added this piece of homage to the moujik because of what was happening as I wrote—at the beginning of 1944. This lays me open to the two charges of sentimentality and dramatic incongruity. The latter I deny; that the Soldier should go to war again and that the Landlord should toast Mother Russia are no more out of key than the characterisation of Death (see above). As for sentimentality (and the Mother Russia theme has nothing to do with the policy of the Soviet Union) I greatly admired and admire the courage of the Russian soldier; this story after all was about the same type of man and it was the same type of man who made this story.

THE MARCH HARE RESIGNS

Page 139. *'Not yet All Fools' Day'*: When I suggested this programme, I meant it for April 1st, 1945, but, as this was dis-·covered to be Easter Day, the date had to be changed.

Page 139. *'The paws of the March Hare'*: a talking animal is in pantomime a mere buffoon. To 'see' him as a character, you must not see him. The Dog in *The Witch of Edmonton* must, I imagine, be silly on the stage—but he *would* be 'radiogenic'.

Page 139. *'Daffodils over the microphone'*: we did have some over the microphone.

Page 139. *'The pitch was sticky'*: both the March Hare programmesare full of puns and other plays upon words. These can be very offensive if they are emphasised. My principle in producing is to have them thrown in quickly and matter-of-factly and leave it to the listener to catch it or miss it.

Page 141. *The Public Address Voice* was inspired by the classic example in Baker Street Underground station.

Page 152. *The Safe Hotel*: compare Nathaniel Gubbins. Mr. Gubbins' excellent column in the *Sunday Express* makes a con-

Notes

centrated use of the same brand of salt which the March Hare sprinkles in passing.

SALUTE TO ALL FOOLS

Page 170. '*My uncle won the boat race*': up to the day of transmission he had won the hurdles. But Oxford had beaten Cambridge on March 30th.

Page 171. *The Poet* and his Truth are, of course, misrepresentations. I was thinking of a foolish and tiresome kind of poet and a narrow conception of poetry; had I been writing for a highbrow public, I should have been more specific. To quote—or misquote—Shelley and Pater in such a burlesque may be, by some, thought blasphemy. But without some blasphemy where should we be?

Page 183. *The Gael* is hardly a caricature (see any Irish nationalist paper). To those who accuse me of fouling my own doorstep, let me say that I dissociate the language lunacy from the question of Eire's independence; I am glad that she runs her own house but why need she keep the windows shut?

Page 186. *The Neo-Yogi* was inspired not by the East but by California. It was Laidman Browne (who played the part brilliantly) who had the idea of adding an extra facet by making the Yogi a cockney in disguise.

Page 189. *Nuclear fission*: if anyone deplores the burlesque of this serious subject, I hold to what I said about blasphemy.

Page 191. *The Two Hares*, speaking or snarling at once, were achieved by pre-recording Esmé Percy and 'dubbing' together two sets of discs.

Page 194. *Salute to the Public*: some of them rose to it.

D1436016

THE NEW NATURALIST

A SURVEY OF BRITISH NATURAL HISTORY

AN ANGLER'S ENTOMOLOGY

EDITORS:
JAMES FISHER M.A.
JOHN GILMOUR M.A. V.M.H.
SIR JULIAN HUXLEY M.A. D.Sc. F.R.S.
SIR DUDLEY STAMP C.B.E. D.Litt. D.Sc. LL.D. Ekon.D.

PHOTOGRAPHIC EDITOR:
ERIC HOSKING F.R.P.S.

The aim of this series is to interest the general reader in the wild life of Britain by recapturing the inquiring spirit of the old naturalists. The Editors believe that the natural pride of the British public in the native fauna and flora, to which must be added concern for their conservation, is best fostered by maintaining a high standard of accuracy combined with clarity of exposition in presenting the results of modern scientific research. The plants and animals are described in relation to their homes and habitats.

The text and line illustrations are here reproduced unaltered, but the process of manufacture used to achieve an economic price does not, unfortunately, do full justice to all the photographs; and those originally in colour appear in black and white.

AN
ANGLER'S
ENTOMOLOGY

by

J. R. HARRIS

M.A. (Dubl.)

SOMETIME DEMONSTRATOR IN LIMNOLOGY, DEPARTMENT OF ZOOLOGY,
TRINITY COLLEGE, DUBLIN

Bloomsbury Books
London

To
MY WIFE
with gratitude for
her help

First Edition 1952
Second Edition 1956
Reprinted 1966

This edition published 1990 by
Bloomsbury Books an imprint of
Godfrey Cave Associates Limited
42 Bloomsbury Street, London WC1B 3QJ
under license from William Collins Son's & Co. Ltd.

ISBN 1 870630 49 9

CONTENTS

CONTENTS

vi

* PLATES IN COLOUR

vii

COLOUR PLATES

PLATES IN BLACK AND WHITE

It should be noted that throughout this book Plate numbers in arabic figures refer to Colour Plates, while roman numerals are used for Black-and-White Plates

EDITORS' PREFACE

J. R. HARRIS is that happy combination, an angler and a scientific naturalist; and angler-naturalists are one of the pillars of British natural history. They have succeeded, through the years, in arranging that art and science should march happily together with the object of catching sporting fish in as deft, delicate, dashing and dramatic a method as possible.

The narrow view, that angling is simply a method of killing fish, receives no support among many thousands of people in the British Isles. The science and art of angling has always carried with it a curiosity about the world around, and particularly into the nature and habits of the animals upon which sporting fish feed, and into the scientific basis of the simulation of certain of them as lures for the fish.

It has been clear for many years that a thoroughly scientific anglers' entomology, which would effectively and completely make a bridge between scientific entomology and the rule-of-thumb field methods of the sportsman, was necessary. Mr. Harris, who is un-doubtedly the best qualified to try this task, set himself to do it many years ago, and this book is the product of his vast experiences in fish-ing and collecting and fly-tying, related to the experiences of others. We believe that an enormous number of people have been waiting for this book — not only anglers. Some anglers who read it, indeed, will approach their fish from an entirely new angle!

One of the tasks which Mr. Harris has successfully performed has been the construction of what might be called a glossary-dictio-nary of the names of flies. These are now clearly and unequivocally linked with the scientific names of the stages of the insects concerned, so that when anglers from Ireland and England meet and discuss the different kinds of nymphs, duns and spinners, they can be quite certain precisely what it is that they are talking about. Mr. Harris's references to the literature of angling has shown that the writers of the past were not always quite so certain.

Moreover, even when anglers are well aware that the Claret Dun is *Leptophlebia vespertina*, and that the Great Red Spinner may refer to the spinners of *Ecdyonurus venosus*, *E. dispar* or *E. torrentis*, they wish to be certain of their identifications. This book makes identification possible and entirely practical with keys, descriptions and plates.

Although in many ways this is the most specialised volume in the *New Naturalist* series which has appeared to date, it never was the object of the *New Naturalist* to produce *highly* specialised books. On the other hand, we have always believed it our duty to fill obvious gaps in the literature of natural history, and *An Angler's Entomology* was such a gap. It is a subject with a very much wider following than many people imagine, and, as Mr. Harris has so interestingly shown, is also a subject of considerable biological importance. The publication of this book we feel convinced will lead not only to further scientific researches, but to a reawakening of critical practice and study in what is quite the most fascinating part of angling.

Mr. Harris's book is illustrated by colour photographs taken, with his collaboration, by Mr. T. O. Ruttledge from living or freshly killed specimens. We believe that nothing of the kind has so far appeared in any book, and are convinced that the amateur naturalist and angler will be able to identify the various forms of all the more important species, with the aid of the key which Mr. Harris has constructed and these remarkable photographs.

THE EDITORS

AUTHOR'S PREFACE

DURING the past one hundred years angling entomology has become complicated. Up to the publication of Ronalds's *Flyfisherman's Entomology* in 1836 anglers were interested only in the superficial characteristics of flies — that is, in their general colour, size and habits.

But the study of these flies has now become more highly specialised, and in order to be conversant with modern literature on the subject it is necessary to have a certain amount of technical knowledge. This change has followed the great advances which were made in systematic entomology towards the end of the last century. In so far as the Ephemeroptera are concerned, the advances in systematic entomology were largely due to the work and publications of the Rev. A. E. Eaton. Eaton completely revised and modernised the systematics, and actually described and named fourteen of the forty-seven species known in Britain and Ireland today. It is not surprising, therefore, that the late F. M. Halford, in writing of the flies soon after the publication of Eaton's works, attached considerable importance to the application of the correct technical name to the various species he dealt with.

This was only following the fashion which had been set by Ronalds, who was the first author to correlate the vernacular and technical names. It is unfortunate that, owing mainly to the confusion which existed in systematic entomology at that time, most of the technical names employed by Ronalds were incorrect. But Ronalds's book possessed the great advantage that the technical name was always subservient to the vernacular name. In recent books, and particularly in recent articles appearing in various periodicals, there is a tendency to overemphasise the importance of the technical name. For example, we now constantly read about *Ephemerella ignita* and *Bibio johannis*, instead of about the Blue-winged Olive and the Black Gnat.

Anglers identify flies by superficial characteristics and entomologists are concerned with precise details of structure of parts
which are often microscopic in size. But it is not generally appreciated that once an entomologist has identified a species, and has
become thoroughly familiar with its appearance, he identifies subsequent specimens of that species by the superficial characters, often
by the same characters, such as the colour, size and shape, which
an angler uses. Only in cases of doubt does the entomologist refer
again to the detailed structure.

The great disadvantage under which most anglers labour is
that they have not got the knowledge or the facilities (or probably
the desire) to make their initial identifications by, for want of a better
term, entomological methods. And, when original identifications
are made solely from superficial characters the identifications are
very liable to be inaccurate, because such characters, whilst they
are easy to remember and recognise once they are known, are extremely difficult to describe. By far the best way to convey these characters is by the use of coloured pictures and it is hoped that the series
of colour photographs of the insects appearing in this book will
prove satisfactory in this respect. In addition to these colour photographs there are included detailed descriptions of the commoner
species of the Ephemeroptera in their various stages. So that this book
is primarily intended to provide a means by which anglers may
identify the more important aquatic flies.

Of the three main orders of these flies, namely the Ephemeroptera, the Caddis-flies and the Stone-flies, the first is by far the most
important. It is the order in which anglers are most interested; yet
no text-book, popular or otherwise, has appeared which deals with
the general natural history of those species which are found in these
islands. It is hoped that this book will remedy that deficiency to some
extent; and it is for this reason that so much space has been given to
the Ephemeroptera in preference to the other orders.

Finally, it is hoped that the book will serve as a connecting link
between the popular angling, and the purely systematic entomological
works. There must be many anglers who would like to take up the study
of these flies from a systematic viewpoint but who have been discouraged
from doing so by the difficulty in becoming familiar with the various
methods and technique. It has been with this end in view that details
of structure, of taxonomic features, and of various technical terms re-
lating to the Ephemeroptera, have been explained in the text.

I have endeavoured to write a book for the angler-naturalist, that is, for the angler who is interested in natural flies. Interest in the natural water flies is not only one of the most intriguing of the side studies which combine to make the art of angling so everlastingly interesting, but it is of obvious practical importance to the fly fisherman who desires to improve his skill as an angler. As Mr. J. W. Dunne truly said "The fly fisherman who knows nothing of his flies is as great an anachronism as the painter who knows nothing of his paints. More, he is a bad man of business."

I hope that imperfections in the text will be compensated for by the excellent photographs. All the colour photographs, with the exception of that of the Hawthorn-fly, are flies which were freshly killed and were then photographed before their colours had visibly altered. I collected the flies mainly in Ireland, but found it necessary to bring some of them from the south of England; but they were all delivered alive for photographing. After it was agreed by what method the flies should be killed, fixed if necessary, and then mounted in suitable lifelike positions, the setting up of the flies and the photography was carried out by Mr. T. O. Ruttledge.

I am glad of this opportunity to acknowledge the encouragement which I have received from Professor J. Brontë Gatenby of the Department of Zoology, Trinity College, Dublin, during the compilation of the manuscript, and I am indebted to him for reading and criticising it both from the point of view of an angler as well as a biologist. I wish also to thank Dr. B. P. Beirne, formerly of the same department, for reading each chapter and suggesting many necessary alterations.

Mr. D. E. Kimmins of the British Museum (Natural History) and Mr. Theodore Savory most kindly read the typescript also, and made several suggestions for the improvement of the text, and I am exceedingly obliged to them for the trouble which they took in the matter. Finally I should like to thank the members of the Editorial Board for much help and encouragement, particularly James Fisher, who has been most generous with time and advice.

J. R. HARRIS

THE PROGRESS OF A FLY FISHERMAN

THIS INTRODUCTION is intended as an apologia, or a *raison d'être* for the compilation of the book. It is in the nature of a brief autobiography of a fly fisherman who, through necessity, became interested in and learnt something about artificial fishing flies, as well as about those natural species which are found in and around fresh waters.

I started angling with wet flies and, when very young, learnt how to tie flies after a fashion; and at eleven or twelve years of age was inordinately pleased to catch a ¾-lb. fish on a fly designed and dressed by myself. Several years later I was able to catch a few fish on nondescript dry flies, but always felt that it was from luck and not through any deserving efforts on my part. Some dry flies were noticeably more effective than others, and at times fish would rise reasonably freely to such patterns as a Ginger Quill or a Blue Quill; but more often they ignored these or else rose to them only reluctantly and usually short. Over several years, as a result of reading all angling books which I could obtain, I gradually compiled a set of patterns which gave reasonably successful results. These patterns included a Pheasant Tail, Hare's Ear, Olive Quill, Black Midge, Rusty Variant and Small Dark Sedge. When using a selection such as these there is little need to pay attention to the natural flies on the water. If one pattern is unsuccessful, another pattern is tried instead. After a while it became noticeable that these patterns were more effective on upland and bog rivers than on limestone streams, and that trout were often most difficult to catch with these patterns when they were rising very frequently. Concurrently with using these patterns, I also carried a set of flies tied as "exact imitations" (mostly Halford's patterns) and had varying success with them. Occasionally a pattern was quite successful during the period when fish were rising strongly in the evening. One such pattern was Halford's female Pale Watery Dun, which once got me five fish all over 2 lbs. during the evening rise, and on another evening eight fish which averaged 1 lb. 3 ozs. On other evenings all patterns were ignored.

From angling books I had learnt a certain amount about the entomology of water-bred flies, and was able to identify, or thought I was able to identify, several of the commoner species. But such identifications were more often than not made with considerable doubt. Such flies as the Greendrake, Alder, Silverhorns, Yellow May Dun, Yellow Sally and the large Stonefly were fairly easily recognised from Ronalds's and Leonard West's books. Identification of the Blue Winged Olive, Iron-blue Dun, Large Dark Olive Dun and the Yellow Upright were made with reasonable certainty with the aid of Halford's books and a magnifying lens, but the small stone-flies, most caddis-flies, and in particular most of the Ephemeroptera could not be identified with any certainty whatsoever.

Among the smaller Ephemeropterans were several flies which appeared to be either pale wateries or small olives, one of them could be called a small dark olive; there were also larger olives which were paler in shade than those flies recognised as Large Dark Olives, and these were assumed to be Medium Olives; there were several other brown and very dark coloured specimens which I found impossible to identify at all. The caddis-flies were even more difficult to place. What was the difference between a Cinnamon Sedge and a Brown Sedge? What were the names of the very numerous brownish-grey sedges which were abundant on most rivers, and which sedge could be identified for certain as the Welshman's Button? Among the smaller stone-flies I tried in vain to recognise which was the Willow-fly which Mr. Skues recommended should be imitated by a spent pattern; also none of the small brown stone-flies found in the early spring could be correlated with descriptions of the February Red.

Assistance obtained from other anglers was of little or no value, as opinions differed so much, and also some anglers of experience disagreed with several of my determinations of flies in cases where I was confident that I was correct.

Owing to the uncertainty in the whole position, I turned to the study of these three orders of flies from the systematic entomological viewpoint. This was with the intention of acquiring sufficient knowledge about the species to enable identifications to be made with reasonable accuracy, and also with the idea of compiling some time in the future a simple entomology to provide other anglers, who might have experienced similar troubles, with a ready means of recognising those flies which are important for angling purposes.

But the systematic study of the flies became interesting for its own sake, and this had the great advantage that it dovetailed so well into my angling activities that I could always collect flies (to be brought home for examination) when the fish were not rising. As a natural corollary it followed that an interest in the habits and in the general natural history of the insects developed.

When I thought that I had collected sufficient data about the flies to compile some sort of an entomology, I realised that it would be essential to have any such work well illustrated with coloured pictures of the species concerned, if the book were to be of practical value. As at the time, i. e. some twenty years ago, this would have necessitated having the flies painted from life, the difficulties appeared too great and the idea was dropped. In recent years, however, colour photography has solved this difficulty, but, owing to additional knowledge which I had acquired about the biology of the natural species in the intervening period, the book is now being produced in a much more ambitious form than was originally intended.

It is hoped that the book will serve the dual purpose both of allowing anglers who merely want to identify different flies which may be found on any river or lake in Britain or Ireland to do so from the coloured plates and from the written descriptions, and of providing those who are interested in the natural history of the flies with a means by which they can increase the scope of their interest and so add to the pleasure and enjoyment of "the contemplative man's recreation".

Most anglers are probably familiar with the appearance and habits of the waterside birds, others have knowledge of the aquatic and semi-aquatic plants. Familiarity with such everyday things as these adds greatly to the contentment derived from a day spent by river or lake.

As one's fishing experiences increase one's outlook changes, and, in so far as the catching of fish is concerned, the matter of importance is not so much how many fish are caught but rather how they are caught. When dry fly fishing, one is apt to find that one loses interest in fish caught on "a good pattern of general fly" and to get satisfaction only when it has been determined on what fly a trout is feeding and then to succeed in catching the fish on an imitation of that fly. Wet fly fishing has often been deprecated, as it is said to be a method of "chuck and chance it", but what method could more aptly be described as "chuck and chance it" than fishing with some general dry fly pattern in the hope that a fish seen feeding will accept it?

It could, of course, be maintained that any type of fishing consists in "chucking and chancing it". But the more the margin of error is reduced, the less is left to chance, and a chief source of error would appear to be in the selection of the particular fly used. As has been mentioned previously, trout often feed more or less indiscriminately on a number of different species which may be on the water at the same time, and when they are doing this any one of a number of different patterns is likely to prove effective. But just as often (more so on some rivers than on others) they will, to a greater or lesser extent, concentrate on one species only, and it then becomes necessary to exercise careful judgment in selecting a suitable pattern.

Normally, such a pattern will, to our eyes, somewhat resemble the natural insect in colour (either by transmitted or reflected light), size and shape. Often, without being able to identify the fly on the water, one can yet, by comparison, select a suitable imitation. But it is much more satisfactory to be able to name the natural species, for then one can utilise one's knowledge of artificial flies acquired from reading fishing books, imparted by other anglers or gained through experience. For instance, if it is ascertained that a fish is feeding on Blue-winged Olives, one can, without opening the fly box, decide which of possibly several imitations contained therein to use. It may be the Orange Quill or other Blue-winged Olive pattern recommended by Skues, Lunn's Hackle Blue-wing or Orange Quill variant, or perhaps one's own dressing of the fly. Whichever of the patterns is selected, it will obviously be fished with much greater confidence, and likelihood of success, than would some general pattern chosen at random, or even some olive coloured pattern selected because of its resemblance to the natural species.

Even though one is able to recognise many of the important natural species in the hand, it by no means follows that one can therefore deduce what fly the fish may be feeding on. The river may be wide and the wind be blowing the flies on the surface towards the further bank, or the bank may be several feet above the water surface so that it is difficult to capture flies from the water. In such circumstances, and probably at all times, preliminary observations,

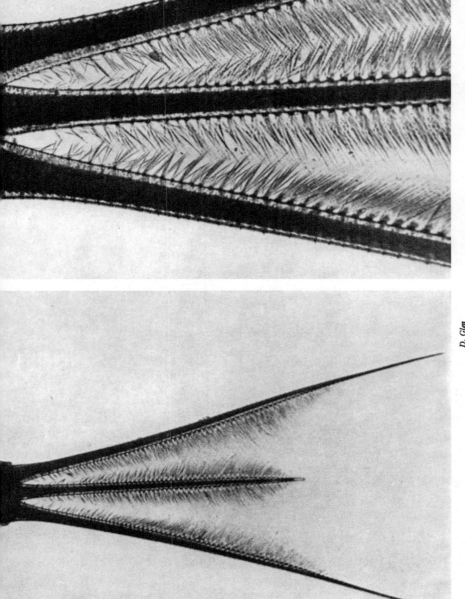

Plate Ia The tails of the Large Dark Olive nymph, *Baëtis rhodani*, enlarged x 25, showing the general arrangement of the fine hairs or *setae*

D. Glen

Plate Ib The basal portion of the tails enlarged x 85, showing the finer ramifications of the *setae* arising from the tails

D. Glen

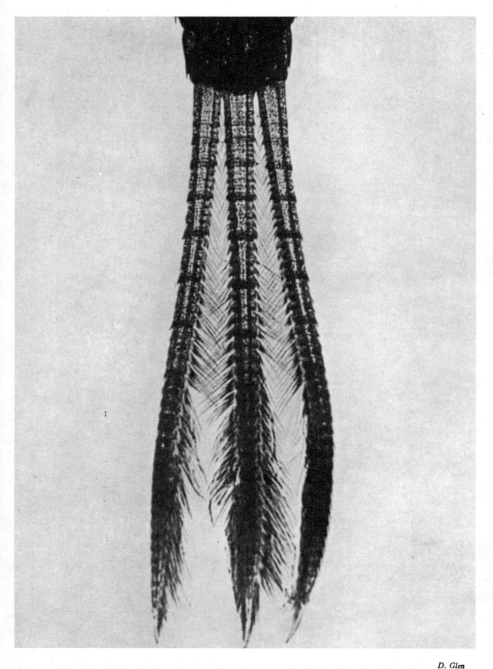

D. Glen

Plate II Tails of the strong swimming nymph of the Pale Evening Dun, *Procloëon rufulum*, enlarged x 60, showing the arrangement of the additional hairs towards the apical portion of the tail which make this type of tail a more effective propelling unit

aided by a knowledge of the habits of the flies, is invaluable. Knowledge of the seasonal and diurnal times of appearance of various species, of how to recognise them by their flight, and of the type of rises trout make to different flies, often enable the angler to decide from a distance of fifteen or twenty yards what a fish may be feeding on. He may often know in advance what the fish will probably be feeding on later in the evening.

For instance, if a strong flight of Sherry Spinners is seen flying upstream on a warm July evening, and if other spinners which oviposit in the evening are not much in evidence, it is extremely probable that within the next half hour or hour the spent flies will be on the water. Should trout subsequently begin feeding with the typical sort of rises they make to spent flies, then it is obviously likely that they are concentrating on these spinners.

The American author E. R. Hewitt refers to three stages through which anglers pass: —

1. When they want to catch the greatest possible number of fish;
2. when they want to catch the largest fish;
3. when they want to catch the most difficult fish and are less concerned with numbers or size.

No matter to which of these categories an angler belongs, he will obviously increase his own efficiency considerably by applying himself to the study of natural flies on which the fish are feeding.

PART ONE
EPHEMEROPTERA

CHAPTER I

CLASSIFICATION

ANIMALS (including insects) are classified on the same general lines as
any collection of individuals might be. They are first divided into
groups composed of individuals which resemble each other in general
features. The groups are then sub-divided several times into smaller
groups which contain individuals possessing finer points of resemblance, until groups are finally reached which contain only individuals
which (special considerations apart) resemble each other so closely that
for practical purposes they are classed as of the same kind. The
special considerations comprise differences of form due to sex or some
other factors.

The features which are considered in arranging the various
groups might be such obvious ones as the colour or size of the animals,
or the number and position of appendages which they carried; or
they might be more fundamental ones, such as whether the animal
possessed bones, whether it was warm — or cold — blooded and so on.
The most natural arrangement is that which takes into consideration
the greatest number of features, and this presupposes an intimate
knowledge of the structure of the animals concerned. This natural
arrangement or classification allows animals to be segregated in
accordance with their real or presumed evolutionary relationships*
and it has been universally adopted.

Taxonomy — the science or practice of classification of living
organisms — is thus based on the affinities of groups. It provides a

---

* As our knowledge of evolution is limited, the arrangement of the organisms in
their classification is, to a certain extent, arbitrary.

framework into which every organism will fit, and when the framework has been filled the relationships between different organisms can be seen at a glance. It is like, and in some respects functions as, a gigantic filing system as used in a modern business house.

Animals are divided into a few large groups, differing in their basic *plan* of construction, called phyla. Each phylum is made up of a number of classes. Classes are divided into orders, orders contain families, families are composed of genera, and genera of species.

Thus the Blue-winged Olive, *Ephemerella ignita*, and the fresh-water Shrimp, *Gammarus pulex*, are classified as follows: —

	BLUE-WINGED OLIVE	FRESH-WATER SHRIMP
Phylum	Arthropoda	Arthropoda
Class	Insecta	Crustacea
Order	Ephemeroptera	Amphipoda
Family	Ephemerellidae	Gammaridae
Genus	*Ephemerella*	*Gammarus*
Species	*ignita*	*pulex*

In addition to these main divisions, divisions such as subspecies, sub-family are also often used.

We are concerned primarily with the Insecta, or insects. Insects, as a class, contain twenty-four orders; the class is divided into two sub-classes, namely: —

(1) *Apterygota:* these are apterous (i. e. wingless) insects in which the wingless condition has been maintained throughout their evolution. Such insects undergo little change of form or metamorphosis, during development and they comprise four orders as follows: —

Diplura	—	Bristletails
Thysanura	—	,,
Protura	—	,,
Collembola	—	Springtails

(2) *Pterygota* are winged insects, some of which have secondarily become wingless. Metamorphosis is nearly always apparent. The twenty orders of this latter sub-class are separated into two divisions.

Division 1, called the *Exopterygota*, is composed of insects in which the wings develop externally, metamorphosis is slight, pupation seldom occurs and the larvae or nymphs show many features in common with the adults.

There are eleven orders of insects in this division:—

Orthoptera	—	Grasshoppers, Cockroaches, etc.
Isoptera	—	Termites or White Ants
Plecoptera	—	Stoneflies
Embioptera	—	Web-spinners
Dermaptera	—	Earwigs
Ephemeroptera	—	Up-winged Flies or Mayflies
Odonata	—	Dragonflies
Psocoptera	—	Book-lice
Anoplura	—	Lice
Thysanoptera	—	Thrips
Hemiptera	—	Plant-bugs, Aphides, Water-boat-men, Corixids

The *Endopterygota* comprise Division 2. They consist of insects in which the wings develop internally and the larvae differ considerably from the adults. They pass through a pupal stage and undergo a complex metamorphosis.

Neuroptera	—	Alder-flies, Lacewings
Mecoptera	—	Scorpion-flies
Trichoptera	—	Caddis-flies
Lepidoptera	—	Butterflies and Moths
Coleoptera	—	Beetles
Strepsiptera	—	Stylops
Hymenoptera	—	Ants, Bees, Wasps, Ichneumon-flies
Diptera	—	Flies, including Gnats, Midges, Reed Smuts, House-flies, Bluebottles, etc.
Aphaniptera	—	Fleas

Those orders which are of interest to anglers are in italics; the various other orders have been included merely for the sake of completeness.

According to modern knowledge, insects have evolved from some common ancestral wingless form. Insects at present show great diversity in their structure, and those which it is considered have diverged the least amount from the ancestral form are spoken of as being primitive, whilst those which show the greatest amount of divergence from the primitive structure are said to be highly specialised.

The various orders of insects are, as far as possible, arranged so as to proceed from the most primitive to the most specialised forms. Hence, according to the arrangement on the list of orders, the Plecoptera are considered to be more primitive than the Ephemeroptera, and both of these orders are more primitive than the Trichoptera.

NOMENCLATURE

The modern scientific system of naming, or nomenclature, was adopted from the proposals of a famous Swedish naturalist named Linnaeus (Carl Linné) as outlined in his book *Systema Naturae*. The giving of names under his system in zoology is taken to start in the year 1758 when the tenth edition of his book was published. Under this system each animal is allotted two names, a generic and a specific name, hence the system is known as that of binomial nomenclature.

The names applied to organisms are usually adapted from Latin or Greek words, and, as they are derived from these dead languages, they possess the advantage of having universal application. That is to say that a fly or a fish, for example *Ephemera vulgata* or *Salmo trutta*, carries these names in any part of the world. But it is only among English-speaking peoples that it is known as a mayfly or a trout.

In order to obtain universal agreement in other aspects of scientific nomenclature and classification of animals, an international code of Rules was agreed upon by zoologists in the year 1901.

Under this code the names of animals are written in Latin or in latinised words, a capital letter being used in the generic name and a small letter in the specific name. The name of the person who first described and named the species follows the specific name, thus:— *Ephemera vulgata* Linné. As the name of Linné is widely known, it is usually abbreviated to Linn. or simply to L. When more than one species of a genus is being referred to, the generic name in the second instance is often abbreviated to its initial letter, for example *Baëtis rhodani* and *B. vernus*. This practice of abbreviating the generic name is also used with well-known insects — provided there is little likelihood of confusion arising. For instance, no one familiar with the

Ephemeroptera is likely to associate *E. ignita* with any genus other than *Ephemerella*, and consequently the generic name is often abbreviated. When a species is moved to a genus different from that in which it was placed by the original author, the specific name is retained and the author's name is parenthesised; thus *Ephemera bioculata* L. is now known as *Baëtis bioculatus* (L). This species was moved to the new genus, *Baëtis*, which was created by an entomologist named Leach in 1815. The ending of the specific name was changed from "*a*" to "*us*" in order to keep it of the same gender as the new generic name. The names of families end with the suffix "-idae", sub-families in "-inae" and orders of insects usually with the suffix "-ptera".

Linnaeus described and named eight species of Ephemeroptera, all of which occur in England today. Since that time (1761) the number of species which have been recorded throughout the whole world has increased by about one thousand, but so far only forty-seven in all have been recorded from Britain and Ireland. Linnaeus placed the eight species which he knew in the genus *Ephemera* and in the order Neuroptera. During the next 130 years other entomologists described many new species and erected additional genera, and at the present time the forty-seven species recorded for these islands (listed on pp. 185-66) are contained in eighteen genera.

CHAPTER 2

GROWTH AND STRUCTURE

THE natural history of any group of organisms can be more completely understood if it is studied in conjunction with the methods
by which the various vital processes of the organisms are performed. The
vital processes, which include assimilation of food, respiration, excretion
and growth, are not effected by insects in the same manner in which
they are by man and other vertebrate animals. In order to counteract
a natural tendency to view such processes from the human stand-
point, it is important to be familiar with their functioning in insects.

The differences in the methods utilised by insects and vertebrates
are directly associated with, and dependent on, differences in the
structure of the two types of animals, and they are, therefore, considered here in conjunction with the various structural parts.

CELLS

If the entire substance of any animal be examined, it will be found
to consist of cells, the products of cells, and various nutritive substances
which have been absorbed by the animal, together with waste products
which are being expelled. For example, teeth, skin and bone consist
of cells, together with material produced by cells.

Most cells are microscopic in size and they vary much in shape.
A typical cell could be said to resemble a minute transparent sphere
filled with a semi-fluid substance, and containing suspended within
it a much smaller and usually more opaque sphere. This smaller
contained sphere represents the nucleus of the cell, and it is the control-
ling centre of activity. The area surrounding the nucleus contains a
mixture called cytoplasm, which has very many functions, and in
which nutritive matter is stored for use by the nucleus in its various

Plate IIIa Magnified (x 72) semi-translucent view of a leg of the Pale Evening Dun nymph, *P. rufulum*, showing how the contracted leg of the dun is contained within the integument of the nymphal leg

Plate IIIb Enlarged view (x 170) of apical portion of same leg showing vestigial hairs on posterior side of leg more clearly

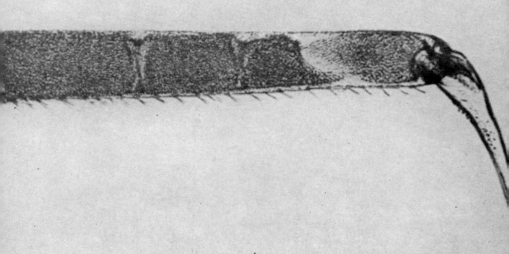

J. R. Harris

Plate IVa A high hill stream in Co. Wicklow (about 1800 feet above sea-level) where the Summer Mayfly, *Siphlonurus lacustris*, and the Olive, *Baëtis tenax*, are found, and the ubiquitous Blue-winged Olive, *E. ignita*, is also common

Plate IVb Troutbeck in Westmorland; a hill stream which provides suitable habitats to such species as the Yellow Sally, *Isoperla grammatica*, and Dark Dun, *Heptagenia lateralis*

John Markham

processes. This nutritive matter is absorbed from the blood through the containing membrane which forms the cell boundary.

Cells multiply by division: that is, a cell will divide into two parts, and each of the two new cells then increases to the size of the former single cell and again divides.

A property of some cells is that they secrete various essential substances. The chemical nature of these secretions varies considerably. Some secretions harden and form bone, others form various softer tissues, whilst anyone who has performed autopsies on fish must be familiar with the white mucus found in the stomach. This mucus is a secretion of some of the cells lining the inside of the stomach wall.

GLANDS

These are groups of cells, often arranged in bulblike shape, functioning as secretory organs. Their secretions are generally of a nature different from those of non-glandular cells and react in a functional, rather than a structural capacity. Examples of such glands in man are the salivary, adrenal and tear glands, and in insects the moulting glands.

A cell can be regarded as a minute chemical plant. The raw materials used by cells are obtained from the food eaten by the animal. When food is swallowed essential nutritive substances are absorbed through the stomach wall and pass into the blood-stream. The blood carries them to the cells which in turn absorb any substances they require through their containing. membranes, and by reaction convert these substances to their own uses.

RESPIRATION

In order to produce energy by the combustion (oxidation) of food, cells require a continuous supply of oxygen and must get rid of carbon dioxide. In vertebrates, such as man, which possess lungs, or fish which possess blood gills, the necessary oxygen is transported by the blood to cells in all parts of the body, and the blood also carries carbon dioxide away from the cells.

Respiration in insects is not effected by means of lungs or blood-gills; instead, insect cells receive oxygen by means of a system of air tubes called tracheae, which lead into ramifications of much finer tubes known as tracheoles, and these penetrate to all parts of the insect body. These tracheae in adult ephemeropterans have a pair of external openings, or spiracles, on most of the body segments. Oxygen, which enters the spiracles, passes along the tracheae by diffusion and reaches the individual cells by means of the extremely fine and numerously branched tracheoles. By a more or less inverse process carbon dioxide is exhaled. Ephemeropteran nymphs and many other aquatic insect larvae absorb oxygen through the body wall. In ephemeropteran nymphs the tracheae, instead of terminating in spiracles, continue into the tracheal gills which arise from the sides of most of the abdominal segments.

SKELETON

A skeleton suggests an internal framework of bone as is found in all vertebrates, but in place of an internal structure of this type the insect skeleton consists of the outer secretions of the skin, or cuticle. The insect's skeleton is, therefore, largely external and is known as the exoskeleton, and contained within it are the muscles, blood and various organs of the body. In structure the exoskeleton somewhat resembles a segmented tube in which the segments are relatively rigid and the joinings are of softer material. This segmented effect is plainly seen in the bodies of any of the Ephemeroptera.

The body wall, or integument, of insects is formed of cuticle together with an internal layer of cells called the epidermis. The cells of the epidermis secrete the substances which form cuticle. One of these substances is known as sclerotin; it hardens and supplies the rigidity and strength to the exoskeleton. The cuticle also contains chitin.

Usually the cuticle consists of three layers, namely an outermost very thin hard inelastic layer, called the epicuticle, which is composed of sclerotin; a thicker middle layer, the exocuticle, containing both chitin and sclerotin; and a soft inner layer, the endocuticle, which contains chitin but not sclerotin and is extremely elastic. The rigidity of the exocuticle depends upon the quantity of sclerotin which it contains.

The investment of cuticle on an insect is spread over the whole body, and covers the wings, eyes, legs and tails as well as the abdomen and thorax. The relative thickness and composition of the cuticular layers vary. They are, for instance, very thin and transparent on the wings and are even more highly transparent on the eyes. On the abdomen and thorax the cuticle is divided into many small relatively rigid areas which are attached to each other by softer membrane. This arrangement, whilst providing an exoskeleton, also permits a necessary flexibility.

The localised areas of more rigid cuticle are known as sclerites. In the abdomen of ephemeropterans each segment consists of two sclerites, namely, a ventral plate or sternite which forms the underneath or ventral surface of each segment, and a dorsal plate or tergite with which the upper, or dorsal, and most of the lateral areas are covered. The cuticle joining segments is flexible and is often slightly infolded. This not only facilitates freedom of movement, but also allows a certain amount of elongation and contraction of the abdomen.

The thorax carries the wings and legs, and the arrangement of sclerites on each of the three thoracic segments is more complicated than on the abdomen. In addition to tergites and sternites on the dorsal and ventral surfaces respectively, the lateral, or pleural region of the thorax carries pleurites.

IMAGINES OR SPINNERS

The body of an adult ephemeropteran is composed of three main regions, namely, a head, a thorax (sometimes known as "chest" or "shoulders") and an abdomen.

The head is small and compact. It carries a pair of feelers or antennae, a pair of large compound eyes, or oculi, as well as three small simple light sensitive organs, or ocelli, and mouth parts which are atrophic and functionless.

The thorax is of three segments, of which the posterior two are closely fused to each other. The foremost segment is the smallest and carries the anterior or forelegs. The second segment is the largest of the three and from it arise the large forewings as well as the centre or median legs, and the third segment carries the hind legs and (when present) the small hind wings. The head and thorax are joined by a very short neck. These three thoracic segments are known respectively as the prothorax, mesothorax and metathorax.

The abdomen, which is attached to the thorax, consists of ten distinct segments. It is the largest of the three body regions and is from one-and-a-half to two times as large as the head and thorax together. The tails arise from the last segment of the abdomen, and in male flies, a pair of claspers, forceps or styli pertain to the ninth segment and extend underneath the tenth segment. Anglers usually refer to the "thorax" of a fly as the "shoulders" and to the "abdomen" as the "body". These alternative terms which are used in regard to artificial flies are perhaps better avoided when referring to natural species. The two or three tails which arise from the extremity of the abdomen are frequently described as "setae" or "cerci". Technically, the two lateral tails are "cerci", but the median tail is not a "cercus", as it differs from the cerci in both origin and structure, and is known as a "median caudal filament" or "telofilum".

The former practice of using the word "setae" to describe these appendages has been discontinued, as under modern usage "setae" is used to describe the very numerous fine "hairs" which arise from the tails. Although the word "tails" is itself technically incorrect, it yet seems a suitable word to use. It has the advantage of being English rather than Latin, and is widely used in speaking of the whisks of artificial flies.

Sub-imagines or Duns

Duns resemble spinners in structure, and they differ from them only in that they have not yet cast their subimaginal cuticle. When the cuticle has been shed, some of the appendages of the dun lengthen, particularly the tails and the forelegs in the males.

Superficially, a dun differs from a spinner in that the body and wings of the dun are sparsely covered with microscopic hairs. These hairs, if examined with a lens, can be seen most easily along the posterior edge of each fore-wing where they form a close fringe. The wings of all spinners found in Britain except *Caenis* species are devoid of hairs. Also duns are dull and generally sober coloured, whilst spinners are more brightly coloured and shining and their wings are clear and transparent.

Nymphs

Nymphs very superficially resemble duns without their wings, and in senior nymphs the wing-cases can be plainly seen on the thorax. Another marked difference between duns and nymphs is the presence of the tracheal gills on some of the abdominal segments of the nymphs. These gills arise from most or all of the first seven segments of the abdomen, but their shape varies considerably on

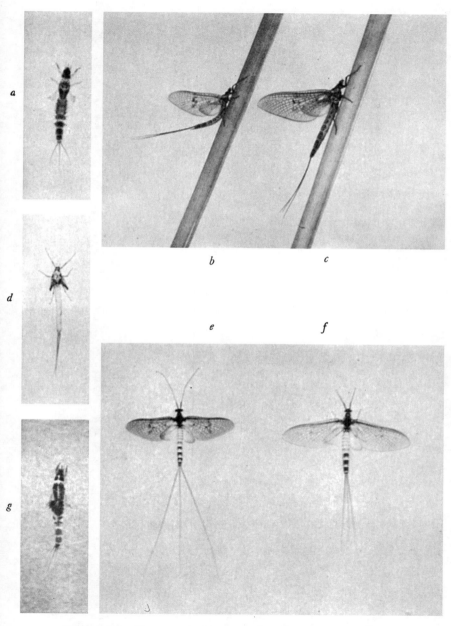

Plate 1: LIFE-HISTORY OF MAYFLY (*Ephemera danica*), natural size
(a) Nymph; (b) and (c) Greendrake male and female; (d) Exuvia of
Greendrake; (e) Black Drake, male spinner; (f) Grey Drake, female
spinner; (g) Nymphal skin or exuvia

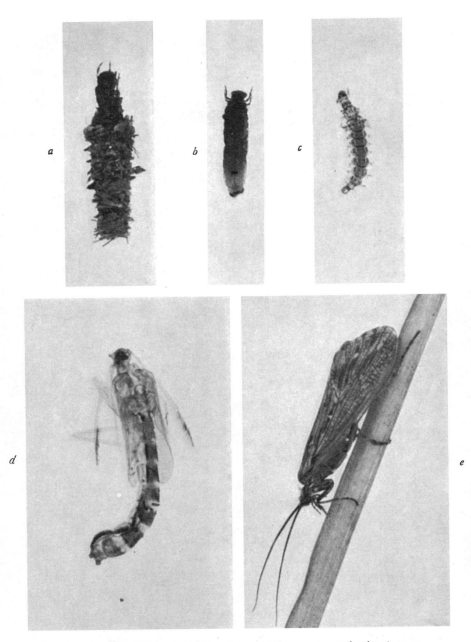

Plate 2: LIFE-HISTORY OF SEDGE-FLY (*Phryganea* sp. and others) × 2
(*a*) Larva in case; (*b*) Larva removed from case; (*c*) Non-case-making
larva; (*d*) Empty pupal skin; (*e*) Sedge-fly, Murragh, *P. striata*

nymphs of different genera. All senior nymphs which occur in these islands also have three tails even in those species in which the duns have only two.

The terms "senior" and "junior" nymphs are used respectively to describe the advanced stages of well-developed nymphs and the early immature stages of nymphs more recently emerged from the egg.

CHAPTER 3

LIFE CYCLE

DUNS

IN THE development of the Ephemeroptera the period most important to anglers is probably that of the emergence of the duns. Trout feed extensively on nymphs ascending to the surface and on duns resting on the water. It is, therefore, appropriate to consider the life cycle at this stage.

To an angler waiting on the river bank for the duns to appear, the river may appear devoid of life. The surface is undisturbed by any unnatural ripples, and the river flows past placidly and evenly. Suddenly a small break is seen on the surface. The break merges into widening rings as a trout takes something from the surface film and turns down again. Immediately afterwards a dun floats past, it is followed by several others, some fluttering, others sitting quietly as they are carried along by the current with wings cocked and abdomen and tails held carefully above the water. More duns appear as though from nowhere, soon they may be too numerous to be counted. A few swifts swoop down over the water and dart along the river, screaming with excitement as they capture the duns which are fluttering slowly upwards towards the shelter of trees or bushes alongside the river. The trout which was first seen is now feeding steadily, and several others are rising. The angler picks up his rod, for the "hatch" has begun.

When duns leave the water, the direction of their flight is governed mainly by the wind, and few of them are able to make headway against even a gentle breeze. Their flight is slow and laboured and their characteristic attitude of flying, with the abdomen hanging below the level of the thorax and wings, makes them easily recognisable when in the air. In warm still conditions, or when in a gorge in which there is an updrift of air, duns rising from the water often ascend until they are lost to sight. More usually, however, they deviate towards trees, grasses or other vegetation near the water.

During windy weather they are carried along and are blown in among the foliage of trees, or, if nearer to ground level, among grasses and rushes. At such times the velocity with which they strike the outer foliage carries them through to the quieter regions among the inner layers.

On reaching suitable shelter the flies hide on the underside of leaves, near the roots of plant stems or in any unexposed position which offers shelter from the wind, sun and rain. Unless disturbed they remain quiescent for a period which lasts until moulting occurs. The process of moulting, or ecdysis, consists in the shedding of the outer skin which covers all portions of the dun, the fly then emerging as an imago or spinner. The spinners are the adult flies, and the Ephemeroptera are the only Order of insects in which moulting occurs after the winged form has been assumed. It is only as spinners that the flies are able to breed.

Moulting may take place within a few minutes after the dun comes to rest, as happens with species of *Caenis;* or it may not occur for two or three days, as with some of the larger species; but most species moult in about twenty-four hours. The duration of this sub-imaginal resting period is also affected by temperature and humidity; cold weather acts as a deterrent to development and warm dry weather accelerates it.

When a dun is about to moult it spreads its large fore-wings out sideways. A split appears in the outer skin on the dorsal surface of the thorax and extends forwards to the head. Through this opening the thorax, head and legs of the spinner emerge. The spinner may then use its legs to pull itself completely free from the outer skin. This cast outer skin or exuvia which the spinner leaves behind retains perfectly the shape of the external features of the abdomen, tails, genitalia, legs and lower portions of the thorax and head of the fly. The shape of the wings is not retained, as the delicate tissue which covers them collapses when the wings of the spinner are withdrawn. Exuviae will frequently be found adhering to the undersides of leaves near a river or lake.

SPINNERS

Spinners are most noticeable during warm calm weather, when large numbers of them may be seen in flight in the vicinity of a river or lake. The males like to collect into swarms, each swarm being joined by some females. A swarm retains a more or less fixed position in the air, whilst the individuals, with their very attractive-looking hovering flight, rise and fall and fly to and fro within its confines. Some swarms will remain consistently over the shoreline, others may be over the water, but most of them will be found a short distance inland. The position which a swarm retains in the air in relation to the water's edge depends partly on the topography of the immediate surroundings and on weather conditions, but also on the habits of the species of flies composing the swarm. If a number of swarms, each of a different species, is examined, it will be seen that each species has its own characteristic manner of flight. Familiarity with these habits of the flies is of assistance in quickly identifying their species.

This flight of the male spinners is not an aimless expenditure of energy but is for the express purpose of allowing the sexes to come together.

Two characteristic methods of hovering will be observed; spinners of the mayfly *Ephemera danica*; the Pale Watery, *Centroptilum luteolum*, and of the Iron Blue, *Baëtis pumilus*, constantly rise and fall in the air. An individual will propel itself rapidly upwards for a foot or so and will then descend by falling and gliding down. While ascending, the wings beat extremely rapidly, but in falling they are held motionless and point upwards, so that when the fly is viewed from the front the wings form a wide V.

Other ephemeropterans such as the Yellow May Spinners, *Heptagenia sulphurea*, and the Yellow Uprights, *Rhithrogena semicolorata*, have a much steadier flight. They do not rise and fall continuously and rapidly and their wings beat without cessation. A fly seen hovering, motionless in the air except for the rapidly flickering wings, may move slowly forwards and then fly rapidly upwards or obliquely sideways and again hover. Their movements are more erratic though less rapid, and the course of their flight tends to be horizontal rather than vertical.

If a swarm of male spinners is kept under observation, sooner or later a female will be seen approaching. She may enter the swarm and fly in it for a short while until she attracts the attention of a male, or she may fly only in the vicinity of the swarm until one or more males leave the swarm and pursue her. In both cases copulation takes place in the air, but the pair may alight on the ground or water before separating. After separation the male spinner returns to the swarm, and the female either flies at once to the water on her egg-

J. R. Harris

Plate Va R. Avonbeg, Glenmalure, Co. Wicklow : the moss-covered granite stones of the river bed which are here exposed by low water are firmly embedded and provide shelter for a large population of Ephemeropteran nymphs

Plate Vb R. Avonbeg, Glenmalure : although this reach is only about four miles upstream from that shown above the stones are loose and therefore carry little or no moss, and Ephemeropteran nymphs are present only in small numbers

J. R. Harris

Humphrey and Vera Joel

Plate VIa R. Dart, Dartmoor : on fast-flowing rocky rivers such as this, where small brown stone-flies abound and where the Large Dark Olive and the Blue-winged Olive are usually the commonest of the Ephemeropterans, the hackled wet-fly patterns as recorded by Cutcliffe dressed with stiff cock's hackles are very effective

Plate VIb A stretch of the river Teith in Perthshire a typical " wet or dry fly stream " where most of the common species of Ephemeropterans occur

John Markham

laying flight or else again seeks shelter on the shore. Those species which seek shelter after copulation remain quiescent for a period, the length of which depends on the habits of the particular species concerned. Should the weather become unsuitable, this resting period may be considerably prolonged; species which would normally return to the water in one or two hours may be delayed for at least as much as twelve hours. The chief deterrents to their flight, either before or after copulation, are low temperature or heavy rain.

There are three general modes of flight adopted by female spinners, each of which is associated with a different egg-laying habit. Spinners of *Baëtis* require an object projecting from the surface down which they can crawl, in order to attach their eggs to some submerged rock or weed. They tend to fly close to the water and to zig-zag back and forth across the river in their efforts to locate a suitable spot.

Species of *Ephemerella* (Sherry Spinner etc.) and of *Siphlonurus* fly steadily and evenly along the river, usually upstream; as they progress, their eggs are exuded and collect in a round mass under the posterior end of the abdomen at the oviducal openings. As the egg-mass increases in size, the extreme end of the abdomen is bent downwards and slightly forwards in order to keep the eggs in position. The tail threads also incline downwards and give these flies a very characteristic appearance so that they can readily be recognised when in the air. The flies gradually approach the water and either drop the egg mass or else let the tip of the abdomen touch the surface so that the eggs are washed off.

Other spinners such as the Grey Drake, *Ephemera danica*, and the Great Red Spinner, *Ecdyonurus venosus*, lay their eggs in batches. Each batch is laid by the female flying down to the surface, resting there momentarily while she presses the tip of her abdomen on to the water, and then flying up again. After each visit to the surface she may rise steadily and then gradually descend again. She may fly some distance parallel to the surface, or she may remain in the air for some minutes rising and falling, much after the manner of the swarming flight of many male spinners. During the intervals between visits to the surface, more eggs accumulate at the openings of her oviducts.

When oviposition has been completed, the spinners die and are usually found floating on the surface of the water. These spent spinners provide most interesting fishing, as they are highly appreciated by the trout, who feed on them extensively, and often concentrate on them in preference to any other flies which may be on the water at the same time.

The identification of the spinners on the water is obviously important if advantage is to be taken of the opportunity offered by the rising fish. Familiarity with the swarming flights of the male spinners not only provides a ready means of inferring what females may be on the water, but in the case of many species it allows a forecast to be made as to when they may be expected to be on the water.

EGGS

Those eggs which are laid on the surface of the water sink quite rapidly. Most of them possess organs of attachment which keep them anchored to the bottom or to rocks or weeds with which they come in contact when sinking; they can thus hold their position in fast-flowing water in rivers or in shallow areas in lakes where wave action causes agitation. The attachment organs are of various types. Some consist of numerous fine thread-like appendages arising from various parts of the egg and each terminating in a small adhesive knob or disc, others consist of large polar caps which anchor one end of the egg firmly to the bottom. Other eggs are enclosed in an adhesive transparent jelly. Eggs of species of *Baëtis*, which are applied directly to and adhere to rocks or other underwater objects, do not possess any such specialised means of anchorage.

The rate of development of eggs is affected by the temperature of the water. Those which hatch in about two weeks when kept at room temperature may take twice as long under natural conditions where the water is colder. Some spinners may retain their eggs for a period of a week or more after fertilisation before ovipositing, and thus reduce the subsequent incubation period. Spinners of the Pond Olive, *Cloëon dipterum*, at times retain their eggs until they are ready to hatch; and on several occasions on the continent of Europe it has been observed that the eggs have hatched in the oviducts of the female spinner, and that the spinner has thus given birth to living nymphs.

NYMPHS

After eclosion, or hatching from the eggs, nymphs are so small that they are scarcely visible to the naked eye. In shape they bear only a general resemblance to mature nymphs. Some of the more obvious differences are the lack, or incipient state of, the abdominal gills, the small size of the compound eyes and the absence of wing-cases on the thorax. Also in these newly-hatched nymphs the segments of the thorax bear a much closer resemblance to those of the abdomen than in more developed specimens.

As the nymphs develop they moult at intervals. Moulting consists in casting an outer skin. As explained in chapter 2 (p. 14), the outer skin, or epicuticle, is composed mainly of sclerotin, and one of the properties of sclerotin is that it hardens on exposure to water or air. After the epicuticle has hardened, the nymph is unable to alter in shape or size. Consequently, changes associated with growth can occur only while the epicuticle is still soft and extensile.

Nymphs moult in much the same manner as duns. The epicuticle on the dorsal surface of the thorax and head splits apart and the nymph draws itself out through the aperture so formed. The colour of the newly-moulted nymph is at first a pale translucent whitish but it gradually darkens. The newly exposed epicuticle remains soft for a short time, and before it hardens the necessary changes occur in the external features. These changes consist in the erection of additional appendages, which have developed beneath the old skin since the previous moult, and of alteration in the general shape or increase in body size.

Thus internally development is continuous, but externally growth proceeds by a series of steps or stages. The form assumed by a nymph during any one stage is called an instar. Thus, first instar nymphs are those in the stage lasting from eclosion to the first moulting, fifth instar nymphs are in the stage between the fourth and fifth moults, and nymphs are in their final instar during the stage immediately preceding emergence as a dun.

The number of nymphal instars has not been ascertained for any British species of Ephemeroptera. In America, two broods of a species of Baëtis were reared in succession by Dr. H. E. Murphy*, who recorded that nymphs of each brood passed through 27 instars. The first and second instars each lasted for two or three days, while instars in the latter half of the nymphal life lasted from seven to eleven days each.

These early stages in the life history of the Ephemeroptera have been studied in only a few species. From what is known of the deve-

* See Needham, Traver and Hsu (1935).

lopment of some species of *Baëtis* and *Ecdyonurus*, the tracheal gills have all appeared and assumed the shape of the gills of mature nymphs by the tenth instar. The wing cases, which first appear as small protuberances on the dorsal surface of the thorax, are visible during the fourteenth or fifteenth instar. They continue developing until the final instar, when they have become large and are often dark coloured and constitute one of the noticeable features of mature specimens. The development of other parts of the nymph is more or less parallel with those described above.

The total length of nymphal life is affected by temperature and varies in different species. The mayfly nymph, *Ephemera danica*, matures in two years, but most species probably complete their development in a single year. Four successive broods of a *Baëtis* species were reared under natural conditions by Dr. Murphy, and it was demonstrated that there were three broods in every two years, the adults appearing in May, August and October. Eggs laid in May produced adult flies in the following October, the October eggs produced adults in the following August, and the progeny of the August flies appeared in the following May. The nymphs matured in six months during the summer, but took nine months when they had to survive the colder winter period.

Dr. Murphy also reared two broods simultaneously from eggs laid in October. One brood was kept indoors at room temperature and the adult flies appeared in the following May; the other brood, kept out of doors under colder conditions, took three months longer to mature. As water temperature can control the length of nymphal life, it is apparent that seasonal or local variations in the times of appearance of Ephemeropterans may be due to variations in water temperature during the year.

Nymphs feed mainly on vegetable matter, either algae or the decaying portions of larger plants. If some *Baëtis* nymphs are placed in a shallow aquarium containing water-plants, they can be examined under a lens while feeding. A nymph on a plant stem will be seen grazing on the algae coating the stem in much the same manner as a sheep grazes on pasture land. The nymph methodically feeds along the stem, eating continuously. As it eats it advances step by step. At intervals it may lift its head to chew an unusually large mouthful or, if the algae are scarce—perhaps owing to cropping by another nymph—the feeding nymph will advance rapidly to an area containing a more luxuriant growth.

As with most herbivores, the jaws of nymphs are of no value as weapons of defence. For protection against its enemies the nymph depends on its agility in escaping attack and on the effectiveness with which it can hide. Hiding may consist in crawling beneath stones, into cracks in rocks or penetrating more deeply into a weed bed. When a quick-swimming nymph is disturbed, it darts away very rapidly for a short distance and then stops abruptly and remains motionless. This abrupt cessation of flight is a most effective way of escaping observation: owing to their colour and shape, which blend in with their natural surroundings, nymphs then become very difficult to detect.

If collections are made both from the rapid and the slow-flowing reaches of a river, it will be seen that the shapes of nymphs from different environments vary considerably. Many of them are long and slender, others are short and stumpy, and some are rather wide and flattened. These variations in the form of the nymphs can be correlated to a large extent with their habitats. In this connection Professor J. G. Needham classified nymphs into two groups, each with three sub-divisions. These, with certain modifications, are as follows:—

1. Still or slow-flowing water forms.
   a) Climbers among vegetation, agile streamlined forms.
      Siphlonurus, Cloëon, Centroptilum.
   b) Crawlers upon the bottom, silt-dwellers.
      Caenis.
   c) Burrowers in the bottom.
      Ephemera.
2. Rapid water forms.
   d) Agile, free-ranging streamlined forms.
      Baëtis, Paraleptophlebia, Centroptilum.
   e) Close-clinging limpet-like forms found under stones.
      Ecdyonurus, Rhithrogena, Heptagenia.
   f) Stiff-legged, trash-, moss- and silt-inhabiting forms.
      Ephemerella, Caenis.

These ecological divisions are not exact, as considerable overlapping occurs among the different species. The Pale Watery, *Centroptilum luteolum*, is found in lakes and canals, and in both quick and slow-flowing rivers. The Yellow May Dun, *Heptagenia sulphurea* and *H. fuscogrisea*, occur in stony rivers and on the shallow rocky shores of lakes. On the other hand, species of *Baëtis* and *Ephemerella* do not occur in lakes, although the Blue-winged Olive, *Ephemerella ignita,* occurs in canals where the flow of water is slight.

Dispersal of nymphs depends upon several factors, notably movement, aeration and temperature of the water, geological environment and aquatic vegetation. These factors, which are considerably interrelated, will be discussed in chapter 4.

The most extreme diversities of form among nymphs are found in species of *Ephemera, Caenis, Ecdyonurus, Cloëon* and *Ephemerella.* Some of their important adaptations to habitat are as follows:—

Ephemera: Rather thin build with narrow thorax and pointed head; mandibles and front legs adapted for burrowing, gills arched over in an oblique posterior direction, and lying close to the abdomen in such a position that they do not hinder the movements of the nymphs when in their burrows, but when operating create a current of water which passes through the burrow.

Caenis: Small, stumpy, slow-moving forms, densely covered with hairs which get impregnated with fine detritus and thus provide an excellent protective camouflage. The second pair of abdominal gills is transformed into large opercula, or gill-covers, which overlie the remaining gills posteriorly and protect them from silt or detritus which might interfere with respiration.

Ecdyonurus: Body, and particularly head and thorax, wide and flattened, with the dorsal surface shallowly convex. Legs strong, with the femora broad but thin. These nymphs offer very little resistance to the current when clinging limpet-like to stones in rapid water.

Cloëon: Torpedo-shaped, streamlined body with plate-like gills, the latter being of considerable assistance to the nymphs in swimming; tails with dense lateral fringes of setae emanating from both sides of the middle tail and from the inner sides of the outer tails, which combined make a most effective tail-fin; legs slender and eyes well developed.

Ephemerella: Slow-moving nymphs with strong legs and rather thickset bodies. The gills lie close to the abdomen on the dorsal surface and do not project sideways, an arrangement which doubtless facilitates the passage of these nymphs through the thick moss or other vegetation which they inhabit.

Nymphs of all species may be found in rivers, where the ecological conditions vary tremendously. Extensive pools provide conditions approximating closely to those present in lakes, and in other parts all gradations between these conditions and conditions associated with fast-flowing water will be found. Somewhat similar differences may be present side by side in relatively small areas. For instance, turbulent quick-flowing water in a rapid may be only a yard or two away from still water at the extreme edge of the river. Similarly a current will be less rapid behind or in front of a weed-bed or boulder than it will be on each side, and any nymphs which crawl under the boulder or into the weed-bed may find very quiet conditions. It is thus the micro-habitat, i. e., the habitat of the immediate surroundings, which is of importance to nymphs, rather than the general habitat of a larger area.

EMERGENCE

When a nymph reaches its final instar, it ceases feeding and its mouthparts degenerate. The abstinence from food is noticeable in the alteration in the appearance of the alimentary canal, or intestine, as seen through the skin. When this contains food it is visible as a dark median line in the abdomen, but when empty it is difficult to detect. The wing-cases usually darken considerably, and in those species in which the adult flies possess only two tails, the middle tail of the nymph becomes pale and transparent.

When emerging*, most nymphs swim to the surface and the duns emerge in the manner described previously (pp. 19, 23); others emerge from the nymphal skin under water, and the dun, surrounded by a film of air, either crawls out of the water or else floats to the surface; and the nymphs of some species crawl out of the water before emergence occurs.

It is fortunate that most duns emerge from floating nymphs, as otherwise much of the interest and delight of fly-fishing would be

---

* Anglers speak of a fly "hatching" rather than "emerging" or "transforming", but to do so here might lead to some confusion, as the term "hatching" is more properly used the describe the liberation of a nymph from the egg.

unknown to us. If all nymphs crawled ashore in order to emerge, we should not require such dry fly patterns as the Iron Blue, Pale Watery Blue-winged Olive or Olive Duns, as well as other less well known patterns. The importance of the duns would be relegated to that of any terrestrial insect which appears on the water only adventitiously, usually as a result of having been blown there by the wind. Also, nymph fishing as we know it to-day would not exist, and the scope of wet fly fishing would be considerably reduced.

All that is usually seen of the emergence of sub-imagines and particularly of small specimens, is the sudden appearance of a fly on the water. A fly will appear so suddenly that one is left in doubt as to where it came from. It may have been flying and have lighted on the water, or perhaps have fallen from an overhanging tree, or it may have emerged from the water.

A detailed view is often obtained when Greendrakes or other large specimens are concerned. A nymph may be seen at the surface of the water with the dorsal surface of its thorax appearing much swollen. Often, before it is realised that the swollen appearance is in reality the thorax of the fly itself which is protruding from the nymphal skin, the fly has by a single continuous movement withdrawn itself completely from the exuvia of the nymph and at the same time erected its wings. It is the speed of this final movement which confuses the observer.

Hence much of our interest centres around the actions of the insects immediately before, during, and immediately after their transformation. Present knowledge on this subject is scanty, and valuable additional information could be collected by anglers, who have opportunities which are seldom available to entomologists to make and record observations on habits such as these.

John Markham

Plate VII R. Wye at Symonds Yat : a type of river where the bordering trees offer an abundance of shelter to spinners and other adult water-flies, but where the river bed may not be conducive to the development of an abundance of nymphs owing to the amount of sunlight which the foliage excludes

John Markham

Plate VIIIa R. Spey below Aviemore : a rather quick-flowing lowland type of river where the eroding sandbanks and shifting gravel-beds are a deterrent to an abundance of the very varied stock of fly life which a lowland river may support

Plate VIIIb A placid reach of the Liffey at Lucan, Co. Dublin : the limestone waters of Liffey, like those of Wharfe, support an abundance of fly life ; among the eighteen species of Ephemeropterans recorded from this water are the Yellow Evening Dun, *Ephemerella notata*, and the Pale Evening Dun, *Procloëon rufulum*

J. R. Harris

CHAPTER 4

ADAPTATIONS

Nymphs

IT HAS been explained in Chapter 3 that when nymphs first hatch from the eggs they possess few specialised features, and that all species resemble each other more closely at this stage than at any other period of their lives. Their structure resembles the structure of primitive nymphs more closely than it does mature modern nymphs. As the young nymphs grow and additional structural features appear, the points of resemblance between nymphs of different genera gradually lessen and specialisations in the structure become apparent. Among the more obvious specialisations are:—

(1) The wide head and thorax and the general flat appearance which is noticeable in the genera *Ecdyonurus*, *Heptagenia* and *Rhithrogena*.

(2) The long torpedo-shaped build of the free-swimming stream-lined genera, among which *Cloëon*, *Siphlonurus* and *Baëtis* are examples.

(3) The stubby compact build with protected gills, as found in *Ephemerella* and *Caenis*.

(4) The specially-shaped mandibles, anterior legs and gills of the burrowing nymphs of the genus *Ephemera*.

Specialisation in structure is intimately connected with differences in habitat, and in order to appreciate the necessity for these structural differences in nymphs, it is necessary to consider the various habitats frequented by the species concerned.

Habitats include:—

In flowing water:—
  (1) Large smooth stones.
  (2) Rough stones.
  (3) Moss-covered stones and boulders.
  (4) Various aquatic weeds.
  (5) Sand and mud.
  (6) Various types of detritus.

In still water:—
  (7) Exposed wave-washed rocky shores of lakes.
  (8) Shallows carrying aquatic weeds.
  (9) Mud and sand bottoms.
  (10) Small ponds, and sheltered bays in lakes.

The following descriptions show a connection between the structure of the common nymphs and the surroundings in which they live.

FLAT NYMPHS

The wide and flattened nymphs are the late March Brown, *Ecdyonurus venosus*, the August Dun, *E. dispar*, the Yellow May Dun, *Heptagenia sulphurea*, the early March Brown, *Rhithrogena haarupi*, and the Yellow Upright, *R. semicolorata*. They also include the other (five) species of the genera *Ecdyonurus* and *Heptagenia*.

There are easily observed structural differences between nymphs of each of the three genera concerned, but the different species in each genus closely resemble each other. The following descriptions are placed under headings of individual species but apply almost equally well to all other species of the same genus.

August Dun Nymph, *E. dispar*. Pl. 4a, p. 33. The head is wide and flattened and shallowly convex. It somewhat resembles half an inverted saucer with the perimeter of the saucer forming the front and sides of the head and the cut portion of the saucer forming the back of the head where it joins the thorax.

The thorax is wide and is also shallowly convex. The dorsal surface of the first segment of the thorax, the pronotum, is produced sideways and backwards, the backward projections lying outside the anterior portion of the second thoracic segment. This expansion of the pronotum is found only in species of *Ecdyonurus* and distinguishes them from species of *Heptagenia* and *Rhithrogena*. The thighs (femora) of each leg are wide and flattened and are slightly turned on their long axis so that their flat upper surfaces slope downwards in a forwards direction. The femora slope obliquely backwards from the thorax, the knees are sharply bent and the remaining leg-joints, which are rounded and slender, point forwards and end in strong hooked claws.

When a nymph of this type is clinging to a rock by means of its claws in fast-flowing water and is facing the current, the pressure of the water, acting on the sloping surfaces of the femoral joints of the legs and on the curved surface of the head and possibly of portions of the thorax, presses the nymph against the rock, and, as the nymph offers little resistance to the water, it is able to maintain itself with ease in such positions.

The abdomen is narrower than the thorax and carries seven pairs of gill-plates, or lamellae, the first six of which have each a tuft of feather-like gills, or fibrils, at its base. The tails are slender and carry only very short hairs. They are held divergent when the nymph is at rest and are probably of assistance to the nymph in orientating itself to the flow of the water.

The nymphs are agile and can swim fairly well, but usually prefer not to lose contact with the stones they frequent. They can run very rapidly over the surface of the stones and are able to move sideways or backwards with as much facility as they move forwards. This habit of crawling sideways and backwards allows them to wander over the stones at will without turning sideways or backwards to the current. When running their motions are crablike.

During daylight they are found on the side of and underneath stones, and they seem to prefer loose stones as they offer a larger underneath surface than stones which are partly sunk in, or attached to, the river bed. They feed on diatoms and other algae which grow on the stones, and their mouth-parts are specially adapted for scraping their algal food substances from flat surfaces.

Yellow May Nymph, *Heptagenia sulphurea*, is noticeably less broad than the preceding. The pronotum of the thorax is not produced sideways and backwards as in that species, and the dorsal portion of this first segment of the thorax is only about the same width as is the second segment. The habits are similar, in that species of both genera are found under rocks and stones, but these *Heptagenia* nymphs possibly show a preference for rougher stones. They are found also along the stony shores of large lakes where the action of waves keeps the water in motion.

March Brown Nymph, *Rhithrogena haarupi,* is very similar in outline to the Yellow May Nymph, *H. sulphurea.* However, the femora are perhaps narrower and the head rather more clearly demarked from the thorax.

These nymphs have developed a most interesting adaptation to enable them to keep their positions on smooth stones in very fast water. The gill-plates are larger than in either of the preceding species and each gill-plate overlaps the succeeding one. They lie in a lateral position and form a continuation, as it were, of the ventral surface of the abdomen, and the first and last pairs meet underneath it. The nymph can press itself against the rock it is clinging to and press down all its gill-plates and thus form a vacuum underneath its body (see Fig. 1). By this means it can obtain a limpet-like grip on the smoothest surface, and maintain its position when nymphs of any other genus would be swept away by the force of the current. As might be expected, these nymphs are found on medium or large-sized smooth stones in fast water, often just in the "hang" at the end of a pool where the water is rapid but not broken. To appreciate the strength of the grip which they obtain it is necessary only to lift a stone from the river and try to remove some of these nymphs from it. They cling with the tenacity of a leech.

The **Olive Upright Nymph,** *R. semicolorata,* has the same method of attachment.

SWIMMING NYMPHS

These comprise a large group and differ from each other mainly in that some of them, being more efficiently equipped, can swim faster than others. The genera are *Siphlonurus, Cloëon, Procloëon, Centroptilum* and *Baëtis.*

The general form of the body of all species is torpedo-shaped and streamlined, the legs are slender, the thorax is as high as or higher than it is wide, and the head is rather small and rounded. In the following paragraphs one species representing each genus is dealt with.

Summer Mayfly Nymphs, *Siphlonurus linnaeanus,* are large nymphs with prominent gill-plates which they can move very rapidly. There

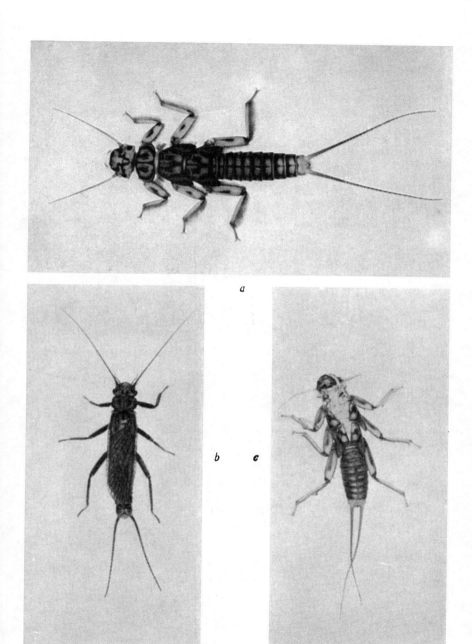

Plate 3: LIFE-HISTORY OF STONE-FLY (Plecoptera spp. and others) × 2
(*a*) Nymph or Creeper; (*b*) and (*c*) Adult Male and nymphal skin

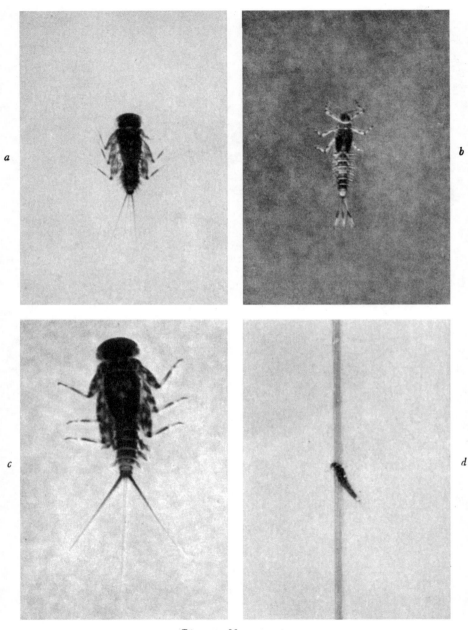

Plate 4: NYMPHS × 2

(a) August Dun, *Ecdyonurus dispar*; (b) Lake Olive, *Cloëon simile*; (c) *Ecdyonurus* sp.; (d) Iron-blue, *Baëtis pumilus*

are dense lateral fringes of hairs on both sides of the middle tail and on the inner side of each of the outer tails. This combination provides the nymph with a most effective tail-fin. The posterior half of the abdomen is somewhat widened by lateral prolongations of the fifth, sixth, seventh and eighth segments. The posterior lateral angles of these prolongations are produced backwards into sharp points. This feature is found only on species of *Siphlonurus*. These nymphs can dart about with great rapidity; they swim with powerful vertical motions of the abdomen and they stop so abruptly in the middle of their swift flight that one momentarily loses sight of them. They utilise their large gill-plates both in stopping and starting their flight.

The chief function of the gill-plates, however, is to create a current of water in order that the nymph may have a continuous supply of fresh water from which it can extract oxygen. When the nymph is stationary and the gill-plates are flickering, a current passes along the abdomen from the tail towards the head. As these nymphs live in the still waters of lakes as well as in rivers, it is necessary that the gills should aid respiration in this way. The antennae are short, their length is less than the width of the thorax, and the nymphs live in more or less open water. They flit along the bottom and around the sides and top of weed beds, but do not penetrate far into them.

Lake Olive Nymphs, *Cloëon simile*, Pl. 4b, p. 33: These nymphs bear a close resemblance to the preceding ones. Their gill-plates are prominent and their tails are similarly adapted for swimming. They, however, penetrate the fronds of weeds and loose water-mosses to a greater extent than do species of *Siphlonurus*, and their antennae are well developed, being longer than the length of the head and thorax together. Their long antennae are probably of advantage to them when they enter such semi-confined habitats; and their powerful though slender legs enable them to climb easily among the open fronds of the plants they frequent.

Pale Evening Dun Nymphs, *Procloëon rufulum*: These nymphs live in the slow-flowing reaches of rivers. Like the Lake Olive Nymphs, their tails are adapted for swimming, but their gill-plates are less prominent, lie closer to the body and are oval-shaped instead of being more or less circular in outline. In flowing water nymphs do not require as efficient a set of gill-plates as they do in still water. Their antennae and legs are well developed and the nymphs may

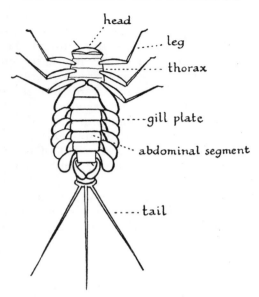

head

leg

thorax

gill plate

abdominal segment

tail

FIG. 1

Ventral view of *Rhithrogena* sp. nymph showing the arrangement of the gill-plates Nymphs of this genus, e. g. the March Brown *Rhithrogena haarupi* can obtain a suction grip on smooth stones with their abdomens aided by the gill-plates which latter can be pressed inwards and downwards at will.

be found clambering among loose vegetation, but will also be found distributed over open portions of the river bed which are devoid of weed.

Little Sky-blue Nymphs, *Centroptilum luteolum*: These nymphs are not so restricted in their choice of habitats as the previous species, as they occur in both quick- and slow-flowing water as well as in lakes. They are not quite so efficiently equipped for swimming. Their gill-plates are narrower and more pointed, and offer little resistance to the water or to the passage of the nymph through weed beds. Their tails are rather less hairy than those of the Lake Olive or Pale Evening Nymphs, but they carry sufficiently long hair fringes to provide an efficient tail-fin.

Large Dark Olive Nymph, *Baëtis rhodani*, Pl. 5a, p. 48: These and all other *Baëtis* nymphs are found only in flowing water. In rivers and streams they occur in fast and medium-paced water, less commonly in slow-flowing stretches, and .they avoid still pools. In water which suits them they will be found clinging to anything which offers them support in counteracting the force of the current, whether it is the rocky bottom of the river, clumps of moss, or larger aquatic plants. They are streamlined, as are all the swimming type of nymphs, in order that the water can slip past them easily, but their gills are less well developed and are immobile, as the nymphs do not require to create a current of water for themselves. Their tails are not as effectively designed for swimming as are those of the swimming nymphs previously mentioned. Their antennae are of moderate length.

CRAWLING NYMPHS

Crawling nymphs live at the bottom of the river or lake among detritus, mud, sand, gravel or stones, and also in weed beds or in the moss which grows on stones. Most of them crawl about slowly and they are all poor swimmers; their tails are evenly covered with very short hairs and are of little use as a tail-fin, see Plate 5, page 48. Their antennae are of moderate length.

Purple Dun Nymph, *Paraleptophlebia cincta,* is the most active of the crawling nymphs. These nymphs are slender and streamlined, their tails are very long and their gills are long and ribbon-like. They live in rapidly-flowing reaches of the river among weed or moss and also among small stones on the bottom; apparently they require more highly oxygenated water than the following species.

Claret Dun Nymphs, *Leptophlebia vespertina,* are less slender than the Purple Dun Nymphs, and their gills are oval-shaped with only their end portions produced into pointed ribbon-like processes. These nymphs are lethargic in their movements and are found in the shallow areas of lakes and in the slow-flowing reaches of stony streams. They are particularly fond of areas with a peat bottom, and so well do they blend with the colours of peat that they are extraordinarily difficult to locate when clinging closely to a peat substratum or to the sides of the stones, which often acquire a dark reddish-brown colour in such surroundings. Their peculiarly shaped gills not only allow the nymphs to live in still water, as they can effectively create a current, but they also tend to camouflage the nymph by breaking up the even contour of its outline. This latter factor may be of some importance, as these nymphs seem to depend on the thoroughness with which they can merge into their surroundings in order to escape observation rather than on the speed with which they can retreat when danger threatens.

Blue-winged Olive Nymph, *Ephemerella ignita,* Pl. 5b,—cast skin, Pl. 5d, p. 48: These nymphs do not live in lakes or ponds. In rivers they penetrate deeply into weed beds and are often seen near the roots of weeds, such as *Ranunculus,* which grow in fast-flowing water. They commonly occur also in clumps of moss growing on stones, and among rubble and litter, mainly leaves, which collect on the upstream side of stones and other obstructions. In most of the habitats which they select there is little movement of the water, although it may be flowing very rapidly an inch or two away, but there is sufficient movement to keep it constantly changed and it is renewed from water which is flowing rapidly and is, therefore, fairly low in temperature with probably an equivalently high oxygen content. They possess strong legs and a compact thorax, and, as befits a species which has to pass through close-packed vegetation or other confined spaces, the gill-plates are small and lie inclined close to and on the upper surface of the abdomen. The most posterior pair of gill-plates lie underneath the penultimate pair and are, therefore, even more efficiently protected.

Caenis Nymphs, Pl. 5c, p. 48: These nymphs live in both rivers and lakes. They are found on the bottom on mud or sand, and also on stones or in thick weed in sluggish or still waters. The nymphs are covered with fine hairs which collect a coat of algae and detritus which provides a most effective camouflage. Owing to their small size and to the manner in which they blend with their surroundings they are difficult to find, and as they are extremely sluggish in their movements, they depend on their camouflage and not their agility in order to escape from their enemies. They are often to be found half buried in loose fine detritus or mud, and their gills are specially adapted to cope with such conditions. The second pair of gills are large and platelike, and lie on the upper surface of the abdomen inclining towards the tail. The remaining posterior four pairs of gills lie beneath and are protected by this second pair. So well hidden are the posterior pairs of gills that they cannot be seen from above, unless this second pair are first raised or removed.

BURROWING NYMPHS

The only burrowing nymphs which occur in these islands are nymphs of the mayflies, *Ephemera danica, E. vulgata* and *E. lineata*.

These nymphs burrow into mud and sand and live in the holes or tunnels which they excavate. For digging they are provided with a pair of long tusk-like mandibles and short, strong forelegs with flat joints. The head is pointed and narrow, and the body and thorax are slender and rounded.

The femora of the middle legs, which swing from a backward to a forward direction when the nymph is crawling, are abnormally short, and in consequence the legs project sideways to only a slight extent as the nymph moves along the confined space in its burrow. The femora of the hind legs are longer, but they incline in a backward direction and do not swing out at right angles to the body.

The gills, which are plume-like and are arched over and lie close to the dorsal surface of the abdomen, are adapted for operating in the confined space in the burrows. Their action keeps a slight current of water passing through the burrow and past the nymph.

CHAPTER 5

EMERGENCE

A PARTICULARLY dangerous period in the life of an ephemeropteran is that immediately before, during, and immediately after the emergence of the dun from the nymphal shuck. At such a time many nymphs are eaten by fish and many of the newly-hatched duns are eaten by fish or birds; but the heaviest mortality is caused either by the failure of the dun to emerge from the nymphal skin, or else by its inability to take flight from the surface of the water. Mishaps at this stage may occur through some mechanical cause which prevents the dun emerging successfully from the shuck, or else through the dun's becoming entangled in the surface film.

The final nymphal moult, which results in the emergence of the dun, differs from earlier nymphal moults. In the earlier moults, the nymph remains in the same medium and the change in form is not very pronounced. But in the final moult the nymph usually moults under the water, and the dun emerges into the air. Also, the differences in the external structure of the insect at the two stages are marked, mainly in that the dun has fully erected wings in place of the small wing cases of the nymph.

Nymphal moults have been studied in regard to several insects and a certain amount is known about the method by which the insects rid themselves of the old cuticle. But, as well as considering how the insect actually leaves its exuviae, it is interesting to consider some of the changes which take place within the insect's integument and which lead up to the actual moulting.

The skin, or integument, of a nymph is composed of four main layers. These are called the epicuticle (the outermost layer), the exocuticle, the endocuticle and the epidermis (the innermost layer composed of cells). In his *Outlines of Entomology*, Dr. Imms briefly describes moulting in insects. A portion of his description, which is appropriate to this chapter, is as follows:—

"The initiating factor in moulting is the secretion of a hormone into the blood. The source of this hormone appears to be the corpora allata. In some cases blood from an insect, near to the moulting stage, has been transfused into another individual in a normal condition, with the result that an accelerated moulting has followed.

"Prior to ecdysis an insect ceases to feed and may become for a time quiescent. Owing to recent growth the epidermal cells become greatly elongated and often thrown into folds which results in the old cuticle being separated from them. A thin new covering, composed of epicuticle and exocuticle, becomes formed and a moulting fluid is discharged into the narrow space separating the old from the new cuticle. The fluid is the product of epidermal moulting glands that become functional at this time, and it has the property of liquefying the endocuticle. It does not attack the epicuticle or exocuticle of the new skin which function as interposing layers between the moulting fluid and the developing endocuticle. The old skin, thus reduced to epi- and exocuticle, is now ready to be cast off.

"The insect, by contracting its abdominal muscles, increases the pressure of blood in the thorax. The tergal region comes to bulge upward until the old skin ruptures along a predetermined line of weakness. This line is marked by the absence of exocuticle: it commonly runs mid-longitudinally along the back of the thorax. Many insects swallow air, or water in the case of aquatic forms, and thereby enhance the disruptive force employed. When the skin has split the insect escapes gradually by peristaltic movement, often aided by gravity, since many insects suspend themselves head downward during the moulting process. As it issues from the old skin, the limbs are withdrawn from their coverings and the creature escapes with a soft and pliant cuticle. It swallows considerable quantities of air (or water) and by this means again increases its bulk. Many of the muscles remain for the time in a state of contraction and, in this way, pressure of the blood serves to expand the wings and other parts to their full dimensions. The cuticle hardens and darkens, processes which appear to be effected by an oxidative change since neither takes place in an atmosphere of nitrogen. If the crop of a newly-moulted cockroach be perforated with a needle, air escapes and distention of the new cuticle is prevented. If the wings of newly-emerged insects be pricked, blood is seen to issue freely and their proper expansion cannot be attained."

From this description it is not difficult to picture the moulting of a nymph. The insect can swallow water, contract its muscles, and exert pressure on the cuticle in the region of the thorax. A split then appears on the dorsal surface and runs longitudinally across the thorax and extends forwards to the head. When it reaches the posterior-dorsal region of the head (called the epicranium), the split divides into two parts, and passes down each side of the head capsule behind the eyes. This provides an opening large enough to allow the contained nymph to emerge. If a large number of nymphs is collected alive and placed in a wide dish in shallow water and kept under observation, it will not be long before one of them will be seen moulting.

It is less easy to determine in detail what occurs when the dun is emerging. In effect, duns emerge in one of the following ways:—

1. The nymph may swim to the surface and the dun emerge from the nymphal skin while the latter remains suspended from the surface film. Most species can emerge in this way.

2. The nymph may crawl partly or completely out of the water by way of emergent vegetation or a protruding rock, and the metamorphosis takes place in the air, as happens with dragonflies. Any nymph, apparently, may adopt this method at times, but with some species, those, for instance, belonging to the genus *Siphlonurus*, this seems to be the method normally used.

3. The dun may leave the nymphal skin while it is several inches below the surface and while the nymph is clinging to a rock or other support. The dun then either crawls up above the water or else floats to the surface.

The first of these methods is by far the most important in so far as angling interests are concerned and it would be interesting to determine exactly what occurs. There are several points to be considered. When a nymph is moulting (between two nymphal stages) it swallows water and thus increases its size. This helps in rupturing the nymphal skin. After the skin has been cast the nymph maintains its increased bulk until the new cuticle has hardened. It then expels the water from the gut and continues feeding.

When a dun emerges, its gut must be filled with air or some other gas, instead of water, in order that its flying powers will not be hindered by undue weight. In addition to this it is usual to find a film of air lying between the loosened skin, which a nymph is about to cast, and the body of the contained dun. How nymphs obtain the necessary air which is found in the gut, and the method by which it penetrates beneath the nymphal skin, is not known. Various suppositions have been advanced, and it seems probable that air is drawn into the gut by the nymph's swimming or crawling to the surface and protruding its head sufficiently far above the water to enable it to swallow the air. This may occur some time before the nymph hatches. More usually, perhaps, nymphs do not rise to the surface until they are actually ascending in order to hatch, and the air is perhaps then swallowed by the dun, while in the process of hatching, or just after it has hatched.

The air (or other gas) which accumulates beneath the cuticle shortly before emergence begins may be supplied by the tracheal tubes, which at this stage become severed at the spiracular openings on the abdomen of the dun. In the nymph the tracheal tubes (air-tubes) of the abdomen are united to the tracheal gills, but the gills and their contained tracheal tubes remain with the cast skin when the dun hatches.

Or, as has been suggested by Mr. Kimmins, air may creep beneath the loosened nymphal skin from the air which the nymph has swallowed. The skin which the nymph casts not only covers all the outer parts of the nymph, but it also lines the mouth cavity and the fore and hind ends of the gut. It is at the point inside the gut, where the skin becomes detached from the wall of the gut, that the air may penetrate beneath the skin.

Other aquatic insects are able to obtain air from the dissolved gases in the water. For instance, the pupae of the Reed Smuts, which are anchored to submerged weed, can do so. When the pupal case breaks open, the adult Reed Smut emerges already enveloped in a film of gas. This gas keeps the insect dry and buoys it to the surface. It is possible, but not necessarily likely, that ephemeropteran nymphs also utilise the dissolved gases in the water for this purpose. It is apparent that there are considerable opportunities here for further research.

The presence of the gas beneath the nymphal skin is easily detected as it imparts to the nymph a sort of glistening appearance. The extent to which the glistening can be seen varies with the angle of light under which it is viewed. At some angles it is difficult to see it at all. But at particularly favourable angles the air film may reflect so much light that it becomes difficult to determine the colour of the nymph.

When a nymph starts to hatch, the abdomen of the dun is partially withdrawn, so that a space appears between the tail end of the dun's body and the tail end of the nymphal shuck, and this space becomes filled with the gas. The tail end of the hatching nymph then immediately assumes a much increased lustre, and in fact it strongly resembles a section of a glass tube which has been filled with mercury.

This effect is even more noticeable in the pupae of those long-legged midges, the chironomids, when they are hatching at the surface of the open water of lakes, and I think that it explains the added attraction which a flat tag of gold or silver gives to many artificial flies.

When a nymph ascends to the surface in open water prior to the appearance of the dun it may do so, apparently, either voluntarily or involuntarily. Those which ascend voluntarily are probably attracted by the light and they appear to swim deliberately to the surface. But nymphs may also be buoyed to the surface by the gases contained beneath their integument. I had a clear illustration of this one September day on a reservoir in the west of England. During the afternoon I noticed some Lake Olives, *Cloëon simile*, emerging from shallow water near the shore. As some of the flies were hatching within one or two feet of the shore, from water which was from about 6 ins. to 1½ ft. in depth, I examined the bottom in order to ascertain if any nymphs were visible. A close scrutiny revealed several nymphs clinging to the upper layers of some completely submerged aquatic moss which covered the bottom. Most of the nymphs were about six inches or a foot from the surface, and instead of darting away and then clinging to some other support, as is their usual habit when disturbed, each of these nymphs swam to the surface, and within a second or two the dun emerged. Other nymphs hatched when the moss further from the shore was disturbed with aid of stones or a stick. From a closer scrutiny of the nymphs it appeared that when they were disturbed and swam away they endeavoured to reach some other support, but that they were buoyed upwards as they swam, and so passed over their objective and were carried to the surface.

In order to try to confirm this supposition I immersed a glass tube and allowed it to fill with water. I then induced a nymph to swim into the tube and, while the tube was still under water, corked it. This resulted in my obtaining a nymph in a tube full of water from which all extraneous air had been excluded. When the tube was removed from the water, the nymph was found floating against the uppermost end of the tube, and when the tube was inverted, the nymph immediately floated up to the other end.

As this nymph had been captured nearly a foot below the surface, and, so far as I was aware, had never been in contact with the atmosphere, it was obvious that there was sufficient gas beneath its cuticle to buoy it to the surface. It also seemed apparent that the only reason why it had not been carried up to the surface, at any rate during a short period before I captured it, was because it was clinging to the submerged moss. This incident brought to mind the numerous occasions on which flies are seen hatching behind an angler wading through weed in a river, or along the shallow shore of a lake. One can, in fact, at times bring on a local hatch of fly by disturbing the mature nymphs in their habitat. When nymphs become mature, and for some time before they hatch, they will be found in exposed positions on the upper sides of stones and on the upper layers of weed. They become restless, and swim or crawl from one exposed point to another. They often make preliminary ascents to the surface.

Many times in rivers, I have seen nymphs of the Iron-blue Dun, *Baëtis pumilus*, and of the Large Dark Olive, *B. rhodani*, (Pl. 6c, d, p. 49), make such preliminary ascents by swimming to a protruding stone or weed and then crawling up to the surface. The object of these preliminary ascents to the surface is not known, but it is generally supposed that the nymphs at such times gulp down air from the atmosphere, and that this air is of help to the nymph when it is finally hatching. Nymphs also, at times, make preliminary ascents by swimming instead of crawling upwards, but many, and possibly most, nymphs hatch without having made any such preliminary visit to the surface.

It is, however, perhaps more usual for nymphs which ascend to the surface of open water in order to emerge, to do so by swimming upwards without also being buoyed up by contained air. Nymphs of the Greendrake, *Ephemera danica*, swim to the surface and appear to be continuously active during their ascent. Nymphs of the Iron-blue, *B. pumilus*, swim and rest intermittently as they ascend. The following description of the ascent of an individual Iron-blue Nymph, which I recorded immediately after observing it, is, I think, fairly typical for this species.

"A nymph was seen near the bank moving restlessly across the surface of a stone about five inches under the water. After a minute or so it suddenly swam actively out towards the faster-flowing water. It swam and was carried along by the current for about two yards and then it ceased swimming and drifted for a few feet. It again commenced swimming actively and reached the surface of the water and continued swimming, so that it was pressing against the under-side of the surface film. It did not succeed in penetrating the film and again ceased activity and drifted inertly with the current. While drifting in this manner (which it did for two or three feet) it was rolled over by the underwater currents and sank a few inches. It once again commenced to swim vigorously upwards, and this time after reaching the surface it succeeded in penetrating the surface film with the upper portion of its thorax. It again drifted inertly, but this time it did not sink as the tension of the surface film held it securely. By the time that it had drifted about two yards in this manner the dun had emerged."

The whole process from the time the nymph swam away from the submerged stone until the dun emerged occupied about twenty-five seconds, and during this time the nymph was carried and swam about six yards downstream. Other nymphs hatch more rapidly and are not carried along so far by the current, whilst nymphs which are unfortunate enough to reach the surface in an area where there is scum on the water may be carried very long distances, and often fail entirely to penetrate the surface and hatch.

Surface tension plays a very important part in the hatching of these flies. When a nymph reaches the surface, the thorax either of the nymph or else of the emerging dun possesses water-repellent properties, so that when the water retreats from this area the surface tension exerts an upward pull on the nymph. This effect is explained in Chapter 17. This upward pull of the surface tension holds first the nymph and then the discarded nymphal shuck in position and greatly facilitates the safe emergence of the dun.

In consequence, factors which lower the surface tension hinder the safe emergence of the flies. A common cause of reduced surface tension is scum, and scum may be present without being very noticeable. There is always a certain amount of scum distributed over the surface of a river. Under conditions when a cross wind is blowing, the scum will be gradually blown across to the lee side of the river and will become concentrated along that shore. The glass edge which forms on a lee shore always contains scum. In turbulent, quick-flowing, or rippled water, the scum is dispersed and broken up, and consequently duns can usually hatch from water of this type more easily than from still water.

When a dun has successfully emerged from the nymphal shuck, it still has to take flight from the water without getting wet or entangled in the surface film. The dun has several features which aid it in doing this. The skin of a dun is covered with very fine minute hairs and these hairs are water-repellent, with the result that if the dun is suddenly pulled underneath the water, or is blown over on to its side water does not necessarily come in contact with the insect, as a very thin film of air automatically envelops the dun owing to the cohesion of the water molecules. But in practice, the strength of the surface film is often reduced because of the presence of small traces of scum, and the dun is then liable to get wetted.

When a dun is resting on the water, usually only its legs, but sometimes the under surface of its thorax, are in contact with the surface. Its wings are held upright and at first sight it would appear to be very vulnerable to the levelling effect of the wind, for its wings are tall and relatively broad in proportion to the size of the fly. But for several reasons the duns are not as vulnerable as might at first sight appear. Owing to the somewhat sail-like appearance of their upright wings duns have often been likened to miniature yachts. Their reactions to the wind are most easily appreciated if some of the fundamental dynamics as applicable to yachts and duns are compared.

When a yacht or rowing boat is lying sideways to the wind, there is considerable resistance to movement of the boat sideways through the water, owing to the nature of the hull. Lake anglers make use of this lateral resistance by drifting with the boat lying sideways to the wind. And a certain place about midway between the bow and the stern which is the fulcrum of the lateral resistance is known as the centre of lateral resistance.

Similarly, there is lateral pressure exerted by the wind on the sails, mast, and exposed portion of the hull of the boat. The centre point of this lateral pressure is called the centre of effort. When the centre of effort lies anywhere along the upright vertical line of the centre of lateral resistance, then the boat will drift straight downwind. But if the centre of effort lies to one side of the centre of lateral resistance, the boat will turn so that the centre of lateral resistance is

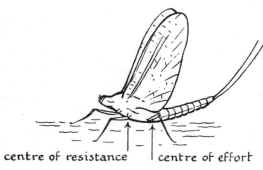

centre of resistance   centre of effort

FIG. 2

When an Ephemeropteran is resting on the water it reacts in weathercock fashion to the wind. Normally, only the insect's legs are in contact with the water surface. If its tails should become entangled in the surface film the insect is liable to be blown over on its side and ultimately drowned.

upwind from the centre of effort. Owing to the nature of the keel and to the pressure which the water exerts on it, the boat will only partially turn around.

In a dun which is resting on the surface of the water in the normal manner, the centre of lateral resistance lies somewhere near the middle legs, and the centre of effort lies posterior to this (see Fig. 2) so that the fly tends to turn and face upwind. But a dun differs from a boat in that it rests entirely *on* the surface film, whereas the boat is partially submerged, and therefore both the lateral resistance and the resistance to turning of the dun are very slight. The ease with which the dun can turn on the water is further increased by the fact that the points of contact of the six legs with the surface are arranged so as to lie nearly on the circumference of a circle. In fact, a dun resting on the water reacts to the wind in much the same manner as a weathercock. It is less likely to be blown over when it is facing the wind than in any other position, and it also is in the most suitable position for taking flight. This reveals another objection to scum, as the facility with which the dun can be turned by the wind will be reduced when scum is present. If the dun is unfortunate enough to get its tails or abdomen caught in the surface film, then it will not be turned towards the wind in the normal manner. The relative positions of the centres of lateral resistance and of effort will have altered, and will either coincide or else be reversed.

When a dun hatches it may take flight at once, or it may remain on the water for some time. It has often been remarked that when the sun is shining, the wings of duns dry rapidly, and that the flies can then quickly fly away. But a factor which never seems to be considered, and which may be of greater importance, is the temperature of the flight muscles contained in the thorax. It has been demonstrated by Krogh and Zeuthen that bees are unable to vibrate their wings rapidly enough to enable them to fly until their wing muscles reach a certain minimum temperature. The insects are able to increase the temperature of their muscles by vibrating their wings, and if the temperature of the muscles when at rest is only slightly below the required minimum for flight, then by rapidly vibrating their wings the insects can increase the temperature and then take flight. If these findings are applied to ephemeropterans, it is not unreasonable to suppose that temperature exercises just as much control over their flight as it does over the flight of bees. There is a nearly untouched field here for observation and experiment. But from the angling viewpoint the important thing is to ascertain what conditions induce the duns to remain longest on the water. It would appear to be dull cold weather.

CHAPTER 6

MATING AND FLIGHT

MATING

IT HAS been mentioned already that the purpose of the swarming flight of male spinners is to allow the two sexes to find each other and mate.

When swarming, the males take up more or less fixed positions in the air and remain hovering over an area of usually only a few square yards in extent. They do not move from place to place outside this area in their search for females, but wait until the female spinners fly within their range of vision.

The nature of the structure of the large compound eyes of the males gives them a wide range of vision, but it is unlikely that they can distinguish small objects at any considerable distance.

If the compound eyes of a male spinner are examined, it will be seen that they are spherical in shape and that their surfaces are composed of several hundred minute facets. These facets are so small that it is usually necessary to use a magnifying glass in order to see them. Each of these facets is a separate lens of the eye, and each lens lies at the end of a separate optical tube called an ommatidium. A rough model, which illustrates the principle of these eyes, can be made by holding a bundle of seventy or eighty unused match sticks in the hand, with the heads all pointing in one direction. A more accurate model would be obtained if each match stick were tapered slightly towards the end away from the head. Then if the centre of the bundle at the tapered end were pressed inwards in a rounded fashion it would cause the match-heads to protrude in a complementary manner at the other end. Thus the head end of the bundle, which represents the outer surface of the eye, would

Plate 5: NYMPHS, × 3
(a) Large Dark Olive, *Baëtis rhodani*; (b) Blue-winged Olive, *Ephemerella ignita*; (c) Angler's Curse, *Caenis* sp.; (d) Blue-winged Olive, *Ephemerella ignita*, cast skin of nymph

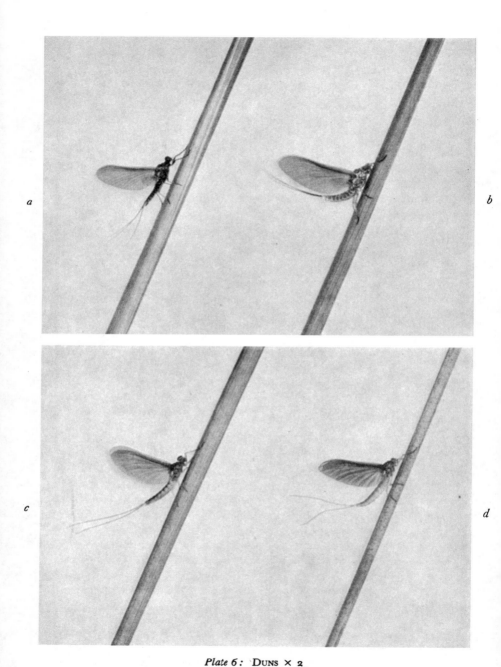

Plate 6 : Duns × 2
(*a*) and (*b*) Iron-blue, *Baëtis pumilus*, male and female; (*c*) and (*d*) Large
Dark Olive, *Baëtis rhodani*, male and female

assume a convex instead of a flat surface, and the match sticks, which represent the ommatidia, would converge inwards.

The manner in which an eye of this nature operates is quite different from that in which our eyes operate. In the insect eye each ommatidium is a separate optical unit, and, owing to its structure, has a very narrow field of vision. It is as though the field were viewed through a narrow tube. Owing to the great number of these ommatidia which are present and to the arc which they cover, the complete compound eyes have a very wide panoramic range of vision. Such eyes are very sensitive to moving objects, but have low resolving power so that it is unlikely that an object will be seen distinctly unless it is within a few yards range. A moving object will be appreciated easily as it will pass through the field of vision of a number of the ommatidia in turn.

The male spinners appear to be primarily attracted to the females by sight. If a female spinner flies within a few feet of a hovering male of the same species, the male usually pursues her. But the males frequently make mistakes in this initial pursuit. They will not only fly up to females of other species, but at times are attracted to any fly of reasonable size which passes within a few feet of them. If an artificial Spent Gnat is tied on to a cast which is attached to a rod and line in the normal manner, and is then allowed to swing out in the wind near a swarm of male spinners, many of the spinners will fly over to it. The artificial fly becomes more attractive if it is drawn against the wind at about the speed at which a female spinner flies. The males then pursue it and knock against it, or even make abortive attempts to grasp it. But once they touch the artificial fly they lose interest, and return to the swarm. Similarly, when they pursue a fly other than a female of their own species, they lose interest when once they have come into contact with it. It appears therefore, that even though male spinners are attracted to the females by sight, they can identify them only by touch. Perhaps, as has been suggested by Dr. H. B. N. Hynes for stoneflies, the ripe females exude some substance by which males of the same species can recognise them.

Mating takes place in the air. The male approaches the female from underneath, and grasps her with his long reversibly jointed forelegs in the region of her thorax. Then, by tilting his abdomen upwards and partly forwards over his own back, he clasps the eighth or ninth segment of her abdomen with his abdominal forceps and copulation is effected, usually while the pair continue flying.

FLIGHT

When watching male spinners hovering one wonders how such fragile insects can have sufficient strength to remain flying for perhaps several hours without resting. All the muscles which operate the wings are contained within the thorax, and they do not extend along the wing as in birds. There must, therefore, be tremendous leverage exerted by the whole wing against the comparatively small wing root. The largest and most powerful of the flight muscles are those which control the downstroke of the wing. These are longitudinal muscles and they extend from the rear to the front of the thorax. When these muscles are contracted, the front and rear walls of the thorax are drawn nearer to each other, and this forces the dorsal portion of the thorax upwards. Owing to the nature of the articulation of the wing with the thorax, this action forces the wing downwards. The muscles which operate the upstroke of the wing pass at right angles through these longitudinal muscles and are attached to the dorsal and ventral walls of the thorax. The contraction of these muscles pulls the dorsal portion of the thorax down again and forces the wing upwards. There are many smaller muscles also concerned, some of which revolve the wing slightly on its long axis, and others which control its forward or backward movement.

It is mainly for the purpose of containing these powerful wing muscles that the thorax of an ephemeropteran is so well developed. The rigid nature of its structure is required so that the wing muscles can obtain sufficient support and purchase when in action.

SWARMING FLIGHT

When spinners are ready to mate, the two sexes locate each other in the air whilst flying.

The male spinners appear on the wing and collect into swarms, often some considerable time before any females are seen. A swarm of these spinners may consist of several hundred or several thousand individuals which will take up a definite position in the air in relation to the water's edge, and seldom deviate appreciably from within surprisingly narrow confines. When hovering, the flies always face up wind, and they seem to prefer flying in a light wind rather than in still conditions. Their hovering flight propels them forwards at the same speed as the wind blows them backwards, and within certain limits they hold a more or less fixed position in the air. They are unable to counteract the force of a very strong wind, and during windy weather they fly in the lee of bushes or other obstacles which provide shelter; or if in open situations they fly near to the ground where the wind velocity is reduced. Except under storm conditions, wind does not directly prevent their flight and rain has not necessarily as much effect as might be expected. The factor which has the greatest effect is the air temperature, for spinners are unable to fly in very low temperatures. Changes in the temperature are rapidly effected by sun, wind and rain. Under conditions of cold north or east winds accompanied by bright sunshine, three widely different temperature readings can be obtained simultaneously in the following positions:—

(1) In the wind but sheltered from the direct rays of the sun.
(2) In the direct rays of the sun but sheltered from the wind, and
(3) In the wind and in the direct rays of the sun.

As an example of the variations which occur, the following temperature readings which I recorded in Co. Meath one day in March 1947 may be quoted:—

(1) 55° F. (2) 81° F. (3) 62° F.

In general, an increase in wind velocity causes a drop in air temperature, and falling rain has a similar effect, so that both wind and rain have, therefore, a secondary prohibiting effect on the flight of spinners. But large swarms of spinners can be seen in flight during periods of strong warm winds and during "warm" rain.

The presence or absence of sun is of considerable importance, primarily by reason of its effect on temperature, but also because of the sensitiveness which many species exhibit to the intensity of light. Some species prefer to fly in direct sunlight, whilst others deliberately avoid it and are seldom seen on the wing except at dusk. Still other species seek intermediate light intensities, whilst a few species apparently fly at night time.

Very light-coloured and translucent spinners are best observed against a dark background with the sunlight coming obliquely through the swarm towards the observer. The individual flies are then shown up in much the same manner as particles of dust suspended in the air become clearly visible when the sun's rays penetrate a darkened room. It is, of course, important that the observer's eyes should be shaded from the sun's rays. Under such suitable conditions light-coloured pale watery spinners can be seen sixty to eighty yards away, while they would not be visible at even two yards distance if looked for against the light background of the sky, with the sunlight coming from behind the observer.

Conversely, dark and more opaque spinners, such as the Black Drakes, *Ephemera danica*, or the Great Red Spinners, *Ecdyonurus venosus* and *E. dispar*, are clearly visible against a light background, such as that provided by grey clouds.

It is normally very difficult to watch insects in flight owing to the rate at which they travel but the male spinners of Ephemeroptera can be examined with comparative ease, for they remain in approximately the same positions in the air often for several hours at a time. And if it is remembered that most species are more easily seen against a dark background, and under conditions of transmitted light, there should not be undue difficulty in studying them. When one becomes familiar with the flight of the spinners, most species can be recognised when they are in the air. Many differences in the manner of flight adopted will be discerned. Some of these differences are fundamental and easily observed and described, others are more fugitive and, though fairly easily observed, are extremely difficult to describe.

The following descriptions refer only to the more obvious features in the flight of different species; and it will be found by anyone who becomes familiar with the habits of any of these flies that many other and more subtle characteristics will become apparent. Most species can then be recognised in the air in much the same way as birds can be recognised by their flight.

The commonest hovering flight is that in which the spinners rise and fall continuously. They rise by flying obliquely upwards, and slightly forwards into the wind, and, as their forward motion is usually counteracted by the force of the wind, they actually rise vertically, or at times may even be blown slightly backwards during the ascent. They fall by gliding downwards and slightly forwards, and the forward motion is also normally counteracted by the wind so that they may either drop perpendicularly or else be blown backwards. When the spinner is falling, the wings, abdomen, tails and front legs slope upwards, and the centre of gravity is centred in the thorax.

Some species rise and fall continuously. Others intersperse the rising and falling with short horizontal flights. Species which do not adopt this rising and falling motion hover more after the manner of a kestrel, that is, a fly will remain in the air motionless, except for the rapidly beating wings and a vibration which is often seen in the body as it absorbs the wing beats and tremors in unison with them. While hovering in this manner, some species will often at the same time move slowly forwards, downwards or upwards.

With many species it is probable that the larger portions of the swarms are too high in the air to be visible from the ground except in very favourable circumstances, and it is only the individuals comprising the lower portions of a swarm which an observer normally sees. Under favourable conditions of light I have seen a swarm of Jenny Spinners which extended from a few feet above ground level to at least forty feet in the air. The upper portion of the swarm appeared to be about ten yards in width, and the swarm tapered downwards to a yard or two in width at the base. A swarm of these dimensions is often made up of a number of scattered small swarms which when viewed from a distance (and from one side) appear to merge into each other. It is only the small swarms which form the base of the main swarm which one normally sees, and the characteristics of the flight of the flies are described from the spinners composing these lower swarms.

When considering the distance from the water's edge at which various species may be found, allowance should be made for the effect of local conditions on the swarms. In this connection a typical river is one which flows through open country containing scattered hedges or trees, or through a valley with a flat or gently sloping floor. Complications are caused by the presence of thick woods, paths or roads near the river and by bridges. When the banks of a river or lake are occupied by plantations of trees, the spinners may be obliged to hover over the trees, and in consequence are seldom visible from the ground. All spinners appear to be attracted to roads and footpaths, especially when the surfaces are wet. Female spinners oviposit on them and the presence of a road often distracts the attention of male spinners from the river. Consequently, when a road passes alongside a river, or a bridge crosses the river, spinners which normally hover over or on the edge of the river may, instead, be found flying over the road. They are also attracted, although to a lesser extent, by footpaths, and when swarming spinners are being watched, and notice is being taken of the distance the swarms are from the water's edge, allowance should be made accordingly.

Grey Drakes, *Ephemera danica,* hover over hedges, trees, long grass or flags, or in general over whatever vegetation had sheltered them in the dun stage. Normally they fly from about six to twelve feet above the ground, but when in the vicinity of trees they hover over them irrespective of the height. They are found at varying distances from the water's edge, their relative position to it seemingly depending on the situation of whatever vegetation they sought for shelter. Owing to their large size these flies are easily observed, and most anglers are probably familiar with their attractive rising and falling flight. An individual fly will propel itself rapidly upwards for three or four feet and then fall again on its outstretched wings. A swarm of these spinners presents a scene of great animation and liveliness and, as with most species, the tempo of their flight increases roughly in proportion to the number of flies present in the swarm.

These spinners do not usually begin hovering until afternoon, and are in greatest abundance about three or four hours before sunset. If the afternoon sun is unusually strong and the air very warm, their appearance may be delayed; while during sultry thundery weather, when a haze obscures the sun, they will often be seen flying appreciably earlier in the day. They seldom continue flying until darkness, and usually seek the shelter of the trees at about sunset.

Pale Watery Spinners, *Centroptilum luteolum* (Pl. 17 a, b, p. 92), hover over the edge of the water, usually partly over the water and partly over the land, and seldom move even a few yards inland. They are most persistent in this selection of a site at the water's edge in which to fly. Their rising and falling flight is similar to that of the Grey Drake, *Ephemera danica.* An individual fly will ascend very rapidly for a foot or so and then glide down again. Owing to their light colouring they are difficult to see unless viewed against a rather dark background.

They fly in the morning, afternoon and early evening, seldom late in the evening. They are quite tolerant of sunshine, although they seem to prefer conditions when the sun is slightly obscured. The distinctive reddish-amber colouring of their turbinate eyes and of the last two or three abdominal segments and their small size makes them easily recognisable if captured.

Jenny Spinners, *Baëtis pumilus* (Pl. 14 c, d, p. 81): These Iron Blue Spinners are most noticeable in windy weather when thick groups of them may be seen in the lee of bushes or other shelter near the river. They also like to hover over beds of rushes or flags, and when a particularly strong gust of wind comes they seek momentary shelter in the vegetation and reappear immediately the gust lessens. In calm weather they will fly at a considerable height, and it is then extremely difficult to observe any individuals except those composing the lowest layers of the swarms. They adopt a jerky motion when in flight. Their ascent is extremely rapid and is in contrast to their rather slow fall; in order to prevent themselves from being blown too far backwards during their descent it is of short duration.

These flies delight in sunshine and fly during the morning and afternoon, but they tend to cease flying towards evening. They are essentially daytime flies. The very dark brown or puce brown colour of the last two or three abdominal segments, the black thorax and dark red-brown eyes, all of which are in marked contrast to the pure transparent white colour of the first six or seven abdominal segments, serve to distinguish them from Pale Watery or Olive Spinners.

Small Dark Olive Spinner, *Baëtis scambus* (Pl. 16, p. 85): The flight of these spinners is rather similar to that of the Jenny Spinner, *Baëtis pumilus*, but it is less active and the change of direction between the falling and the rising flights is less abrupt, so that instead of the line of flight forming an acute angle at this point it follows a more rounded course.

The spinners hover at various distances from the river during the afternoon and early evening; the sites chosen seem to depend largely on the location or distribution of the sheltering vegetation, but they are seldom further than forty or fifty yards from the bank. The faint brown-olive tinge in the first five or six abdominal segments and the dark brown olive colour of the last two or three segments serve to distinguish them from the Jenny Spinners.

Large Dark Olive Spinner, *Baëtis rhodani* (Pl. 14 a, b, p. 81): These spinners do not appear to be consistent in their manner of flight. Their most usual flight consists of a rising and falling motion with noticeably short ascents and descents, and this is varied with a relatively steady type of flight in which individuals remain hovering in the air, and then perhaps slowly fall and rise again, or move sideways or forwards or drift backwards on the wind.

A swarm of these flies may be seen in which the individuals are continuously weaving in and out between each other at a fairly constant speed. At other times they adopt a more pronounced rising and falling flight similar to but somewhat slower than that of the Jenny Spinner. They fly at various distances from the edge of the river, inland for thirty or forty yards, and are most numerous during the afternoon and early evening.

Olive Spinners, *Baëtis tenax* and *B. atrebatinus*: The flight of both these species is rather similar to the flight of the Jenny Spinner. They rise and fall repeatedly and rapidly, but they vary this at intervals by adopting a steady flight in which a fly will remain hovering with little movement. This variation is more noticeable with the *B. tenax* spinners. Both these species fly in the sunshine and they will be found during the afternoon and early evening. They hover on the edge of the river or a few yards inland.

Purple Spinner, *Paraleptophlebia cincta* (Pl. 18a, p. 93): These spinners are difficult to observe when flying, owing to their being both dark-coloured and yet translucent. They adopt a very rapid rising and falling flight and they are seen hovering over or alongside rapidly flowing portions of the river. They are not consistent in their choice of a site, as they may also be found hovering at varying distances from the water in the vicinity of sheltering vegetation. They appear to delight in sunshine and are found on the wing during the morning, afternoon and early evening.

Pale Evening Spinner, *Procloëon rufulum* (Pl. 17c, d, p. 92): These Pale Watery Spinners do not rise and fall with the regularity found in any of the previous species. A fly in a swarm may rise and fall once or twice and then perhaps fly forwards or obliquely sideways, and drift backwards again on the wind, and the general course of the flight is horizontal rather than vertical (see Fig. 3). They rise and fall only intermittently and then in a "shallow" fashion, and it is difficult to perceive whether the wings cease beating when they are falling. The flight on the whole is fairly steady and is easy to distinguish from that of other similarly-sized Pale Watery Spinners such as *Centroptilum luteolum* and *Baëtis scambus*.

In the air, these flies appear very white when viewed against a dark background, and as they fly in the late evening they are often seen in rather dark surroundings. Their flight period is from about

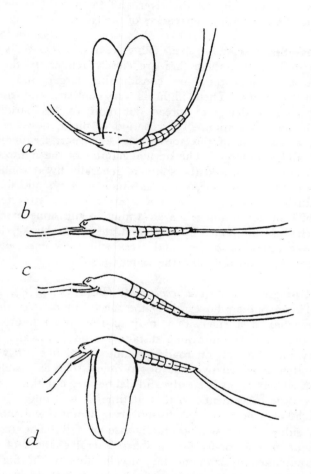

FIG. 3

FLIGHT OF SPINNERS: a) The position of the body and appendages as seen during the controlled 'fall' in the hovering flight of species of *Baëtis, Centroptilum* and others which adopt a pronounced rising and falling flight; b) Position adopted by species of *Heptagenia, Rhithrogena* and others when hovering motionless in a steady breeze; c) Position of the last-named genera in very light air currents; d) Position of body, legs and tails when a species is flying vertically upwards.

one hour before to one hour after sunset or until darkness, provided the air temperature in the late evening does not drop too low for them. They hover on the edge of the river and for a yard or two inland, opposite to the slower-flowing reaches of the river.

Lake Olive Spinner, *Cloëon simile* (Pl. 22 c, d, p. 101): As is suggested by the generic name, these flies are closely related to the previous species, even though they are considerably larger and are much darker in colouring. Their flight is very similar, and the swarms have the same tendency to spread out more or less parallel to the ground in open formation. Their period of flight, however, is quite different, as spinners of this species are seen most frequently in the mornings and afternoons. The normal habitat of the nymphs is lakes and other still waters, and the spinners generally fly at some distance inland from the shore line, often as much as fifty, one hundred or two hundred yards. They do not appear to be attracted to the vicinity of lush vegetation when swarming to the same extent as are such species as the Jenny Spinner and the Grey Drake, and often fringing vegetation of bushes and trees will intervene between the sites selected for swarming and the water's edge.

Yellow Upright, *Rhithrogena semicolorata* (Pls. 15 c, p. 84, and 18 d, p. 93). These spinners hover along the shore line or over the rapidly flowing reaches of a river, they may also be often found in small numbers or singly at quite long distances from any water. At such times they may be seen on roads, or lanes, and, like other spinners, they are often attracted by some bright object such as a well-polished motor car. Their flight is steady and deliberate, but this is varied by frequent erratic movements, so that at times it is strongly reminiscent of the flight of a house-fly. A fly hovering steadily will move slowly forwards, sideways, or will gradually rise or fall. The resemblance to the flight of a house-fly lies in sharp lateral changes of direction, often accompanied by a momentary acceleration in the flight. When viewed from the side, a swarm gives an impression of suppressed or controlled animation, as the motions of the flies in flying upwards or downwards are so steady and deliberate in comparison to the quick abandon of the rising and falling flight of such species as the Jenny Spinner and the Grey Drake.

As with all spinners which move slowly in the air, the angle of the body to the ground varies with the strength of the wind. In conditions of still air the body hangs very much, and in lateral view forms a sort of zig-zag with the line of the extended forelegs and tails (see Fig. 3). When the insect is flying in the wind, the tails, body and forelegs tend to form a straight line as the flies stretch out more or less parallel to the ground.

Large swarms of these Yellow Uprights are often seen during the sultry conditions which precede heavy rain, or during thundery weather. They fly in the afternoon and evening and often continue swarming until dusk.

Yellow May Spinner, *Heptagenia sulphurea* (Pl. 15a, b, p. 84). The flight of these spinners is rather like that of the Yellow Upright, but it is even more restrained. In a wind these spinners hover nearly motionless for periods lasting up to a minute or longer at a time; then they may move slowly upwards or downwards or in any direction for short distances, perhaps for a foot or so, and then hover once more. In still conditions they fly to and fro over a stretch of several yards of water at a slow, even speed. Their slow rate of flight is seldom exceeded except when a fly darts suddenly towards another fly, under the assumption (presumably) that it is a female of his own species. This addition to the variations of flight is common to all spinners, but by contrast it is most noticeable in those species whose flight otherwise is slow and deliberate.

These spinners swarm in the late afternoon and evening, and at times continue flying until darkness. They consistently hover over the edge of the lake or river on which they occur, often at a height of twenty or thirty feet. The dark colour of the male spinners contrasts strongly with the pale lemon or whitish yellow of the female.

Brown May Spinners, *Heptagenia fuscogrisea*: The swarming flight of these is very similar to that of the Yellow May Spinners, and the males of both species will at times be seen flying in one swarm. The diurnal times of appearance differ somewhat, as these species will fly during the morning, afternoon and early evening, but they both show a reluctance to swarm more than a few yards away from the shore line. The wings of both species beat continuously. The light reddish-coloured bands on the femora of both the males and the females serve to distinguish these flies from the preceding.

Great Red Spinner, *Ecdyonurus venosus*, adopts in general the slow steady type of flight of the Yellow Upright. A fly which is hovering motionless in the air at a height of perhaps ten feet may suddenly swoop sideways for some yards, then in a moment or two rise steadily upwards perhaps eight or ten feet higher, and then gradually fall again, often by dropping and hovering intermittently.

They differ from the Yellow Uprights in that they fly greater distances during their vertical and lateral peregrinations, and that their flight is not interrupted by such abrupt lateral changes of direction. They are seen in flight mainly during the afternoon and evening and may be found at varying distances inland from the water's edge, but normally within about fifty yards of it.

August Dun Spinner, *Ecdyonurus dispar* (Pl. 21 c, d, p. 100). The flight is very similar to that of the previous species; the general trend is vertical, but both the rising and falling flights are interrupted by devious variations sideways, backwards or forwards. The rate at which the spinners move, whether in rising falling or deviating sideways, is very constant. Spinners can be seen at heights varying from one or two feet up to twenty or thirty feet. They often appear most numerous at about eight to fourteen feet when in open country, but they fly higher in the neighbourhood of tall trees or cliffs. Many of these dark opaque spinners are not observed when they fly at a level lower than six or eight feet, as they have by then fallen below the light skyline background and are difficult to see on darker backgrounds.

They hover at distances up to about forty or fifty yards inland from the water, but male spinners will also frequently be seen flying over the water. At such times they often adopt a different type of flight; individual flies will fly steadily up or downstream for a few feet above the water, and when they reach broken water tend to remain in that place either by hovering in the normal manner or else by flying back and forth over the area of water selected.

Green Spinner, *Ecdyonurus insignis* (Pl. 15 d, p. 84): These spinners hover over the water, usually about two or three feet above the surface, although in situations where both banks of the river are bordered with high vegetation they tend to fly higher. Typically they fly back and forth along a few yards of river. Their flight is steady in that they do not rise and fall but they sway sideways as they fly along. Their tails are held very widely apart and their wings beat continuously. At other times they hover steadily against the wind and show very little movement. When viewed against a dark background their pale greenish-grey colouring is usually visible. They fly in the later afternoon and evening and may remain on the wing until dusk.

Caenis **species** (Pl. 20 b, p. 97): The swarming flights of the five species of *Caenis* have not been distinguished from each other, and therefore some of the characteristics described here may not apply to all species.

The flies usually hover over the water near the shore line and they have an irregular and rather impatient way of flying. Individual flies may momentarily hover motionless and then move steadily forwards or sideways, then suddenly drop rapidly and rise again. They may vary this by rising and falling repeatedly for a while. At other times (or perhaps with other species) the flies fly very quickly up and down, in long ascending and descending lines of flight of five or six feet in height.

It seems to be characteristic of the flight that the flies may at any time suddenly drop below the general line of flight and rise again. These spinners will be seen in the early morning, seldom later than three or four hours after sunrise, and in the evening, but they seldom fly during the hotter periods of the day.

Sherry Spinner, *Ephemerella ignita* (Pl. 19 a, b, p. 96): The flight of the male Blue-winged Olive Spinners varies between the relatively steady type of flight of the August Dun Spinner, and the rising and falling flight of the Small Dark Olive Spinner, *Baëtis scambus*.

If an individual Sherry Spinner is watched when flying steadily, it may be seen hovering nearly motionless against the wind, and then perhaps it will move sideways or forwards and gradually fall a foot or so and slowly rise again. When in a swarm, it will be seen slowly weaving in and out between its companions who all are flying in a similar fashion. When such a swarm is viewed from one side the spinners may usually be recognised by the oblique slant of their wings. When the wing has been raised above the body it inclines backwards, and at the end of the downstroke it inclines forwards to a greater extent than is apparent with species of other genera. If the flies are viewed against a dark background it is usually easy to see the blur of the wings and, therefore, the extent to which they slope.

These spinners also indulge in a rising and falling flight, and at such times the falling flight, instead of being an uninterrupted fall, often consists of a "stepped" fall. The descending fly interrupts its fall by making a few momentary pauses. It is as though during the fall the fly gave a few beats of its wings at intervals so as to check its falling speed.

As well as being somewhat inconsistent in their method of flight, the flies are also inconsistent in the distance they hover from the water. At times a swarm will be over the water's edge, or it may be forty or fifty yards inland. The swarming period is during the late afternoon and evening, and the flies tend to spread out in loose swarms.

Yellow Evening Spinner, *Ephemerella notata* (Pl. 18c, p. 93): These spinners apparently hover a considerable distance from the river and will be seen in the early evening as far as one hundred or two hundred yards from the water's edge. Their flight in general is similar to that of the Sherry Spinner and the swarms spread out in a similar fashion.

Summer Mayfly Spinners, *Siphlonurus linnaeanus* (Pl. 21 a, b, p. 100): These spinners hover either over the water within a few yards of the shore or else more or less over the shore line. They will be seen flying at heights varying from six feet or so up to thirty or forty feet. They do not rise and fall quickly, but, like species of *Rhithrogena* and *Heptagenia*, they prefer to remain motionless for periods, and then perhaps they will ascend ten or fifteen feet and slowly fall again. The wings beat continuously, and the flight, particularly in descent is slow and deliberate. Owing to their large size the flies are easily seen when in the air, and can be distinguished from the Grey Drakes or Spent Gnats at a glance. Apart from the very obvious differences in the manner of flight these Summer Mayflies have only two tails.

They will be seen swarming during the evening and are most numerous at about sunset. Spinners of the nearly related *Siphlonurus lacustris* adopt a similar type of flight. On mountain streams they will be seen flying at considerable heights, either over the stream or else within a few yards of it, and they have the same habit as the former species of rising at times as much as ten or fifteen feet in the air during their ascending flight. They fly during the late afternoon and in the evening.

CHAPTER 7

EGG-LAYING

FEMALE SPINNERS deposit their eggs on the surface of the water or crawl down beneath the surface and fasten their eggs directly on a sub-surface support, usually the underside of a stone. The species which adopt the latter method all belong to the genus Baëtis. It is easy to observe one of these female Baëtis spinners crawling down to lay. If one wades into a shallow rather fast-flowing stretch of a river and stands in the current, preferably on a warm, dull afternoon, it should not be long before some of the commoner species appear. I have many times watched spinners of the Iron-blue, B. pumilus, the Large Dark Olive, B. rhodani, and the Small Dark Olive, B. scambus, ovipositing in this fashion. They all adopt the same method. A female fly will alight on one's wading boot an inch or so above the surface and will at once walk down to the surface and gradually crawl beneath the water. Immediately before submerging the wings are held upright and pressed together. As the fly enters the water, it becomes enveloped in a film of air and so does not get wet. The pressure of the water and of the surface tension forces the large forewings backwards until they lie close against the abdomen and impart to the fly a somewhat nymph-like shape. The flies appear to prefer to lay their eggs on the side of or underneath stones, and they will sometimes wander for relatively considerable distances over the bottom in order to locate a suitable site. When ovipositing, the spinner lays her eggs in contiguous rows by slow lateral movements of her abdomen and she advances perceptibly as each row is completed. The eggs adhere to whatever surface they are applied.

When the spinner has finished egg-laying, she may die under water beside her eggs, or she may crawl or float up again to the surface. In this latter event, if the film of air surrounding her has remained intact, she will probably appear on the surface quite dry and may succeed in flying away. Usually, however, these spent spinners are carried downstream in, on or under the surface film.

It is not yet known if all species of *Baëtis* crawl beneath the surface in this manner, but it is possible that the female spinners of the Pale Watery, *B. bioculatus*, may not do so, as they are reported to have been seen ovipositing on the surface.

Other genera always oviposit on the surface. The two species of *Ephemerella*, namely the Sherry Spinner and the Yellow Evening Spinner, fly along the river, usually upstream. As they progress, their eggs are gradually extruded through the oviducts and collect at their openings under the eighth or ninth abdominal segments. The mass of eggs assumes the form of a ball and slowly increases in size as more eggs are added. In order to keep the ball of eggs in position, the two or three posterior segments of the abdomen are curved downwards and slightly forwards. The tails also incline downwards and thus give the flies an easily recognised and characteristic appearance.

The spinners fly along the river for a considerable distance before they release the mass of eggs; on suitable evenings they will be present in tremendous numbers and form a regular procession which, as it passes by, appears to be never-ending. The flight of an individual spinner is steady but is constantly varied by dipping movements, as a fly momentarily drops below the line of flight but immediately returns to it.

Individual flies then gradually approach the water, and, particularly in the neighbourhood of fast-flowing or broken water, they approach the surface and then either drop the egg-mass from the air or else release it on touching the water. They then usually fall on the water and get carried downstream, but occasionally fly back to sheltering foliage on the shore.

Females of the Great Red Spinner, *Ecdyonurus* spp., of the Yellow May Spinner, *Heptagenia sulphurea*, and probably of most other species oviposit by first flying over the water for a distance and then gliding down to the surface. While resting there momentarily they allow any eggs which have been extruded to come in contact with the water. This causes the eggs to be washed off and sink. The spinner rises again and continues flying, often with an undulating or rising and falling flight, again glides down to the surface and releases more eggs. This continues until all the eggs have been laid, and the fly then usually falls on the surface spent. However, at least two species

Plate 7: Duns, × 2
(*a*) and (*b*) Yellow Hawk, Yellow May *Heptagenia sulphurea*, male and
female; (*c*) Yellow Evening, *Ephemerella notata*; (*d*) March Brown,
Rhithrogena haarupi

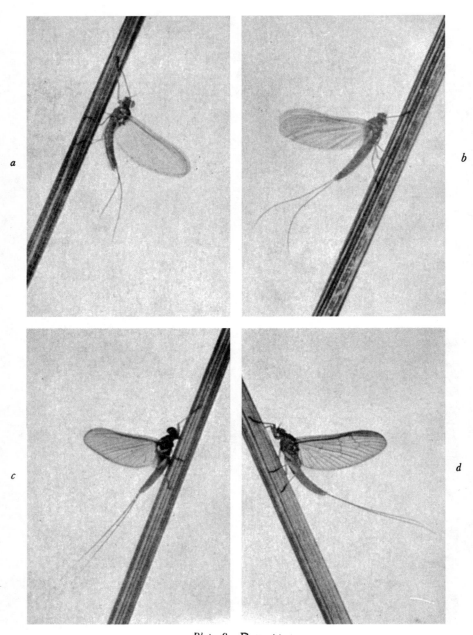

Plate 8: DUNS × 4
(a) and (b) Little Sky-blue (Pale Watery), *Centroptilum luteolum*, male and female; (c) and (d) Small Dark Olive (Pale Watery), *Baëtis scambus*, male and female

at times adopt a different method. They remain flying for quite a considerable period and their eggs are extruded until the two lobes of eggs (one lobe from each of the two oviducts) have increased to such a size that they appear to include most if not all the eggs which were contained in the abdomen. The fly then approaches the water and releases the whole mass at once. I have seen both the Greydrakes, *Ephemera danica*, and the Pale Watery Spinners, *Centroptilum luteolum*, do this. After the Greydrakes have shed all their eggs they may continue dipping to the surface for some time before finally falling spent.

Most spinners fly along the river in an upstream direction before ovipositing, though the direction of their flight appears to be governed partly by the wind. The flies apparently prefer to fly against a gentle breeze, but it may be that they exhibit a positive orientation to the current, in that they fly in a direction contrary to that in which the water is flowing. Most species are attracted to quick-flowing or broken water between calmer stretches, and they will often proceed up a river and not oviposit until they reach such places.

CHAPTER 8

DISTRIBUTION AND ECOLOGY
OF NYMPHS

T HE DISTRIBUTION of Ephemeropterans is controlled largely by
factors which affect the distribution of the nymphs. It is as nymphs
that these insects eat and grow, and in this form they spend by far
the longest part of their active lives. The time spent as winged flies is
comparatively very short, and, whilst it is of the greatest importance
to the race as it covers the period of mating and egg-laying, it is
yet of little importance in affecting the distribution of different
species.

The normal climatic conditions prevailing in these islands suit
all or most duns and spinners, and local differences in the terrestrial
habitats do not appear to be of much importance in restricting the
dispersal of species.

The ecology of any group of organisms is the study of the rela-
tionship between the organisms concerned and their surroundings.
In the case of the Ephemeroptera, this resolves itself mainly into
the study of the nymphs and their environment.

Ephemeropteran nymphs live only in fresh water, and the various
types of fresh water habitats vary in certain physical and chemical
features. The physical features include the general shape and form,
or topography, of the bed of the river or lake, and variations in the
movements, the temperature and the amount of dissolved oxygen
in the water. The chemical features refer mainly to the chemical
content of the water.

A certain amount is known about the effect of the physical features on the dispersal of nymphs and these are considered here.

For convenience, fresh water habitats can be separated into generalised divisions as follows:—

(1) Rapid water flowing over rocks. (2) Rapid water flowing over weeds. (3) Slow-flowing or still water over mud and fine sand. (4) Slow-flowing or still water over weeds.

Included in type (1) are the rocky shores of lakes which are exposed to wave action.

None of these four types of habitats is clear-cut and exact, as innumerable modifications and combinations of them occur. In chapter 4 the adaptations of nymphs are considered in some detail and it is apparent that differences in their distribution are due largely to the physical features of the environment. For instance, the flat nymphs of *Ecdyonurus* and allied genera are confined to the first of the habitats mentioned above, whilst species of the burrowing nymphs *Ephemera* are confined to mud and fine sand. *Baëtis* species have a wider distribution, since they can live both among weeds and on rocks in flowing water, and species of *Caenis* are even less particular, since they occur among weeds in both still and flowing water, as well as among detritus and mud on the bottoms of rivers and lakes.

Apart from the effect of the topography of the lake or river bottom, the movement of the water has a considerable influence. There is the mechanical effect of the force of the water with its tendency to sweep nymphs away. Of all nymphs which are exposed to the direct flow of the water, species of *Rhithrogena*, the Yellow Upright and the March Brown, are best able to cope with it, and they can retain their positions on smooth rocks in rivers in which the pace of the current is so rapid that nymphs of other genera would be swept away.

Exposed to the current on stones in less rapidly flowing stretches *Baëtis* nymphs, such as those of the Large Dark Olive and the Iron Blue, may be found alongside nymphs of the Late March Brown and other *Ecdyonurus* species, but the flow of water in these places will still be too strong for such nymphs as the Lake Olive, *Cloëon simile*, and species of *Caenis*.

The movement of the water also affects the amount of dissolved oxygen available to nymphs. Nymphs breathe by absorbing oxygen from the water; and normally it is necessary that there should be some movement of the water past the nymph so that a continuous supply of oxygen is made available. In flowing water the nymph has merely to retain its position on the substratum or weed in order to achieve this end, but in still water the nymph has to create a current for itself. This it does by working its tracheal gills, and all nymphs which live in still water are able to keep the water renewed by this means. Only few rapid-water forms have this habit and most of them, therefore, cannot live in still water.

Apart from the rate of flow, the amount of oxygen available will depend on the amount which is dissolved in the water. Oxygen is commonly absorbed by water in three ways, (1) by direct diffusion at the surface from the atmosphere, (2) by diffusion from air carried below the surface by the water itself, as occurs beneath waterfalls and in other turbulent places, (3) by a process called *photosynthesis* which takes place when the sun shines on algae and other plants beneath the surface. The action of the sunlight on the green colouring matter in all plants brings about a chemical activity in which carbon dioxide is absorbed from the water and oxygen is released. The oxygen forms very small bubbles which float up to the surface, and diffusion occurs during the time they are held by the algae and during their passage to the surface.

Oxygen is absorbed from the water by insects, fish and other aquatic animals, and also by decaying vegetation or other organic matter. One of the dangers of pollution in rivers is that the discharges may extract most of the oxygen from the water with resulting fatal effects on fish and fly life.

Some very interesting experimental work has been carried out which has a direct bearing on the ecology of ephemeropteran nymphs. The results of much of this has been published in the *Journal of Experimental Biology*, and some of the more interesting findings are as follows:—

Mr. C. A. Wingfield demonstrated with nymphs of the Pond Olive, *Cloëon dipterum*, that no diffusion of oxygen takes place through the gill plates, but that the gill plates function as accessory respiratory organs in that they create a current of water and thus ventilate the respiratory surface of the nymph's body. This aids oxygen consumption by the nymph, particularly in water which has a low concentration of oxygen.

He found also that the gill plates of a *Baëtis* nymph do not aid oxygen consumption nor do they function as accessory respiratory organs, as they do not move.

In contrast to these, the gills of the Mayfly nymph, *Ephemera vulgata*, which are fibre-like instead of being plate-like, and move

Plate 9: DUNS × **2**
(*a*) and (*b*) Large Green, *Ecdyonurus insignis*, male and female; (*c*) and (*d*)
Olive Upright, *Rhithrogena semicolorata*, male and female

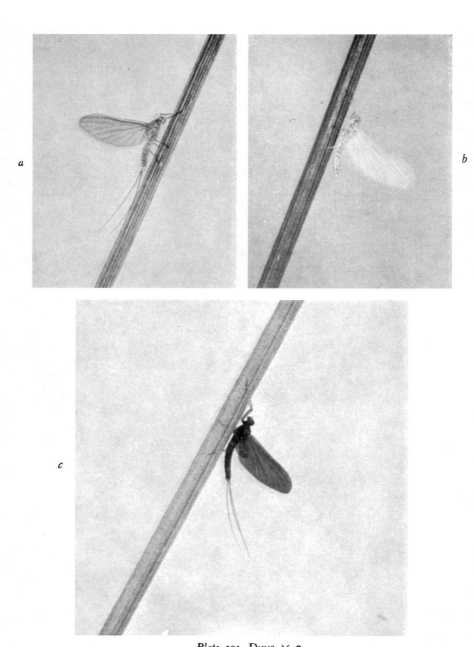

Plate 10: Duns × 3
(a) Pale Watery, *Baëtis bioculatus*, male; (b) Pale Evening (Pale Watery),
Procloëon rufulum, female; (c) Purple, *Paraleptophlebia cincta*, male

freely and cause a current of water to pass through the burrow in which the nymph is hiding, act also as respiratory organs by allowing oxygen to diffuse through their surfaces.

Mr. R. J. Whitney carried out experiments which demonstrate that the thermal resistance, i. e., the resistance to heat, of the nymphs varies among different species.

He collected nymphs from various habitats and, by keeping them in well-oxygenated water at controlled temperatures, he ascertained at what temperatures 50 per cent. of each species were killed within twenty-four hours. The temperature which he ascertained in each case he called the thermal index. The following table shows the thermal indices for several species.

SPECIES	THERMAL INDEX
Baëtis rhodani (large nymphs)	21.0° C
do. (small nymphs)	21.3
Baëtis tenax	21.3
Rhithrogena semicolorata (A)	22.4
do. (B)	24.7
Ecdyonurus venosus	26.6
Caenis sp.	26.7
Cloëon dipterum (large nymphs)	28.5
do. (small nymphs)	30.2

The two different figures obtained for nymphs of *R. semicolorata* are apparently due to the fact that the nymphs marked (A) were collected from a stream which at the time of collection showed a maximum temperature of only 11.6° C., and those marked (B) were from a stream in which the maximum temperature at the time of collection was 14.5° C. This suggests that not only are there differences in the thermal resistance of different species, but that nymphs can adapt themselves to a very gradual increase in temperature. A very gradual increase may mean an increase spread over several weeks.

It is interesting to note from the tables that those species which live in quick-flowing water have a lower thermal index than those living in slower-flowing water, and that the pond species have the highest index of all. It is well known that in a river the quick-flowing water is colder than the very slow-flowing shallow water near the shore, and that normally the water in shallow ponds will reach higher temperatures than the water in a neighbouring river.

BURROWING NYMPHS

The burrowing nymphs of the Greendrake or Mayfly, *Ephemera danica*, live in mud and sand. They show a preference for alkaline water, possibly because the nature of the bottom in such waters suits their requirements. As has been pointed out by Wingfield, the mud requires to be sufficiently soft to allow the nymphs to excavate their burrows, and yet it must not be so soft that the burrow will collapse. The species occurs in lakes, rivers and canals and is widely distributed in Britain and Ireland, mainly in low lying or flat regions. The normal time of appearance of the adult is during the latter part of May and the early part of June, but locally it may be common at any time from the beginning of May until August, and individual specimens have been seen in March and September. It occurs in great abundance on the large Irish limestone lakes, and here fluctuations in its time of appearances in different localities and in different years are easily noticed. It hatches from the shallow areas of the lakes some days before it appears in the deeps, and, at any rate on Lough Derg on the Shannon, it is seen nearly a week earlier at the northern end than at the southern end of the lake. On the Westmeath lakes its season is one or two weeks earlier than on Loughs Corrib and Mask.

These differences in times of emergence are almost certainly due to differences in water temperatures, and for similar reasons nymphs may vary their time of appearance in any one locality in different years. For instance, on Lough Sheelin the mayfly fishing usually begins about the middle of May, but in 1938, following a very hot spring and with low water in the lake, the mayflies were seen hatching in April and the fishing began at the end of April. In that year some of the local fishermen caught trout while dapping with the natural Greendrake as early as 26 April. In 1947, the spring was abnormally severe, with many weeks of frost, and the commencement of the fishing on Lough Sheelin was delayed until the third week in May, whilst on Loughs Mask and Corrib it was so late that many anglers spent a fortnight on the lakes at the end of May and beginning of June, and returned home without having even seen a mayfly.

The other Greendrake, *Ephemera vulgata*, occurs in rather slow-flowing rivers with warmer waters than the preceding species. It is less common than *danica* and is found in the south and midlands of England. The adults emerge from May to August.

CRAWLING NYMPHS

There are five species of *Caenis* (Pl. 5 c, p. 48). One or other of these species is found in most parts of Britain and Ireland. The times of emergence of the duns are more or less confined to the evening, early morning and the night. Infrequently they may be seen during the warmer hours of the day.

Caenis macrura is common in large rivers and in the slow-flowing and flat reaches of smaller rivers, possibly with a preference for alkaline waters. This is one of the few ephemeropterans which hatch from the very slow-flowing water of long still flats on rivers. On some rivers it appears nearly every morning during June and July and less regularly in late May and August. On fine mornings it often appears at about sunrise, and, as happens with all species of *Caenis*, the change from the dun to the spinner stage takes place very quickly, usually within an hour of the emergence of the dun. The spinners swarm and the females proceed at once to lay their eggs and then fall spent on the water, so that the insects live as flies often for less than a couple of hours.

Caenis moesta is very similar in appearance to, and is easily confused with, the preceding. It also is an early morning species but seems to be more widely distributed. It occurs on lowland rivers with alkaline water as well as on stony mountain streams where the water is acid. It occurs on some of the large Irish limestone lakes; Mr. Kimmins has recorded it from Windermere in the English lake district. The adults fly in June, July and August.

These two species differ from the two following in several respects.

(1) They usually, but not invariably, emerge in the early morning rather than in the evening.
(2) They are slightly larger in size and the general colour is white and blackish, or dark brown, instead of white or cream and light brown. The darker markings pertain to the fore edges of the wings and to the thoraces, and to the abdomens of the males.

Caenis horaria appears from the end of May until September on lakes and large rivers. The duns hatch from a silted or muddy type of bottom and occur in alkaline and slightly acid waters; they emerge at, or shortly before, sunset, less frequently in the late afternoon.

Caenis rivulorum is the smallest of the Ephemeropterans. It occurs in small rivers and streams. In spite of its diminutive size trout feed on it as keenly as on the other species.

Fish feeding on any species of *Caenis* may often be recognised by the manner in which they rise. Owing to the great abundance in which the flies are usually present, an individual fish will rise very frequently, often in fact at about one second intervals.

Caenis robusta, a species recently recorded from Southern England, from still and very slow-flowing water.

Blue-winged Olive, *Ephemerella ignita* (Pl. 5 d, p. 48): very widely distributed in flowing water throughout Britain and Ireland. It occurs in both large and small lowland rivers and brooks, also in upland rivers and hill streams. It is tolerant of a wide range of hydrogen-ion concentration as it is found in extremely acid streams as well as in highly alkaline waters. It seldom occurs in lakes or other still waters, although it may be plentiful in some canals where the flow of water is very slight. Its micro-habitats include nearly any position in quick-flowing water which offers shelter from the direct force of the current. It is particularly partial to deposits of refuse which collect on the upstream side of stones and weedbeds.

Normally the duns appear about the middle of June and continue emerging until October; but the insect has been recorded from some rivers as early as April and May, and as late in the year as December. During hot weather, particularly in July and August, the main hatch of the duns takes place at dusk, but earlier in the year, and in the late autumn and during cool, wet or cloudy weather, the hatch is often spread out over the forenoon and afternoon.

The records would suggest that the **Yellow Evening Dun,** *Ephemerella notata,* is much more local in its distribution than is the preceding, but, owing to its short season—for it emerges from about the middle of May to the middle of June—and to the late hour at which the duns appear (usually at dusk), it has almost certainly been over-looked in many localities. When examined superficially it is easy to confuse the duns of this species with those of the Yellow May Dun, *Heptagenia sulphurea*. The most obvious way to distinguish the two species is by the number of tails. *E. notata* has three and *H. sulphurea* has two; but in the gloaming it is extraordinarily easy to overlook the third tail on *E. notata*. In a good light the two flies can be separated at a glance.

It occurs on medium and large-sized rivers, and, judging from its known distribution, it apparently prefers alkaline to acid waters. The duns emerge from the faster flowing stretches of the rivers.

Claret Dun, *Leptophlebia vespertina*: occurs in lakes, ponds and small stony streams which are of an acid or peaty nature. In lakes, the nymphs are most commonly found in areas where there is a bottom of peat. This selection of sites is most noticeable on some of the large Irish limestone lakes. In bays in these lakes in which there is a peat or bog bottom the Claret Duns may be common, whilst in neighbouring bays which have a limestone, marl, or limestone-mud bottom they may be very scarce. A probable partial explanation for this lies in the extent of camouflage afforded by the different environments.

The Claret Dun nymphs are a very dark red brown and are nearly invisible against wet peat, but they are plainly visible against the light greeny-grey colour of the limestone. The nymphs are much less likely to be noticed in the former environment than in the latter by shoals of predatory fish, such as perch and rudd, or other fish or predatory insects which hunt by sight.

The species occurs in greatest numbers in mountain and other peat lakes, and at times trout feed keenly on the nymphs and the duns, and doubtless, under suitable conditions, on the spinners also. It is widely distributed in suitable localities in Britain and Ireland, and although it has been seen from the end of April until August it is generally most plentiful in May and June.

Leptophlebia marginata is somewhat similar in its distribution to the previous species; it occurs in lakes and in the slower parts of stony streams and hill burns. It is widely distributed in Britain and Ireland, but is seemingly less common than the Claret Dun and has not received any popular name. Mr. Kimmins records it from April to the middle of June. The nymph is similar to the preceding in its general appearance.

The nymphs of the **Turkey Brown,** *Paraleptophlebia submarginata,* and the following species have a rather more streamlined appearance than the nymphs of *Leptophlebia,* and they are found only in flowing water. They occur in fairly fast-flowing and medium-paced rivers and streams, and the adults are seen in May, June and July. It is doubtful if this species is of much value for angling purposes, even though it is frequently mentioned in the literature, but on some local streams it may perhaps be common enough to be of importance in this respect.

Purple Dun, *Paraleptophlebia cincta*: occurs in small and large streams and in moderate-sized rather fast-flowing rivers. It apparently has a preference for alkaline water, and nowhere have I seen it so abundant as on the R. Greese in Co. Carlow. This is a very fast-flowing stream with exceedingly clear water. There is a pebbly bottom and a lush growth of *Ranunculus* and other weeds. The duns emerge from May to August, and are at times taken by the trout in preference to the Iron Blue or Olive Duns which may be on the water at the same time. Like several other less well known species, this fly can be quite important in local areas from the angling view point.

The duns are found in grasses and other herbage bordering or overhanging the streams where they occur.

SWIMMING NYMPHS

Baëtis nymphs. The nymphs of all species of *Baëtis* are confined to flowing water and do not live in ponds or lakes. The slender stream-lined bodies of the baetids are of advantage mainly in that they offer little resistance to the current in which they live, and the nymphs are found in nearly all types of streams and rivers.

Large Dark Olive, *Baëtis rhodani* (Pl. 5a, p. 48): This is one of the most widely distributed and commonest of the ephemeropterans. It occurs in the quicker flowing parts of large rivers, also in medium-sized and small rivers and in streams. It does not show a marked preference for alkaline water and occurs in mountain as well as lowland rivers. The dun may be seen all through the year but is commonest in spring and autumn. This is the dun which one sees when salmon or trout fishing in February and March, and it is just as common in April. It is less common during the summer, but increases in numbers again in September and October, and may be seen at any time during mild weather in the winter.

The nymphs are found in a variety of habitats in fast-flowing or medium-paced water. In small stony brooks they will be seen on the upper surfaces and on the sides of stones in the smooth water where the current accelerates on leaving each pool. In very fast water they shelter under the stones, and then seem to prefer roughened surfaces such as are found on broken cement blocks, probably because such surfaces are easier to cling to. They are found also in weeds, often in considerable numbers, but in rivers with a suitable fixed stony bottom which carries a growth of moss and algae they are as plentiful, if no more so, as in rivers well stocked with the larger aquatic plants such as Water Buttercups, *Ranunculus sp.*

Iron-blue, *Baëtis pumilus* (Pl. 4d, p. 33), is also distributed generally over Britain and Ireland, and is perhaps the second commonest of the baetids. It occurs in rivers and streams in medium-paced and in fast-flowing water in similar habitats to those suitable for the Large Dark Olive Nymphs. But the Iron Blue Dun Nymphs can live for longer temporary periods in still water than can the preceding. This is due perhaps to a peculiar habit which these nymphs have adopted of swaying from side to side. This swaying motion is quite dissimilar to the habit, which all species of *Baëtis* appear to have, of whipping their abdomens from side to side. The motions of these Iron Blue Nymphs involve the swaying of the whole insect from side to side on its legs. Doubtless this motion ensures that the water in the immediate vicinity of the nymph is constantly renewed and thus provides a better supply of oxygen to the nymph.

This species is found in the acid waters of mountain rivers as well as in alkaline waters. It (probably) occurs in greatest numbers in (moderate-sized even and rather fast-flowing) limestone and chalk streams. The adults emerge from April to November and are perhaps commonest in May and October.

Iron-blue, *Baëtis niger*: This Iron-blue Dun is less widely distributed than *B. pumilus*. It has not been recorded from Ireland and Mr. Kimmins has records of it from only five counties in England.

It occurs in rivers and slow-flowing weedy streams from May to September.

Medium Olive, *Baëtis vernus*, is much less common than the Large Dark Olive, *B. rhodani*. It is common locally in the south of England on the chalk streams and elsewhere, but it has not been recorded from the Lake District, and its reported occurrence in Ireland needs confirmation. Mr. Kimmins points out that it possibly has a preference for non-acid waters. The adults may be found from May until October.

Medium Olive, *Baëtis tenax*, is widely distributed and fairly common. It occurs in Britain and Ireland in both alkaline and acid rivers and streams. It is found on medium and rather large-sized limestone rivers as well as in small brooks, and it also occurs on mountain rivers and hill streams up to nearly 2,000 feet. It is found on the wing from April until September.

An **Olive, *Baëtis buceratus*,** is an uncommon species which has been recorded from the River Kennet and Holybrook near Reading in June and in September. It does not appear to have been found in the north of England, Scotland or Wales and is not known in Ireland.

Pale Watery, *Baëtis bioculatus*, is found in England and Wales and is common in the south of England, but its reported occurrence in Ireland needs to be confirmed. It apparently shows a preference for alkaline rivers as it has not been recorded from the Lake District. The adults emerge from May until October.

Small Dark Olive, *Baëtis scambus*. This small Olive is widely distributed on rather fast-flowing limestone and chalk streams but is found also on mountain rivers containing acid waters. In Britain the adult has been recorded from February to November; in Ireland it occurs commonly from May to August.

Dark Olive, *Baëtis atrebatinus*, is fairly widely distributed in Ireland but perhaps less common or more local in Britain. It shows a preference for alkaline streams and rivers and occurs in both weedy and stony waters. The duns are most frequently seen in August, September and October, but occur also in May and June.

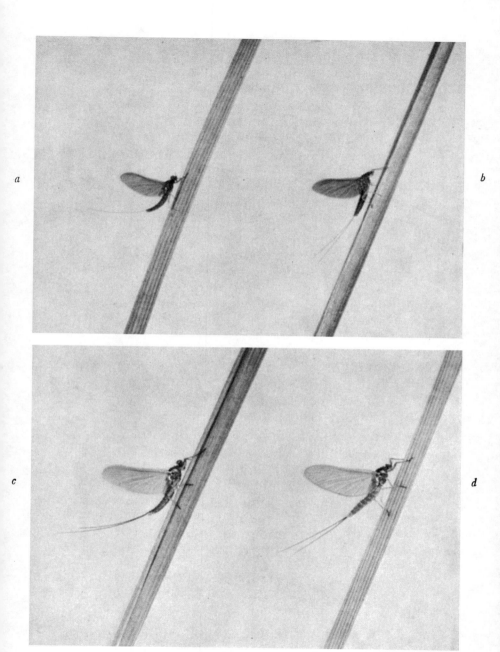

Plate 11: Duns × 2

(a) and (b) Blue-winged Olive, *Ephemerella ignita*, male and female (female used to be called July Dun); (c) and (d) Blue-winged Pale Watery, *Centroptilum pennulatum*, male and female

Plate 12: DUNS × 3
(a) August, *Ecdyonurus dispar*, male; (b) Angler's Curse, *Caenis macrura*,
female; (c) Dark, *Heptagenia lateralis*

Little Sky-blue (Pale Watery) Dun, *Centroptilum luteolum*, is widespread in Britain and Ireland. It occurs in both slow- and quickflowing rivers and streams, and in large and small lakes. The nymphs frequent weed beds and in very fast-flowing water doubtless escape the full force of the current by penetrating among the fronds of weed. In slow-flowing and in still waters they are also found where the vegetation is sparse. They occur in acid rivers but are commoner and more plentiful in limestone and chalk streams. They occur also in most of the large, and many of the small, Irish limestone lakes, as well as in Windermere and several of the Scottish lochs.

The adults have been observed from April to November but are perhaps commonest in May and June, September and October.

Blue-winged Pale Watery Dun, *Centroptilum pennulatum*, is rarer than the preceding. It is unknown in Ireland and, although it occurs in Britain from the south of England to as far north as Aberdeenshire, it is yet apparently localised in its distribution. The nymphs have been found only in rivers and Mr. F. E. Sawyer records that on the Avon above Salisbury the nymphs live in both slow- and fast-flowing water. In slow-flowing water they may live in more open situations, and on the River Kennet below Hungerford, on a short two-day visit, I saw many of the duns emerging on each afternoon between four and five o'clock. On the second afternoon these Blue-winged Pale Watery Duns appeared on the water in greater numbers than any other species of the Ephemeroptera and I saw them emerging only from the deep sluggish reaches of the river.

The adults appear from May until October and are seen most frequently perhaps in the autumn.

Pale Evening Dun, *Procloëon rufulum*: This species is widespread and common in Ireland where it occurs in slow-flowing and rather sluggish rivers, and in large pools and other quiet reaches of quicker-flowing rivers. There are a few records of it from mountain rivers, but in such habitats it is very sparse in numbers and the nymphs are probably restricted to the still pools.

It has been recorded from England, Scotland and Wales but does not appear to be as common there as in Ireland. Perhaps it has been overlooked in many localities owing to its nocturnal, or at least crepuscular habits.

It is at times found in company with *Centroptilum luteolum* and the female duns of these two species closely resemble each other. During the summer months, particularly in hot bright weather, the duns emerge in the evening, often very late, and at times they continue hatching until, or after, darkness. They are found from May until October. On some rivers this fly appears in great numbers and the trout feed most keenly on it. I have on several occasions seen the fish ignoring Blue-winged Olives in preference for this smaller and lighter species.

Lake Olive, *Cloëon simile* (Pl. 4b, p. 33), is found on still waters throughout Britain and Ireland. The nymph occurs in greatest abundance in rather shallow, clear water, alkaline lakes of moderate size. In large lakes it is commonest in the shallow sheltered bays and inlets. The nymphs delight in a tranquil lake bottom covered with moss and other aquatic plants which do not grow very high. They are found in a variety of other habitats also but avoid wave-washed rocky shores which are exposed to the prevailing winds. In the south of England the fly appears on lakes such as the Enton Lakes in Surrey, and on Blagdon and neighbouring reservoirs in Somerset, and it doubtless occurs on similar types of water throughout Britain. It is found on all the large Irish limestone lakes and probably on most of the small ones. It is less common in acid mountain lakes where it is often replaced by the Claret Dun, *Leptophlebia vespertina.* The Lake Olive is of considerable importance to lake anglers as the fish feed on the nymphs, duns and spinners, but it occurs on very few streams in sufficient numbers to interest the trout. Those streams on which it is at all common generally consist of a series of deep cup-shaped pools in which the water is very clear and in which the current is slight and disturbs only the upper water layers of the pools where the nymphs live. The duns emerge in various localities from March until November, but are most plentiful in April and May, September and October. They are seen on the water, usually in the forenoon and early afternoon, but during hot weather in the summer months they often do not emerge until the evening.

Pond Olive, *Cloëon dipterum,* is also generally distributed over Britain and Ireland but probably occurs most commonly and in the greatest numbers in the south and midlands of England. The nymphs thrive in small ponds which acquire quite a high summer temperature, and are commonly found in ornamental garden ponds and other small areas of still water. It is the most domesticated of the ephemeropterans and will establish itself and thrive in garden ponds which are only a foot or so in width. It is the most suitable of all species to keep in an aquarium, as it will live under conditions of oxygen deficiency and high temperature which would prove fatal to other species.

The species is also found in large ponds up to one hundred or one hundred and fifty yards wide, particularly if they are well sheltered by trees or other means from cold winds. In such waters the flies at times become extremely common and very large hatches of duns may be seen. If trout are present they feed freely on the flies in both the dun and the spinner stages. In more extensive areas of water the flies occur in much smaller numbers, possibly because lower water temperatures may prevail, and they apparently avoid the open waters of large lakes.

The duns emerge from May until November but are most plentiful in July and August.

The nymphs live among the weeds growing on the bottom, and on and among dead leaves of trees and other decaying vegetation which may have fallen into the pond. They can swim very quickly for short distances and when they are disturbed they can generally be seen darting rapidly away in all directions.

A **Summer Mayfly, Siphlonurus linnaeanus**: The large fast-swimming nymphs of this species show a preference for alkaline waters. They are found in several of the limestone lakes in Ireland, such as Lough Sheelin and Lough Mask, and they occur also in slow deep reaches of the River Fergus in Co. Clare, which passes through a chain of lakes, including Dromore Lake and Inchiquin. It has been recorded also from Lake Gartan in Donegal and the River Tummel in Scotland, but so far it does not appear to have been found in either England or Wales.

Owing to its local distribution the fly is not of much general interest to anglers, but where it does occur it is at times important. Local anglers on the River Fergus, for instance, have observed a strong rise of fish to the spent spinner in July and August, and, as the spinner is as big as the Black Drake, *Ephemera danica*, it is a useful pattern to be familiar with.

As those of other species of *Siphlonurus*, the nymph of this species

may swim ashore and climb up a reed-stem or protruding rock before
the dun emerges; but at times I have seen the duns sitting on the
open waters in a lake which suggests that they can emerge at the
surface in the manner normal to most species.

The habitat of another **Summer Mayfly,** *Siphlonurus lacustris,*
is markedly different from that of the preceding. The nymphs live
in the cool waters of hill streams and mountain lochs, although they
have also been found in low-lying lochs in mountainous areas. Eaton,
in speaking of this species, remarks, "Anglers in Wales, mistaking this
for *Ephemera danica,* are greatly astonished at seeing the subimago rise
out of the cold tranquil 'llyns'." This species is common in suitable
habitats in Britain and Ireland and the adults are seen from May to
September. They are perhaps commonest in July and August.

When nymphs of this species inhabit streams, they are found in
the slow-flowing and still reaches. A typical hill burn which has
slowly moving water of the type in which these nymphs are found
is shown in Plate IVa (p. 13).

A further **Summer Mayfly,** *Siphlonurus armatus,* is very local;
it has been recorded from the south of England and from Killarney
and Galway, where it occurs in slow-flowing streams, lakes and ponds.
Adults have been taken from May to August.

FLAT NYMPHS

Little Yellow May, *Heptagenia sulphurea,* is common and widespread in Britain and Ireland in rather fast-flowing rivers and rocky
limestone lakes. It occurs in greatest abundance in lowland limestone
rivers of moderate or large size with a rather fast even flow and a
rough stony bottom, and it avoids the acid, mountain type of river.
It is common also on the large Irish limestone lakes.

These Little Yellow May nymphs are of the flattened type, but they
are common in some rivers in which species of the other flat nymphs
of *Ecdyonurus* and *Rhithrogena* do not occur. The duns appear from
the end of April until September but are commonest in May and June.
They usually emerge in small numbers during the forenoon and
afternoon and the trout pay little attention to them; but after sunset,
particularly following a hot bright day, they may appear in large
numbers and on occasions the fish will feed keenly on them.

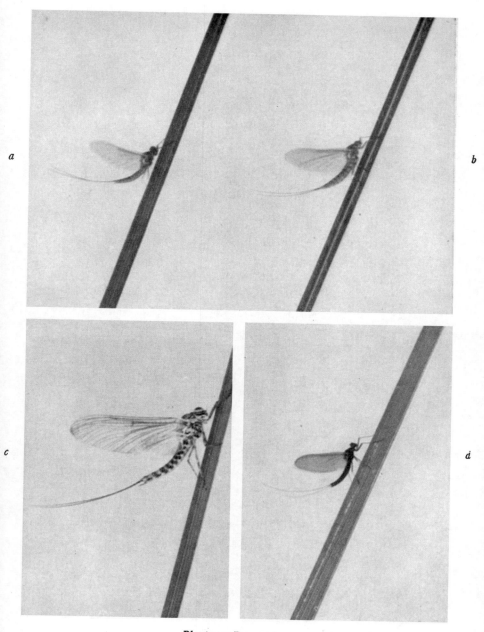

Plate 13: DUNS × 2

(a) and (b) Lake Olive, *Cloëon simile*, male and female; (c) Summer Mayfly,
Siphlonurus linnaeanus, male; (d) Claret, *Leptophlebia vespertina*, male

Plate 14: SPINNERS × 2.5
(*a*) and (*b*) Large Dark Olive, Red, *Baëtis rhodani*, male and female;
(*c*) and (*d*) Iron-blue (Jenny, Little Claret), *Baëtis pumilus*, male and female

August Dun, *Ecdyonurus dispar,* is widely distributed in Britain and Ireland. (An *Ecdyonurus* nymph is shown in Pl. 4c, p. 33). It occurs on the stony shores of large lakes as well as in both quick- and slow-flowing stony rivers of moderate size. It is abundant on some of the shallow and quite slow-flowing limestone rivers in Ireland where there is a hard and partly stony bottom, and is doubtless equally common in suitable habitats in Britain.

The nymphs are found in the shallow or slow-flowing water near the edge of the river and apparently have habits somewhat similar to those of the Late March Brown, *E. venosus.*

The duns emerge usually in the afternoon and are found from June to October. They are commonest in July and August, and at that time of the year the trout will rise freely to the spinners of this species, which are often seen on the water in the late afternoon and evening.

Green Dun, *Ecdyonurus insignis,* occurs on rather fast-flowing alkaline streams and rivers in Britain and Ireland, and is less common than the two preceding species. There appears to be no record of it from a mountain river or lake. The duns, which have a pronounced greenish colour, are found from May to September but are commonest in June and July. They emerge in the afternoon and evening, and on occasions trout feed on them, but more usually the number of flies present at one time is too small to induce the fish to rise.

Late March Brown, *Ecdyonurus venosus*: This species is widely distributed over Britain and Ireland in medium-paced and rather fast-flowing stony streams and rivers. The nymphs are found in the stony regions of both limestone rivers and hill streams, and the adults emerge from April to October but are commonest in May and June. The nymphs live clinging to the underside of stones, and Miss R. Rawlinson has pointed out that their habitat alters with their age. Young nymphs frequent the deeper cooler waters near midstream, and the larger specimens are found in the shallower warmer water near the side of the river where there is usually less current.

They feed mainly on vegetable detritus, which may consist of algae, portions of moss or other portions of decaying plant particles.

The duns emerge usually in the afternoon but, as they frequently do so by clambering out on to a projecting rock and then flying away, they are seldom of use to anglers.

A. E.

G

Ecdyonurus torrentis, in both the dun and spinner stages, is very similar in appearance to the late March Brown, *E. venosus,* but the nymphs are found in small stony streams rather than in rivers. In Britain the species is common and widespread, but it has not so far been recorded in Ireland. The adults are seen in May and June.

Heptagenia fuscogrisea is fairly common in stony limestone lakes and rivers in the midlands and west of Ireland, where it is found in May and early June, but it occurs in small numbers. It is scarce or local in England; one river on which it has been found is the Thames above Pangbourne.

This fly could well be called the Brown May Dun owing to its brown colour, but it is seldom worth the angler's notice as it is so scarce.

Dark Dun, *Heptagenia lateralis,* occurs in mountain streams and on the stony shores of mountain and upland lakes, and it is widely distributed in such localities in Britain and Ireland. In Britain it has been found in Devonshire, Wales, the north of England and Scotland, and in Ireland from the mountainous counties of Wicklow, Kerry, West Galway and Donegal.

This and the preceding species provide an interesting contrast in their distributions. The nymphs of both species are found on stony lake shores or in fast-flowing streams or rivers, but their known distributions, in Ireland at any rate, do not overlap. The former species, *H. fuscogrisea,* is confined to the limestone areas of the midlands, Clare, East Galway and Roscommon, whilst the latter species *H. lateralis* is known only, as stated, from the mountainous counties bordering these areas. The limiting factors which control such distributions are not known. It may be that the mountain-loving species can live only in colder or more highly oxygenated waters, or, as has been suggested in regard to other species, perhaps *H. lateralis* requires less alkaline waters than *H. fuscogrisea.*

The duns of *H. lateralis* emerge from May to September and they are very common along the shores of Ullswater, Windermere and other lakes in the Lake District, and, although trout at times feed on the spent female spinners, this species has apparently not yet received any common name, and is here given one.

Heptagenia longicauda is quite similar in appearance to the Yellow May Dun, but it is apparently very local in its distribution. It has been recorded from the Kennet near Reading and a few other rivers in the south of England. It is unknown in Ireland. The duns emerge generally after sunset, in late May and early June.

March Brown, *Rhithrogena haarupi* (Pl. 7 d, p. 64) the March Brown which is important to anglers. The nymphs are found clinging to flat stones in the fast-flowing stretches of fairly rapid large and moderate-sized rivers. The duns emerge at the surface in the quick-flowing water of the runs, often near the centre of the river. Trout feed keenly on the ascending and hatching nymphs, and less eagerly on the duns. The flies are seen in late March, April and early May, and reference has often been made to the habit which they have of emerging in sudden swarms. One minute no flies will be visible on the water, and a few minutes later they will be seen in large numbers and will be scattered all over the river. A few minutes, or maybe five or ten minutes later, none will be left. A short while afterwards they will again be plentiful.

The flies are found on rivers such as the Tees and Tweed in northern England and Scotland, and the Usk in Wales as well as on several other rivers in Britain. In Ireland they occur on the Liffey and the river Dodder in Co. Dublin; also on the Slaney and the Nore.

CHAPTER 9

NATURAL ENEMIES
AND CONTROLLING FACTORS

FACTORS which affect the numbers of Ephemeropterans are of practical interest. They are directly connected with means and methods of increasing the amount of fly life on trout waters. In general, an abundance of flies is conducive to surface-feeding and to free-rising fish, and the desirability of bringing about such conditions is obvious.

It is not difficult to estimate the likelihood of a mayfly (e. g. *E. danica*) completing its life cycle, provided the whole cycle from the egg stage through the nymph, dun and spinner and back to the egg stage again is included. A Grey Drake lays about 6,000 eggs, and therefore the chances of survival are about 3,000 to 1 against any one fly reaching maturity and ovipositing. If, on any water, every 3,000 eggs laid produced two flies which in turn were able to oviposit successfully, then the population would have doubled itself.

There are undoubtedly fluctuations from year to year in the numbers of Greendrakes which appear in any district. The amount by which they may fluctuate is not known, but even though the number of flies increased by one hundred times it would account for only a very small proportion, actually one-thirtieth, of the eggs which had been laid. The mortality among the developing eggs, nymphs and adult flies is, therefore, extremely high.

The number of eggs laid by female spinners differs among different species. It has been estimated, for instance, that a Spinner of the Large Dark Olive lays about 400 eggs and a Sherry Spinner lays about 1,200. But these species live for only a year or less, while the mayfly cycle occupies two years. There is, therefore, more likelihood

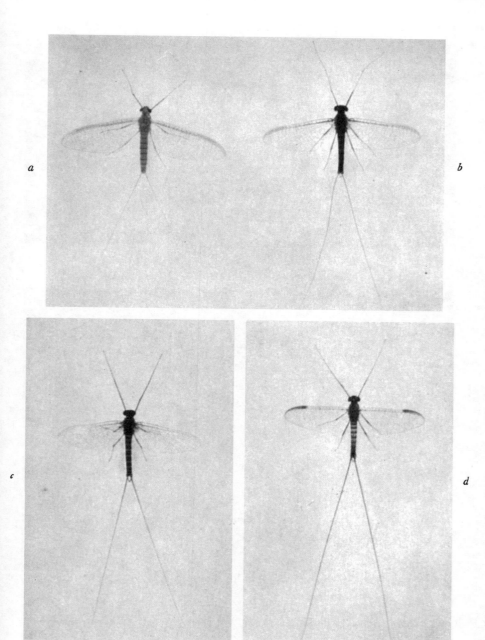

Plate 15: SPINNERS × 1.5

(*a*) and (*b*) Yellow May, *Heptagenia sulphurea*, female and male; (*c*) Yellow Upright, *Rhithrogena semicolorata*, male; (*d*) Large Green, *Ecdyonurus insignis*, male

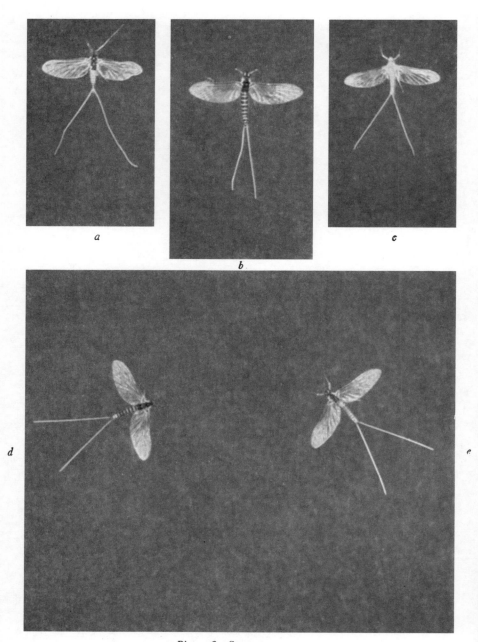

Plate 16: SPINNERS × 2.5
(a) male and (b), (c), (d) and (e) female, Small Dark Olive (Pale Watery),
Baëtis scambus. Showing variations in the colours of the female spinners
owing to age

that individuals of these former species will survive, as the time factor is half as long, or less.

Causes of premature mortality may be divided into

(1) Natural causes, and (2) Man's interference.

The natural causes of mortality are much more severe than is man's interference, but insects in the course of evolution have adjusted their rate of reproduction to these natural causes of mortality and most continue to survive them. This apparent adjustment between reproduction and mortality is often called the "balance of nature". Species unable to maintain this adjustment have become extinct.

PREDATORS

At all stages of its life an Ephemeropteran is in danger of falling a prey to one or other of many carnivorous animals.

Nymphs are very vulnerable to attack, and escape only by their agility, for they are incapable of defending themselves. Their enemies include predators as small as water mites, many of which attack and kill very small nymphs. Larger nymphs are preyed on by the larvae of water beetles, by dragonfly and stonefly nymphs, and by aquatic spiders, whilst they are constantly in danger of being eaten by sticklebacks, minnows, perch, trout and other fish. Nymphs are particularly vulnerable when they are ascending to the surface, and while they are floating at the surface, before emerging as duns. At such times they pay little or no attention to predatory fish and are, therefore, easily captured. Duns resting on the surface are eaten by several of the smaller birds as well as by fish. After they leave the surface their flight is so slow and deliberate that they can be captured while in the air, even by such birds as wagtails, robins and sparrows. The duns are liable also to get entangled in spiders' webs or to be caught by dragonflies.

Spinners are considerably more active than duns and are not so easily captured, particularly those species which adopt a quick and jerky rising and falling motion when in flight. In spite of their activity, however, a considerable number of them are eaten by swallows, martins, bats and dragonflies.

If a female spinner successfully evades these dangers and proceeds to the water to lay her eggs, she may oviposit on the surface, in which case the eggs will sink. If on a river, the sinking eggs may get carried into the small trap-nets which are built by the larvae of several species of Caddisflies in flowing water. Normally, however, they sink and adhere to weed or else lie on the bottom. Here they are in constant danger of being eaten by free-moving caddis or beetle larvae. It was in order to avoid the depredations of caddis larvae that the late W. J. Lunn* first thought of providing floating fly boards. Those species of *Baëtis* which crawl beneath the water to oviposit utilise these boards for the purpose, and the likelihood of a caddis being able to reach the eggs is remote.

PARASITES

Most animals harbour parasites, and ephemeropteran nymphs are not an exception. Parasites may be situated either externally on the animal which they infect, for example sea lice on a salmon, or internally, as are tapeworms.

Little is known about the internal parasites which infect ephemeropterans, but those which are known are mainly round worms and flukes. The round worms, *nematodes*, are found in several species of nymphs, and a well developed specimen of a nematode may be several times longer than the nymph which it infects. It lies curled up in the abdomen, and owing to its size it usually displaces many of the body organs. Nematodes have not necessarily a fatal effect on the nymphs, but they may render any nymph which they infect sterile.

DIRECT AND INDIRECT EFFECTS OF THE ELEMENTS

Even though nymphs have developed many adaptations to the watery environment in which they live, they are, at times, quite unable to counteract the disrupting effect of the water during floods.

Rivers in mountainous districts are subject at times to extremely severe floods. In those rivers which have a precipitous course the force of the water during a sudden violent spate can alter the shape of the bed of the river. Rocks and gravel will be torn up from the bottom and carried downstream to reaches where the current is less severe. Even large boulders can be moved many yards. Nymphs which are clinging to stones which are tossed around or moved

* See J. W. Hills (1934).

along with other stones and gravel are likely to be crushed and swept away. Other nymphs which are clinging to more stable support may be swept off by the unusual strength of the current.

In the quieter reaches of the river, many miles downstream, the effect of such a flood will still be severe, even though the strength of the current may have abated somewhat. Nymphs living in the slower-flowing portions, where the current normally is more stable, may be more vulnerable to severe floods. Banks of mud, sand and shingle will be carried away and redeposited downstream, and nymphs inhabiting such places will at times be quite at the mercy of the current.

Evidence of the destructive effect of floods was obtained by Dr. P. R. Needham* on a stream in New York, U. S. A. He set a net during a flood and obtained a collection of debris which included "practically every kind of aquatic organism which had been collected from this stream during the previous summer. The great majority were dead or injured by the grinding action of rocks and gravel which were being carried downstream. Many parts of insect larvae such as heads, legs, tails and abdomens, offered evidence of the destructive action of high waters."

Lowland rivers flowing through flat country frequently overflow their banks and inundate the surrounding land. Nymphs which are carried out, or swim out, over the newly-flooded areas are liable to be left stranded when the floods recede.

DROUGHT

Very low water is a complementary danger to floods. When the water level falls in the bed of a river, and portion of the bed which normally is submerged is exposed to the air, heavy mortality may ensue among the aquatic fauna. The seriousness of drought varies with the concentration of organisms which the newly-exposed portion of the river bed carried. Also with the extent to which the nature of the bed allows the organisms to retreat when the water is falling.

Normally, preceding periods of unusually low water, the water level falls so slowly that most active organisms can retreat with it. Immobile organisms, such as insect eggs, cannot retreat and, unless

* See Needham, Traver and Hsu (1935).

they are able to survive desiccation, they are likely to perish. During temporary periods of drought many of these organisms which are situated under stones, among moss or other weed will survive, as the proximity of the moisture in such micro-habitats will keep the organism sufficiently moist.

The most serious mortality occurs when the river bed is undulating so that a shallow pool is left isolated as the water falls. Should this occur in a well-populated portion of the river, heavy mortality of larger organisms, including many ephemeropteran nymphs, will follow. Mortality in this instance will be caused by an oxygen deficiency brought on by an increase in the water temperature. The water temperature in shallow still pools is always higher than in the current of the river.

Man's interference includes:—

(1) Control of water supplies.
(2) Pollution.

The control of water supplies may be beneficial to nymphs and other aquatic organisms, as sometimes occurs when a reservoir is built near the headwaters of a river. A reservoir often stabilises the flow of water in the river and thus reduces the severity of floods and droughts. It may, on the other hand, severely curtail the volume of water which enters the river at the outflow. The compensation water which is released may be insufficient to keep the river at its normal height, and it thus reduces the size of the river.

Mills which utilise water power also considerably upset the regular flow in a river. A mill pond usually has to be filled at frequent intervals, and while it is filling, the flow in the river downstream is much reduced, and on some rivers may cease. After the pond has filled, and while it is being emptied again, the normal volume of water in the river below the outlet of the millpond is increased.

Fluctuating conditions such as these, even though each stage may last for only a few hours, can do considerable harm. During periods of high water nymphs may distribute themselves over wide shallows on the river. When the water falls, many of these will be left behind in small pools. In hot weather conditions in such small shallow pools Large Dark Olive and other *Baëtis* nymphs may expire within a few hours.

POLLUTION

So much has been said and written recently about the evil effects of pollution in rivers that it is not necessary to labour the point here.

Pollution can completely exterminate the insect population as well as the fish population in a river or portion of a river; and its evil effects cannot be exaggerated. Domestic pollution is harmful when it removes too much oxygen from the water, and industrial pollution, in addition to removing the oxygen, may have a direct toxic effect on the organisms concerned, in this case ephemeropteran nymphs.

D. D. T.

As extensive use is being made of D. D. T. and other pest exterminators in recent years, it is worth while considering what harmful effects the misuse of the substance can have on ephemeropteran nymphs and other aquatic larvae.

Quite extensive field studies have been carried on in America on the effect of D. D. T. on the insect population of several streams and ponds. The waters were treated by being sprayed from an aeroplane with an oil solution of D. D. T. The extent of the fauna present both before and after treatment was ascertained. It was found that most species were very susceptible to the treatment. On one small stream which was sprayed with about 1 lb. of D. D. T. per acre, about 85 per cent. of the insect population was killed. In another, and larger, stream which was from 10 to 18 feet in width, an application of ¼ lb. of D. D. T. per acre killed about 90 per cent. of the total insect population, and apparently exterminated about one-third of the species studied. Those studied included fifteen species of Ephemeroptera, ten species of Caddis-flies and five species of Stone-flies. It is evident that care should be exercised if ever outdoor sprayings are made near trout streams.

CHAPTER 10

TAXONOMY

IN ADDITION to the colour photographs of natural flies which appear in this book, descriptions of the colours of the flies as seen both by transmitted and reflected light are also included (see pp. 199—237). But, owing to variations which occur in the colours of flies, and to a confusion which exists in the application and interpretation of colour terms, it is advisable when identifying a species for the first time to do so, as far as possible, by means of structural characters rather than by colour differences.

Some of these structural characters are easily seen (e. g. the number of tails present); others, such as the arrangement of veins on the wings, are better examined with the aid of a pocket magnifying lens; but characters which are so small that it becomes necessary to use a compound microscope in order to study them are not included in the descriptions, as it is unlikely that many anglers have microscopes at their disposal.

Once a number of individual flies of one species have been identified, subsequent specimens of that species can generally be recognised at a glance, without resort to the lens. Exceptions to this may be found when examining a few of the closely allied species, but, from the angling viewpoint, the necessity for differentiating between two species diminishes accordingly as the species resemble each other more closely in size, colour and habits.

When it is recommended that one should be able to identify two species which are distinguishable from each other by some structural character, it should be borne in mind that there may also be considerable, though not necessarily such easily described, differences in the general appearance and habits of the two species. For instance, in order to separate the Large Dark Olive Dun, *Baëtis rhodani* (Pl. 6c, d, p. 49), from the Blue-winged Olive Dun, *Ephemerella ignita* (Pl. 11a, b, p. 76), it is necessary only to know that the former has two tails and the latter three tails, but this does not necessarily imply that the flies otherwise closely resemble each other.

The characters which are most often used in identifying winged specimens of the Ephemeroptera are the arrangement of veins on the wings, the shape and size of the wings, the number and colour of the wings and tails, the relative lengths of some of the leg joints, the shape, size and colour of the eyes, the structure of the genitalia of male spinners, and the colour pattern on various parts of the specimens.

In order that references to these various features may be fully understood, one should be familiar with the appropriate terminology and also with the structure of the parts concerned. Some of these parts have been described briefly in Chapter 2, but they are considered here in greater detail.

WINGS

All duns and spinners carry a pair of large anterior wings which arise from the mesothorax (second segment of the thorax). Most species also possess a smaller pair of hind or posterior wings which arise from the metathorax (third thoracic segment). The wing membrane is supported by an arrangement of fine tubes called veins or nervures. The system of these veins is known as the venation or neuration of the wing, and is important in the determination of genera but of less value in distinguishing species.

The main veins run in a longitudinal direction, that is, they arise from the wing base and radiate in a more or less fanwise manner to the apex and posterior margin of the wing. These longitudinal veins are connected by numerous cross veins. Various arrangements in the nomenclature of wing venation have been proposed by different authors. That used by Dr. Needham in *The Biology of Mayflies* is followed here.

The frontal area of the forewing is supported by three strong nearly parallel longitudinal veins which extend from the base of the wing to the apex. Of these veins the Costa (C) forms the front edge of the wing, behind this lie the Subcosta (Sc) and the first vein of the Radius (R_1). At their bases these three veins are supported by a strong curved cross vein known as the Costal brace or Humeral vein. Posterior to R_1 are four other radial veins. These arise at the base of the wing as one vein, which immediately divides into two, and is known as the radial sector. Each branch of the radial sector also divides into two to form the four radial veins R_2, R_3, R_4 and R_5. The Media (M) lies posterior to the radius and divides and forms the veins M_1 and M_2. The remainder of the wing is occupied by the Cubitus (Cu) and Anal Veins (A).

Between many of these longitudinal veins lie shorter intercalary veins, which reach the margin of the wing but do not arise from the wing base. In the wings of several genera, e. g. *Baëtis* and *Centroptilum*, there are characteristic very short marginal intercalary veins (see Fig. 4).

The area, or interspace, between any two longitudinal veins may take its name from the vein which forms the anterior border. Hence the costal area lies between the costa and subcosta and the anal area and cubito-anal area lie respectively posterior to the first anal and first cubital veins. A portion of the costal area near the apex of the wing is known as the pterostigma or stigmatic area. This area is often more opaque than other portions of the wing, and the number and arrangement of the cross-veins in the pterostigma is, at times, of assistance in the determination of species. The general arrangement of cross veins in other portions of the wing may show generic differences, but their precise arrangement is seldom of value in identifying species.

The venation and size of the hind wings differ considerably between different genera. In specimens of *Baëtis* and *Centroptilum* the number of veins is reduced to two or three, but in those species which possess larger hind wings, most of the main veins which are present in the forewings can be located. Differences in the relative sizes of wings, their shape and venation, are more easily understood if the wings are considered in relation to their evolution. Prehistoric primitive Ephemeroptera differed considerably from present-day specimens, they possessed two pairs of long and rather narrow wings of approximately equal size, as is found in present-day dragonflies, Odonata. During the course of ages, as the form of ephemeropterans altered, the hind wings became reduced in size, until, as can be seen at the present time, in only some species, such as *Siphlonurus* and *Ephemera*, are they even as large as from one-half to one-third the length of the forewings. In other genera they are relatively smaller, those of *Baëtis* being only about one-sixteenth the size (linear) of the

Plate 17: SPINNERS × 3
(*a*) Little Sky-Blue (Pale Watery), male; (*b*) Little Amber (Pale Watery),
Centroptilum luteolum, female; (*c*) and (*d*) Pale Evening (Pale Watery),
Procloëon rufulum, male and female

Plate 18: SPINNERS × **2**

(*a*) Purple, *Paraleptophlebia cincta*, male; (*b*) Pale Watery, *Baëtis bioculatus*, male; (*c*) Yellow Evening, *Ephemerella notata*, female; (*d*) Yellow Upright, *Rhithrogena semicolorata*, female

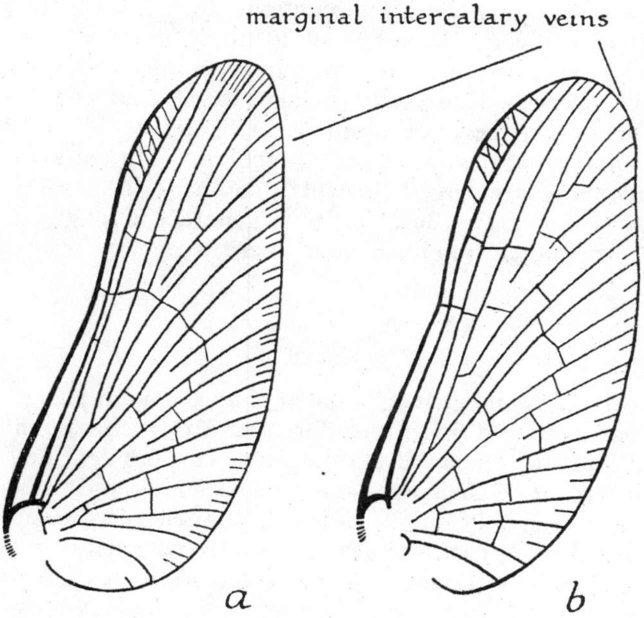

marginal intercalary veins

FIG. 4

a) Forewing of *Baëtis rhodani*; b) Forewing of *Centroptilum luteolum*

The small marginal intercalary veins on the large forewings provide a ready means of identifying species of *Baëtis*. These veins are in pairs in all *Baëtis* sp. and are single in species of *Centroptilum*, *Cloëon* and *Procloëon*.

forewings, and in species of *Caenis* and *Cloëon* they have disappeared entirely.

In order to compensate for the loss of wing area occasioned by the reduction in size of the hind wings, the forewings have increased in width (in an anterior-posterior direction). It can be seen in present-day specimens that the anal and cubital areas of the forewings are most fully developed in those species (*Caenis* and *Cloëon*) which lack hind wings, and are rather less fully developed in species with small hindwings, such as *Baëtis* and *Centroptilum;* whilst the development of these areas is least in those species which possess large hind wings, e. g. *Siphlonurus*, *Ephemera* and *Ecdyonurus*.

Another difference between present-day and primitive Ephemeroptera is found in the wing venation. In primitive specimens all the longitudinal veins were joined at their bases and cross veins were very numerous. In modern genera many of the longitudinal veins have become dissociated at their bases, and cross-veins have become greatly reduced in number. The degree of differentiation of the venation varies in different genera. The most specialised genera in this respect are those which comprise the families *Caenidae* and *Baëtidae* (see page 186). In these genera the longitudinal veins have become much modified and there are very few cross-veins (see page 93).

EYES

The eyes show much variation in shape, colour and size among different genera, and specific differences are often also noticeable; in fact, the male spinners of many species can be identified from the shape and colour of their eyes alone. The compound eyes of female spinners are relatively small and are situated on the sides of the head. In male spinners the eyes are usually considerably larger and occupy not only the lateral regions of the head but also portion of the dorsal surface. The eyes of male spinners can conveniently be grouped into three types:—

(1) Those found on species of *Ephemera* and *Caenis*, in which the eyes are situated only on the lateral regions of the head.

(2) The divided spherical-shaped eyes of such species as the Sherry Spinner, *Ephemerella ignita* (Pl. 19a, b, p. 96), and the spinner of the Yellow May Dun, *Heptagenia sulphurea* (Pl. 15a, b, p. 84), in which each eye is divided into two parts, namely a smaller lateral and a larger dorsal portion.

(3) The divided eyes of species of *Baëtis* and *Centroptilum*, in which the dorsally placed portion of the eye is turbinate or turret shaped, and the lateral portion more or less spherical (see Fig. 9, p. 218).

TAILS

All Ephemeroptera normally possess either two or three tails, and there should be no difficulty in counting the number present. It often happens, however, that a fly inadvertently loses one of these appendages, and, when examining a specimen, it should not be difficult to recognise when this has occurred. The position in which the tails are attached to the abdomen is shown in Fig, 1, p. 34. If a fly normally has only two tails they occupy the position of the outer tails. There is present in place of the normal middle tail a small stump or telofilum. The loss of a tail should, therefore, be apparent, either (1) by the relative position of the remaining tails at their junction with the last segment of the abdomen, when a lateral tail is missing, or (2) by the absence of a telofilum in the event of the middle tail having been lost.

LEGS

The fore, middle and hind pairs of legs arise respectively from the pro-, meso-, and metathorax. Each leg consists of five main joints, the most important of which are the femur (thigh joint), tibia (shin) and tarsus (foot). The femur is separated from the thorax by two short socket-like joints, the coxa and trochanter. The relative sizes of these joints vary in different species. The femur is usually as long as, or longer and stouter than, the tibia. The tarsus is usually rather shorter than the tibia. It consists of four or five small segments, the last of which carries small terminal claws. The fore legs of male spinners differ from the other legs in that the tibiae and tarsi are considerably lengthened. In some species they are twice or thrice as long as in any of the other legs. The lengthened fore legs of the male spinners are used to grasp the female spinners during copulation. Taxonomic features of the leg joints include (1) markings on the femora (the dark medially situated streak in the femur of the Yellow Upright, *Rhithrogena semicolorata*, is often referred to) and (2) the relative lengths of the tarsal joints.

GENITALIA

For taxonomic purposes the genitalia of male spinners is the most important feature. These parts consist of the forceps, or claspers, the base from which the forceps arise, called the forceps base, and the penis. The forceps base pertains to the posterior ventral portion of the ninth segment of the abdomen and it lies beneath the tenth segment; the forceps, which are composed usually of three or four segments, arise from its posterior edge. The penis, a paired structure, usually takes the form of two divergent lobes (see Fig. 5, p. 97).

It arises from between the tenth abdominal segment and the forceps base, and, in ventral view, is seen between the forceps.

It is unfortunate that, owing to their small size, the genitalia cannot be studied without considerable magnification. Much of their structure becomes visible when examined under a lens of x10 or x15, but with several of the closely related species sufficient detail cannot be seen without great magnification. In consequence, means of identifying such species is not included in the keys or descriptions.

ABDOMEN

The translucency of the abdomens of duns and spinners greatly increases the difficulty of describing their colours. This quality is most apparent in male spinners, and an examination of the first six or seven segments shows that this portion of the abdomen contains little more than the air-inflated digestive tract, and that most of the colour and opacity is confined to the integument. The last three or four segments are more opaque, as they contain the internal male genital organs.

The abdomen of a female spinner is completely filled with eggs in the first eight segments, and is, therefore, opaque before the eggs have been passed, but it becomes translucent after the spinner has oviposited.

COLOURS

The difficulty experienced in describing the colours of translucent substances is, of course, due to colour changes which occur according to whether the substances are viewed by transmitted or by reflected light.

When a substance is viewed by transmitted light, that is, when it is held more or less between the observer and the source of light so that the light rays pass through it, the colour seen is that which might be called the contained colour of the substance. It is the colour produced by the mixture of all the pigments which impregnate the substance. If the same substance is viewed by reflected light, that is, if the light comes from behind or above the observer, so that the light is reflected from the substance, then the colour seen will consist of the colours of the surface regions. The extent to which more deeply seated colours may be reflected will depend on the relative translucency of the substance.

Plate 19: SPINNERS × 2.5
(a) and (b) Sherry (Blue-winged Olive), *Ephemerella ignita*, male and female;
(c) Blue-winged (Pale Watery), *Centroptilum pennulatum*, female; (d) Olive,
Baëtis tenax, male

Plate 20: SPINNERS × 2.25
(a) Summer Mayfly, *Siphlonurus lacustris*, female; (b) Angler's Curse, *Caenis macrura*, male; (c) Dark, *Heptagenia lateralis*, male

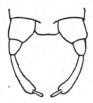

Those surface colours which are visible by reflected light may
be of a pigmentary or of a structural nature, or they may be a
combination of both. Colours seen by transmitted light are mainly
pigmentary.

Pigmentary colours are those produced by the pigments or
natural colouring substances, whilst structural colours are produced
by diffraction or diffusion of light rays due to the presence of minute
ridge formations on the surface of the substance viewed, or due to
very thin differing layers of material comprising the substance.

Structural colours include those of an iridescent or metallic
nature such as are found, for example, on the dried wings of many
spinners, and on feathers such as the green feathers of a peacock
or the vivid blue body feathers of the kingfisher.

In practice, a translucent object such as the body of a spinner is
normally seen under a mixture of both transmitted and reflected
lights, and, as it usually happens that the colours as seen under
transmitted and reflected lights differ appreciably, then colour
changes will occur as the relative proportions of the two types of
lighting are altered.

If, for instance, a spinner is held in one's fingers and is viewed
by reflected light (i. e. with the source of light coming from behind
the observer), light rays will be reflected from the fingers and
hand holding the fly, as well as from other objects in the near vicinity,

A. E.

and some of these light rays will be transmitted through the fly. The great extent to which the light reflected off the background against which a fly is viewed affects the colour of the fly is easily demonstrated. If, for instance, a medium-coloured Olive Dun is placed first against a black background and then against a white one, the colour of the abdomen of the fly will alter from a very dark green olive to a bright light luminous olive.

Colour Descriptions

The colour descriptions of the flies which appear in the appendices were made under the following conditions. Flies described under reflected light were placed on a light-coloured surface, such as the underneath of the inside of a match-box or the observer's hand, and were examined only in daylight. The transmitted light descriptions were made also only by daylight, and when the specimens were being examined, they were viewed against the horizon in a position which allowed the greatest amount of light to pass through the specimens, without the observer being dazzled by the light from the sky or sun.

CHAPTER II

COLLECTING

EPHEMEROPTERA may be collected from the water or else taken in the air whilst flying. Specimens are most easily captured on the water with the aid of a flat net, that is, a piece of fine curtain net or muslin stretched tightly across a net ring of wire which is attached to a handle. If the net is made in the usual bag-like form the specimens are very liable to get damaged through coming into contact with the wet insides of the net as it is being lifted from the water.

But for specimens in the air, a fairly deep net, about twice as deep as wide, of fine muslin is most satisfactory, although, in default, one's hat or cap makes quite a good substitute. Specimens may also be collected from underneath the leaves of trees, flags or other plants. Such vegetation should be shaken so that specimens will fall on to a sheet of some sort laid underneath, or disturbed specimens may be captured as they are flying away, or a net may be swept through the vegetation.

As it is intended that identifications from the illustrations or written descriptions in this book should be made from living or freshly killed specimens, it is advisable to bring specimens home alive. They can be carried in any sort of small container such as an empty match-box or a glass tube which has been covered on the inside with blotting paper. The blotting paper prevents condensation and subsequent injury to the specimen. Alternatively, empty compartments in the usual type of dry fly box make excellent carrying boxes, and duns or spinners will often live for several days, or nearly a week in such places. A very satisfactory type of special carrying box is like a strongly constructed pill box with a strong piece of clear celluloid forming the end of the deeper part of the box.

For permanent collections, or for forwarding through the post, flies can be collected and put first into a tube of about 60 per cent alcohol, and then transferred to a tube of 3 per cent formalin. The alcohol wets the flies and ensures that they will sink when placed in the formalin. Tubes of specimens which are transmitted by post should be filled as full as possible and a piece of cotton wool then inserted to protect the specimens from any air bubbles which may be left in the tube after it has been corked. If tubes are shaken much, as is liable to happen during transit, an air bubble may considerably damage specimens.

The easiest flies to identify are male spinners, and it is often necessary to capture duns and keep them alive until they moult. Consequently, when duns are being collected they should be handled very carefully, and particular care should be taken to ensure that their wings do not get squashed by the collector's fingers, otherwise they may not succeed in moulting. Even moderate pressure on the tips of the wings will often result in the spinner being unable to withdraw its wings from the shuck of the dun.

For permanent collections, apart from specimens kept in formalin, specimens may also be set and pinned in much the same way as butterflies; but, unfortunately, when such specimens dry they contract considerably and become very brittle and fragile. They are less liable to get damaged if they are fastened to pieces of stiff paper by celluloid or gum tragacanth, but they are then less valuable for comparative purposes.

To anyone who wishes to undertake systematic work on the Ephemeroptera the following notes may be useful.

Acquire a low-power microscope which will magnify to about x 30 or x 40. Microscopes are of two types. In the commoner and cheaper type the image of anything being examined is inverted. This in itself is not of importance, but it means that if the specimen being examined is moved it will appear (through the microscope) to move in the opposite direction to that in which it actually does move. Because of this, some initial difficulty is experienced in arranging specimens for examination, and also in making dissections while the specimens are being viewed through the microscope. But these difficulties are overcome by practice. In the other type, which is called a stereoscopic or dissecting microscope, the image is not inverted, and it moves as it appears to move, and it is easy to arrange or dissect specimens. This type is the most suitable but is more expensive. But either type can be used.

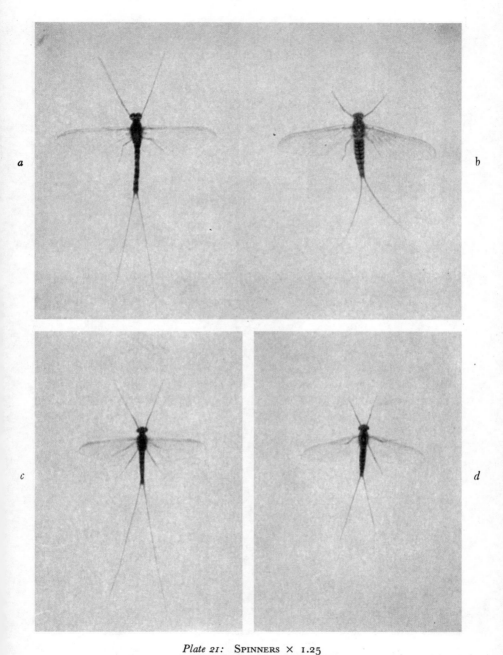

Plate 21: SPINNERS × 1.25
(a) and (b) Summer Mayfly, *Siphlonurus linnaeanus*, male and female; (c) and
(d) Great Red (August Dun); *Ecdyonurus dispar*, male and female

Plate 22: SPINNERS × 2

(*a*) Pond Olive, *Cloëon dipterum*, female; (*b*) Large Claret, *Leptophlebia vespertina*, male; (*c*) and (*d*) Lake Olive, *Cloëon simile*, male and female

Then purchase a copy of Mr. Kimmins' *Keys to the British Species of Ephemeroptera with Keys to the Genera of the Nymphs*, which is published by the Freshwater Biological Association, Wray Castle, Ambleside, Westmorland, and costs only 2 6d.

This is an excellent publication and it contains drawings of the genitalia of the male spinners of all British and Irish species of the Ephemeroptera. It also has illustrations of the wings, and, where necessary, other parts of several of the species. All of the species can be identified by the genitalia, although descriptions of additional features may make identifications more certain.

The genitalia of male spinners, of course, consists of the forceps or claspers, the paired penes, and the forceps base. In making identifications it is of considerable advantage to be familiar with the general appearance and size of the insects to which the drawings of the genitalia refer. In this connection the colour plates and written descriptions contained in this book will be of assistance.

The most satisfactory way to keep specimens for examination of the genitalia is in fluid, either alcohol or dilute formalin. When specimens are set and dried, considerable contraction and distortion occurs. Specimens in fluid can be examined by placing them under the microscope in a small shallow glass dish, preferably a dish which has a flat bottom. A pair of dubbing or darning needles are useful for arranging or dissecting specimens.

PART TWO
OTHER FLIES

CHAPTER 12

CADDIS-FLIES

CADDIS-FLIES, Sedge-flies or, as they are often called in Ireland, Rails, form numerically the largest of the three main groups of water flies. They belong to the order Trichoptera. About 185 species are known in Britain; but of these more than 50 are so small that they are of little or no use as fishing flies. Of the others, only about 40 or 50 are common enough to be important and many of these are local in their distribution, so that even though there is a considerable number of species there are actually only comparatively few which are important from the angling viewpoint.

Caddis-flies differ widely in their development from both stone-flies and ephemeropterans in one obvious respect. The two latter orders pass from the egg to a larval stage and then to a winged stage. But caddis-flies pass from the egg to the larval and then through a pupal stage before they assume a winged form.

In appearance, caddis-flies somewhat resemble moths, particularly when in flight, but on being examined closely will be seen to differ from them in several respects. The wings have not got that powdery appearance which is plainly seen on the wings of moths. This powdery appearance is caused by innumerable minute scales which cover the upper surfaces of the wings. The wings of caddis-flies are covered with hairs, some species more profusely so than others. The hairs are small and are difficult to see without the aid of a magnifying lens, but on a few species the hairs are very thickset and are somewhat club-shaped, and are, therefore, more visible.

Individuals of the two orders also differ somewhat in their general appearance. In comparison to most moths, caddis-flies are less broad across the thorax and when at rest they appear slenderer, partly because their wings are held closer to their bodies.

When the insects are at rest, the wings are inclined at an angle to each other so that they cover the abdomen like a roof, each wing obscures both the dorsum and one side of the abdomen.

STRUCTURE

In general structure caddis-flies resemble ephemeropterans although they differ very much in appearance. The head carries a pair of moderate-sized compound eyes and according to the particular species being examined, there may or may not be three simple eyes or ocelli. The antennae are very long, being sometimes nearly three times the length of the fly. The mouthparts, which are situated on the ventral side of the head capsule, include small jointed protuberances called palps. These palps are easily seen on the Black Silverhorns, *Mystacides azurea*, in which insects they are short and claw-like. On the male Halford's Welshman's Button, *Sericostoma personatum* (Pl. 24a, p. 109), the maxillary palps are curved upwards and lie close to the front of the head, they are relatively very much swollen and noticeably increase the apparent size of the head. The dark brown males of this species are easily recognised by this feature.

The thorax consists of the usual three segments. Each of the segments carries a pair of legs, and the large anterior and posterior wings arise respectively from the second and third segments. The abdomen, which is appreciably shorter than the wings, is formed of nine segments and does not carry any caudal cerci or tails.

LIFE CYCLE

Many anglers are more familiar with the appearance of the caddis larvae, which is also known in Ireland as cor-bait, than with that of caddis-flies. The best known of the larvae are those species which live in tubes made of grains of sand or small pieces of twigs, leaves, shells or other material.

Their cases are constructed in the first place of a tube of silk web, composed of silk threads which the larvae exude from their salivary glands in the mouth. To this tube of web are fastened particles of the particular material which the larva selects. The particles used are not chosen at random and most species are consistent in the nature of the material used. For instance, the larvae of species of Silverhorns, *Leptocerus* spp. (Pl. 25a, p. 112) use sand grains, the Great Red Sedges, *Phryganea* spp. (Pl. 23 a, b, p. 108), collect pieces of plant material which they fasten to their cases so that they lie longitudinally and often in a spiral fashion. Some of the Cinnamon Sedge larvae, *Limnephilus* spp., utilise small lengths of plant stalks, but arrange them in a criss-cross fashion.

Other species utilise small snail shells or pieces of gravel. The cases serve several purposes. They provide an excellent camouflage; most larvae are extremely difficult to detect unless they move. They act as a protection against predators, and also are of some hydro-dynamical importance. The specific gravity of the materials used obviously affects the portability of the cases. Those cases made of small pebbles and sand will be heavier than cases composed of plant material and will doubtless tend to keep the contained larvae on the bottom. Mr. Mosely, in his excellent text book *The British Caddis Flies*, states, " Speaking generally, we find that species inhabiting the fast-running water attach heavy stones to their cases to avoid being swept away by the strong current; others, living in ditches, ponds or slow-running rivers, employ bits of wood which no doubt render their cases more buoyant and enable them to move more easily to fresh feeding-grounds."

Other species of caddis, which do not construct portable cases, are found among moss or other plants, or under stones. Some of them construct a fixed shelter of web on the side of a stone, which not only offers some protection to the larva, but also serves as a net which collects various food organisms from the water.

Caddis larvae feed on plant material and also on animal matter. The animal matter includes insect larvae, crustaceans, and, as Mr. Lunn* pointed out, they feed on insect eggs. They should be kept out of boxes in which trout eggs are being hatched, as in the absence of other food they may kill and eat the ova.

When the larvae are fully developed, they prepare for pupation. This they do either by constructing a cocoon of silk on the side of a stone, or else, as with the case-bearing species, they seal up the ends

* See J. W. Hills (1934)

of their cases with a mesh of web, which is porous and so allows the ingress and egress of water. The change from larva to pupa corresponds to the change from caterpillar to chrysalis in butterflies. To outward appearances the process is accompanied by a moult, and when the larva sheds its skin the pupa is revealed underneath. The pupa is quite different in appearance from the larva, is inactive and does not eat.

Pupae may take a considerable time to develop. Some apparently spend the winter in this stage, but perhaps more usually the period lasts only a few weeks. When the pupa has fully developed, it tears open its cocoon by means of a pair of strong jaws which it possesses for this purpose. When the pupa emerges from its case, it bears considerable resemblance to the adult fly. The thorax and abdomen are well formed and distinct, the contained wings can be seen within the wing cases, the long antennae and the legs are also visible through the pupal skin. The pupa is provided with a heavily fringed pair of legs, which it uses in order to swim to the surface. When the pupa reaches the surface, either the adult fly emerges in open water, or the pupa climbs out of the water by means of some plant stem or other object before the adult appears.

Adult caddis-flies live for much longer than adult ephemeropterans. This is probably largely due to the fact that the caddis-flies are able to absorb liquid foods and can thus obtain nourishment, and at the same time counteract the loss of water caused by evaporation. Loss of moisture is one of the most serious factors with which insects have to contend, and those insects which cannot drink water are particularly susceptible. Warm, very dry air quickly kills them, and they live longest in a wet atmosphere. Under natural conditions, caddis-flies and Ephemeropterans live in a moist atmosphere, as the air in the immediate neighbourhood of rivers and lakes, and in the microhabitats, under and among the bordering vegetation, normally contains much water vapour. But on occasions when flies are captured and placed alive in a matchbox or other container, precautions should be taken to ensure that the atmosphere in the box remains moist. This may be done by enclosing some fresh leaves in the box, or else by wrapping the box in a damp cloth.

Mr. Mosely refers to experiments which were carried out regarding the length of time for which caddis-flies will live. He says "Dohler has found that a caddis-fly fed on sugar and water survived for 105 days. In other experiments, examples kept without food entirely lived from 4 to 20 days. Others, given water only, survived for about 30 days, whilst the specially favoured individuals, which were given sugar in addition, lived for over 70 days."

Normally, it is extremely unlikely that adult caddis-flies live for as long as some of these captured specimens, as under natural conditions their lives would be very much shortened as a result of mating and ovipositing. Perhaps a week to a fortnight would be the normal period, and it would vary with the weather conditions. Caddis-flies, in common with other insects, are unable to fly if the air becomes too cold. If, after hatching, a long cold period followed, then the flies would probably live longer than if the weather remained warm and moist, as under the latter conditions the flies would probably breed, and under the former would remain dormant.

The flies mate while at rest. Sometimes a female fly may be seen setting out on her ovipositing flight immediately afterwards, but at other times a considerable interval elapses. The females lay their eggs in several ways. Silverhorns, *Leptocerus* spp. (Pl. 25 a, p. 112) and *Mystacides* spp., fly out over the water and oviposit on the surface. Brown Sedges, *Rhyacophila* spp., crawl down beneath the water and attach their eggs to some underwater object, and other species lay their eggs on vegetation bordering or overhanging the water. Obviously the species which adopt either of the first two methods are more likely to be found spent on the surface, and will be of greater value as trout-flies than those which use the third method and therefore need not approach the water. But little is known about the ovipositing habits of caddis-flies and there is a very wide field here for original observations by angler entomologists. Unfortunately, the females of some species are extremely difficult to identify, but they could be placed into their correct genus.

DISTRIBUTION AND ECOLOGY

Caddis are found in all types of unpolluted fresh water throughout Britain and Ireland. They occur in lakes and reservoirs, rivers and streams, ditches and ponds. Some species are tolerant of a wide range of habitats, and others are considerably restricted in the type of water in which they can live.

From the angling viewpoint, caddis-flies are sometimes of more importance collectively than individually. That is to say that several species may be present on the water at the same time, each species in sparse numbers, but the total of the individuals of all the species present is sufficiently high to bring on a rise of fish. At other times, of course, one species will predominate and the trout may concentrate on it. Trout feed on the pupae of the caddis during the time that the pupae are swimming up to the surface in order to hatch. They feed on the freshly emerged fly while it is resting on the water, or is scuttering along the surface towards the shore. They also feed on the female flies which are on the surface immediately before or while the flies are ovipositing, and on both the males and females which are lying spent on the water. The governing conditions are, of course, those which affect the larvae, but little is yet known about the habits of caddis larvae, so that the following notes which relate to some of the more important species are very brief.

Grannom, *Brachycentrus subnubilus*: These larvae are confined to flowing water. They live on weed or other support in the current, and collect their food from the water as it flows past them. They pupate on the weed and the pupae swim to the surface in order to allow the adults to emerge. They are widely distributed in Britain and occur on various rivers from Hampshire to at least as far North as Perthshire in Scotland, but they are unknown in Ireland.

Grey Flag (Sedge), *Hydropsyche* spp. (*H. pellucidula*, Pl. 25b, p. 112). These larvae are also confined to flowing water, but they are found among stones and rocks. They likewise collect their food from the current, but instead of doing this by means of their hair-fringed legs, they build a web of silk on the side of, or in a crevice between, two stones or other rigid supports. This web is closely woven and it faces upstream and acts as a strainer, so that various small organisms get caught in it. The larva lies in a protective silk tunnel which is a continuation of the web, and feeds on the detritus which the web collects. In view of its method of collecting food it is easily seen that the species must be confined to flowing water.

The adult flies emerge at the surface in open water in, or below, fairly quick flowing reaches of the river. They are valuable to the angler, as they are one of the comparatively few day-flying sedges. The males may be seen hovering in the sunshine all through the day, but the females do not usually lay their eggs until evening. The flies are easy to recognise with the aid of a lens, as a dark fine spiral line can be seen on the antennae of both sexes of all the species of

Plate 23: CADDIS-FLIES, Trichoptera × 2
(a) Speckled Peter, *Phryganea varia*; (b) The Peter, *Phryganea obsoleta*;
(c) Carperer, *Halesus radiatus*; (d) Large Cinnamon Sedge, *Stenophylax stellatus*

(*a*) Halford's Welshman's Button (Caperer), *Sericostoma personatum*;

(*b*) Medium Sedge, *Goëra pilos*

Plate 24: Caddis-flies × 3

Hydropsyche. The line actually is a series of oblique stripes, but on superficial examination it appears to be continuous.

Silverhorns, *Mystacides* spp. and *Leptocerus* spp. The larvae of these two genera usually construct their cases of fine sand grains, and they often make them slightly curved instead of in the normal straight fashion. The species live in both rivers and lakes, and on some of the large limestone lakes in Ireland they may appear in tremendous numbers. The *Mystacides* species are commonly found also on reservoirs, and will often establish themselves quickly on newly constructed artificial lakes. As trout feed on the larvae (in their cases), the pupae and the adults, they are valuable species to encourage on trout waters. In rivers they occur in the slower-flowing parts, and the males of the Black Silverhorns, *Mystacides azurea*, will often be found hovering along the sides of the still deep flat reaches. A species of Brown Silverhorns, *Mystacides longicornis*, which is also called the Grouse Wing, is common on Blagdon and on other reservoirs and ponds. Species of *Mystacides* may be recognised by the fact that the extreme tip of each wing is bent downwards when the insect is at rest.

Halford's Welshman's Button, *Sericostoma personatum* (Pl. 24a, p. 109) is widely distributed in lakes and rivers throughout Britain and Ireland. The larval cases are formed of sand grains and fine pieces of other hard material, and resemble large-sized cases of some of the Silverhorns. The adults emerge at the surface in open water and they are one of the day-flying species, and when present in abundance are an important fly for angling purposes. The female flies oviposit on the surface, and in flowing water are carried downstream in a spent or half-spent condition.

Great Red Sedge or Murragh, *Phryganea grandis* and *P. striata*: The larvae of these species are found in rivers and lakes throughout Britain and Ireland. They make cases of pieces of plant material arranged in a spiral form and are the largest of the caddis found in Britain. Owing partly to their large size, they are the most predatory in their habits and will even attack and kill small fish.

The adult flies emerge in open water and the freshly hatched flies scuttle along the surface towards the shore. They appear in the evening, and when they are at all plentiful, the trout feed freely on them. They are in greatest abundance during late May and June.

CHAPTER 13

STONE-FLIES

STONE-FLIES, the Plecoptera are found in greatest abundance on rivers and streams with stony and gravelly bottoms. Rivers of this nature are mainly upland rivers and hill streams, and it is on such waters, rather than on lowland limestone and chalk streams, that these flies are of importance to anglers. It is not that stone-flies are absent from lowland rivers, but that most species appear in smaller numbers on these rivers than elsewhere. Also on lowland rivers Ephemeroptera and Sedge-flies are relatively much more abundant and important.

The large stone-fly is unique in that it is the oldest known artificial fly which has retained its original name. It is now just over four and one half centuries since the publication of the *Treatise on Fishing with an Angle*. In this book is found the first mention of the stone-fly, together with the description of a dressing for the artificial imitation. On those rivers on which it is common the stone-fly is of considerable importance as an angling fly. In the north of England it is called the Mayfly and is just as valuable there in its season as is the Greendrake on midland or southern rivers. Several of the smaller species of stone-flies are also important and have received common names. Owing to the close resemblance that there is between many of the species, some of these common names are applied indiscriminately to a number of different species.

As an Order, the stone-flies are numerically small. Dr. Hynes records only thirty-one species in Britain. The common and more important species are:—

Perlodes mortoni *Dictyopterygella recta*	Large Stone-fly

Perla cephalotes
„ *carlukiana* } Large Stone-fly

Isoperla grammatica (Pl. 26a, b, p. 113) Yellow Sally
Chloroperla torrentium   Small Yellow Sally
Taeniopteryx nebulosa   February Red
Leuctra geniculata (Pl. 26c, p. 113)   Willow-fly
„ *hippopus*
„ *fusciventris* } Needle-fly

Protonemura meyeri (Pl. 27a, p. 128)
„ *praecox* } Early Brown
Nemoura variegata (Pl. 27b, p. 128)

STRUCTURE

Stone-flies differ from caddis-flies in several very obvious ways. The wings are hard and shiny and somewhat resemble a bee's or wasp's wing in texture. When not in use they are folded and lie very close to the body and usually protrude beyond the posterior end of the abdomen. Several of the larger species carry two tails, or cerci, which are about as long as the abdomen. In other species the tails are aborted and consist of only one or at most a few joints and are difficult to see.

The larger flies all have a noticeably flat appearance when at rest, and the smaller species, particularly those in the genus *Leuctra*, the Needle-flies, appear flat and also very thin owing to the close manner in which the wings are folded around the body. Stone-flies look insignificant when at rest and, in marked contrast, are most conspicuous when in the air. If a stone-fly is kept in sight as it flies along, with its steady undeviating slow flight, and is watched as it alights and folds its wings, it is quite disconcerting to realise how small it actually is. This applies more particularly to the Needle-flies mentioned above.

If a fly is examined closely it will be seen that the whole body, as in other insects, consists of a head, thorax and abdomen. The three segments of the thorax and the head capsule are all of about equal size and together are about as long as the abdomen. The abdomen consists of ten segments of which nine are clearly discernible. On those species which possess long tails, the tails arise from the posterior lateral end of the last abdominal segment and incline directly to rearwards. The abortive tails on the species in which the joints are reduced to one or a few segments are directed upwards on some species, and on all species are difficult to recognise as tails, as they are reduced to mere stumps. Each of the three thoracic segments carries a pair of legs, and the two pairs of wings arise from the second and third segments.

The wings of stone-flies possess features of unusual interest. The wings of the males of some of the larger species are reduced in size and are useless as organs of flight. The degree of this brachypterous condition varies. The wings on the male fly of *Dictyopterygella recta* are so small that they resemble nymphal wing cases. It is quite difficult to recognise that the specimen is actually a fully developed adult fly. Apart from differences in the size of these wings on different species, it has been found that the size of the wings on the male of some species of flies varies with the altitude at which the specimens live. Dr. Hynes determined in regard to two of the Needle-flies, *Leuctra hippopus* and *L. inermis*, in the Windermere area, that the species were present at heights up to 1800 feet in small stony streams, and that the wings became reduced in those specimens which were collected above 800 feet. This shows a direct connection between a reduction in wing area and the altitude of the habitat.

The legs are sturdy and terminate in a pair of stout claws. The first two joints of the legs, namely the coxa and trochanter, are small and knuckle-like. Of the three main joints, the tibia (shin) is slightly longer than the femur (thigh), and the tarsus (foot joint) consists of only three segments.

Nymphs in structure resemble the corresponding adults without their wings. The wings in mature nymphs are enclosed in wing cases which are on the appropriate thoracic segments, and are easily seen. Nymphs of all species have two tails, whereas in several of the adults the tails are abortive. Obvious differences between stone-fly and Ephemeropteran nymphs lie in the presence or absence and in the position of the tracheal gills. On Ephemeropteran nymphs these are always present on the sides or upper surfaces of the abdominal segments, but never so on stone-fly nymphs. Instead, they arise from various parts of the thorax, and in a few species, from the posterior end of the last abdominal segments. Many stone-fly nymphs have no tracheal gills.

LIFE CYCLE AND HABITS

The life cycle of most species of British stone-flies or *Plecoptera*,

Plate 25: Caddis-flies × 3

(a) Silverhorns, *Leptocerus* sp.; (b) Grey Sedge, *Hydropsyche pellucidula*;
(c) Small Red Sedge, *Tinodes waeneri*

a

b

c

Plate 26: STONE-FLIES, Plecoptera × 3
(*a*) and (*b*) Yellow Sally, *Isoperla grammatica*, male and female (male
inverted); (*c*) Willow-fly, *Leuctra geniculata*

from the time the eggs are laid until the adult flies emerge, lasts for one year. The two large stone-flies, *Perla carlukiana* and *P. cephalotes*, differ widely from this, as they live as nymphs for three years. The only other probable exception is the Small Yellow Sally, *Chloroperla tripunctata*, which Dr. Hynes states probably spends two years as a nymph.

EGGS: The eggs of all species are laid in water, and their incubation period varies from less than a day to more than three months. The quick-hatching eggs were obtained from a dark-coloured species called *Capnia nigra*. This species does not appear to have received a common name; it is found on the stony shores of upland lakes and in some rivers. The eggs of most species apparently hatch in a period of three, four or five weeks, but the eggs of the large stone-flies, *Perla* species, remain for about three months before eclosion occurs.

NYMPHS: The nymphs are essentially insects which crawl rather than swim. They are extremely active on their legs, and, like the flat species of nymphs of Ephemeropterans, they can move as readily sideways and backward as forwards. The best known nymphs are those of the large stone-flies. These are the creepers, which are so important as an angling bait on rivers in which they are plentiful. Plate 3, page 32.

Nymphs of smaller species are quite like these creepers in shape, although most of them are more slenderly built. They should never be mistaken for Ephemeropteran nymphs, as all the latter nymphs which are found in Britain have three tails, whereas all species of stone-fly nymphs have only two tails. Stone-fly nymphs feed on both vegetable and animal organisms. All species eat vegetable matter, but in general it is only nymphs of the larger species, those which comprise the families *Perlodidae* and *Perlidae*, which are carnivorous. The animal organisms eaten by the carnivorous species consist largely of Ephemeropteran and stone-fly nymphs, and of the larvae of caddis, Reed Smuts, *Simulium* spp., and midges, *Chironomidae*. The herbivorous nymphs feed on mosses and parts of higher plants and also on various species of algae.

It would appear that the presence of the large stone-fly creeper in a river is a mixed blessing. Its value as trout food and as a bait for trout is counter-balanced by its noxious habits of preying on Ephemeropteran nymphs and other fly larvae. The method by which the creepers prey on Ephemeropteran nymphs is graphically described by Dr. Hynes, who says "They did not appear to be able to see these nymphs, but as soon as they came into contact with the antennae or cerci they pounced on them, worrying them as a dog worries a rat, after which they were eaten quickly."

In common with other insects, stone-fly larvae moult as they grow. Little is known about the number of times various species of nymphs moult, but Dr. Schoenemund, working on nymphs of the Large Stone-fly, *Perla cephalotes*, recorded that thirty-three moults occurred during the three years of life of the creeper. When the nymphs are fully developed, they crawl to the shore and out of the water in order to allow the adult fly to emerge. The actual moulting is slow, the adult emerging through a split which extends along the thorax and along the epicranial suture on the head.

This habit which the nymphs have of crawling ashore rather than swimming to the surface in order to allow the flies to emerge, renders them of little use as a means of bringing on a rise of trout at the surface. Trout undoubtedly feed on nymphs which are crawling along the bottom towards the shore, as has been shown by Allen in regard to the nymphs of *Nemoura* species in Windermere. During the emergence period of the adults the nymphs of this species were commonly found in the stomach contents of trout caught in the lake. But it would be difficult to fish with an imitation nymph in such a way that the trout mistook it for a nymph crawling along the bed of the lake.

Writing on fishing in a clear water lake in New Zealand, Dr. Mottram describes how he caught trout which were feeding on green beetles, which he could see lying on the bottom of the lake. He tied an imitation of the beetle and then cast out and allowed the line, cast and artificial beetle to sink and lie on the bottom. Several trout which were seen to swim along and suck the imitation beetle off the bottom were caught. To use somewhat similar tactics with stone-fly nymphs would necessitate the added complication of pulling the imitation along the, presumably rocky, bottom of the lake shore.

ADULT FLIES: When the flies emerge from the nymphal skin they are at first very pale coloured, in fact much of their bodies and their wings are white, but after some hours they darken to their normal colour.

During their life, which probably lasts about two or three weeks, the adults are not very active. They spend most of their time sheltering under stones, or banks or among the foliage of trees or other vegetation. The Large Stone-flies are found under large rocks and stones beside and on the shore of the river or lake from which they emerged. Smaller dark brown coloured species, such as the Willow-flies and Needle-flies, are found commonly lying along the thin branches and stems of willows and among the foliage of other trees and bushes which overhang or are growing alongside the water. The Yellow Sally and other yellow or yellowish green coloured species may show a preference for the combined camouflage and shelter of green vegetation, against the background of which they tend to be less conspicuous than elsewhere.

Unlike Ephemeropterans, all stone-flies are able to drink after they have assumed their adult winged form, and many species are able to eat also. The larger species, which comprise the two families *Perlodidae* and *Perlidae* (and include the large stone-fly) do not eat, but smaller species in the other four families do so. These species include the Needle-flies, Willow-fly and Early Brown, and they have been observed feeding on the lichens and algae which grow on trees.

EGG LAYING: The only time at which adult stone-flies are seen on the water in any quantity is during and immediately after the period of oviposition. So far as is known, all the female flies lay their eggs on the surface. This they do in two ways. The female may release the eggs as she swims along the surface, and when on a river she usually swims across and upstream. Alternatively the female will fly over the water and either gradually approach the surface and touch it with the posterior end of her abdomen, or else alight on it momentarily while the eggs are released. Other species fly over the water and then suddenly fall to the surface on their upstretched wings and release the eggs on contact.

Females of the Large stone-fly adopt the first method, and at such times these large flies are most noticeable. They create a considerable disturbance in the water, and, as they are powerful swimmers, they leave a V ripple behind them as they move along. It is not surprising that they are important angling flies and that trout at times feed on them greedily. Several of the smaller species, including the Small Yellow Sally, *Chloroperla torrentium*, oviposit by the flying and dipping method, but the methods adopted by most of the other smaller species have not been closely described.

The eggs of stone-flies are of two general types. Those of the large stone-flies and of the other large species in the families Perlodidae and Perlidae are provided with an adhesive disc at one end. The disc carries numerous small adhesive knobs and when the eggs sink to the bottom these adhesive knobs on the disc anchor the eggs firmly to the substratum. Eggs of many, if not all, of the smaller species are without the terminal discs or adhesive knobs, but are protected instead by an extremely sticky jelly-like membrane which also serves to anchor the eggs to the river bottom.

DISTRIBUTION AND ECOLOGY

The rivers on which stone-flies are found in greatest numbers are those which flow over a stony and rocky substratum. The rivers of the west and north of England, Wales, Scotland and the maritime counties of Ireland are, in general, of this type. It is in these areas, rather than in the south and east of England and the midlands of Ireland, that stone-flies are of importance to anglers, it being remembered that the importance of a fly depends very largely on its abundance.

Of the thirty-one species recorded for Britain, only about twelve are classed as common. The type of habitat of different species varies with stone-flies as it does with all other orders of insects. And whilst most of the species have their most suitable habitat in the stony streams and rivers, which are typical of mountainous and upland districts, a few species occur in greater numbers in lowland rivers. Many of the species which are abundant in mountainous districts are found also in the lowlands, but, owing to their being in a less suitable environment, they may be relatively few in number.

In considering stone-fly habitats, the distributions of only the commoner or, for want of a better term, angling species are dealt with. Habitats of the nymphs include:—

1. Stony rivers (a) with stable substratum.
            (b) with unstable substratum.
2. Small stony streams.
3. Rocky shores of lakes.
4. Slow-flowing rivers with a muddy bottom and rooted vegetation.

Large Stone-fly, _Dictyopterygella recta_. This fly shows a

Plate IXa At Stockbridge

*Humphrey and Vera Joel*

THE RIVER TEST : the abundance of fly life which the Test supports is due, in part, to a low mortality rate among the nymphs and larvae, owing to the stabilised flow of the river, and the absence of very low water conditions or turbulent floods

Plate IXb At Houghton

R. A P. Dexter

Plate *Xa* The Itchen at Shawford

Humphrey and Vera Joel

The gin-clear water of the chalk streams allows light to penetrate easily. This is conducive to strong plant growth, and thus provides food for an abundance of nymphs, which feed mainly on the algae which coat the leaves and stalks of all submerged plants

Plate *Xb* The Test at Wherwell

R. A. P. Dexter

preference for waters of low temperature. It is found on high hill streams and on the stony shores of spring-fed and other cool-water lakes. The nymphs live under large-sized stones and have been found in lakes in the north of England and Scotland, and on some of the large Irish limestone lakes, as well as in many upland streams. The wings of the male flies are so small that they are quite useless as organs of flight. In appearance these males bear a superficial resemblance to the creepers, as the abortive wings are only slightly larger than the wing cases on mature creepers. The adult flies shelter among stones, under cut-in banks, or exposed tree roots along the shores of their water of origin. They are commonest in April and May, and on some lakes they are used as a bait for dapping. A distinct yellow stripe, which traverses the head and thorax longitudinally, serves to distinguish this from the two following species, which are larger in size.

Large Stone-fly, *Perla cephalotes.* This and the following species are the two most generally known and most commonly used by anglers. The creepers are found in stony rivers and streams, at times as high as 2,000 feet above sea level. They prefer a firm substratum of moss-covered stones which are more or less fixed to the river bed and are often partly buried in the bottom subsoil. The subsoil in such places often consists of a matrix of sand, gravel, clay and small stones. These creepers avoid areas of the river bed where the stones are loose and free from moss. The adults emerge in May and June, they are found in the north and west of England, Scotland, Wales and Ireland.

Large Stone-fly, *Perla carlukiana.* This is perhaps the commonest of the large stone-flies. It occurs in streams and rivers but differs from the preceding species in that the creepers show a marked preference for an unstable substratum. They are found in fast-flowing water in rivers, or in those portions of rivers in which the bottom is composed of loose stones which are free from moss. The loose stones on which these creepers occur in greatest quantity often overlie other loose stones rather than the more stable type of bottom in which moss-covered stones become embedded. A possible advantage of an environment of this nature is that during periods of severe floods the creepers can, with ease, penetrate downwards between the stones for shelter.

This species is widely distributed in suitable localities in Britain and Ireland. It is common in the north of England and in Scotland and occurs also in the west of England. The adults emerge in May and June. The adult flies of this and the previous species shelter beneath the larger stones which lie among the shingle along the banks of the rivers on which they occur. The empty skins of the creepers from which the flies have emerged will be found on stones near the water's edge.

Yellow Sally, *Isoperla grammatica* (Pl. 26 a, b, p. 113). This is a lowland rather than an upland species, and, owing to its wide distribution and conspicuous colour, it is probably the best known of the smaller stone-flies. The nymphs are found in stony, gravelly, and sandy rivers and streams. Mr. Mosely records it as being abundant on the River Test but less plentiful on other chalk streams. The species is distributed generally over Britain and Ireland. It is very common on limestone rivers, but has not been found on high hill streams.

The adults emerge from April to August and are occasionally of use to the angler. The female flies oviposit in the afternoon, and trout at times feed on the spent flies.

Small Yellow Sally, *Chloroperla torrentium*. This species is just as common as the preceding, but occurs in greatest abundance in upland and mountainous districts. The nymphs are found among sand and gravel in rivers and streams and also on lake shores. They are widely distributed in Britain, where they occur as far north as Inverness, and they also occur in Ireland. At times trout in upland rivers feed on the ovipositing or spent female flies. The adults emerge in greatest numbers in May, June and July.

February Red, *Taeniopteryx nebulosa*. Of all the stone-flies considered in this chapter, the February Red is the most localised in its distribution, and is one of the few which appear to avoid a stony environment. It is not known on the chalk streams, nor apparently on mountain rivers, and it is doubtful if it occurs in Ireland. It has been recorded from the Midlands, east and north of England, Wales and Scotland; and the nymphs are found in sluggish water in rivers and streams, perhaps usually with emerging vegetation and muddy bottoms. The adults emerge from January to April, and, although they are localised in their distribution, they may be exceedingly common on those rivers in which they do occur.

Early Brown, *Protonemoura meyeri* (Pl. 27a, p. 128): Widely distributed and abundant. The nymphs live in stony streams and in rivers where there is a stable bottom with moss-covered stones and boulders. They occur in suitable localities in Britain and Ireland and the adults emerge in the spring and early summer. The flies of this species quite closely resemble those of the previous species, but may be distinguished from them by the wings which in the Early Brown are greyish instead of brown, and by the abdomen which in the female February Red is pronouncedly reddish-brown in the last two or three segments.

Nemoura variegata (Pl. 27b, p. 128) is a small brown stone-fly quite similar to the preceding in appearance. It differs in habits, however. The nymphs live in slow-flowing and still water, often where there is emerging vegetation and a soft bottom. In consequence they are found in sheltered bays in lakes, in ponds and in the slow-flowing parts of rivers. They are widely distributed in Britain even as far north as the Hebrides, and are common in Ireland.

This is one of the nondescript small stone-flies, which, together with other species, are collectively called Browns. The adults emerge from March to July.

Willow-fly, *Leuctra geniculata* (Pl. 26c, p. 113): This species is common in the south of England on the chalk streams and is found as far north as Loch Awe in Scotland. Its distribution is rather local, however, and it has not been recorded from Ireland. The nymphs inhabit rather deep rivers with fairly soft though stony bottoms. Apparently the nymphs can burrow down through the mud or sand to the underside of deeply embedded boulders, as they have several times been recorded from such micro-habitats. Occasionally they occur in still water and I have found the species on Blagdon in Somerset.

The emergence period of the adults is in the autumn and they are in their maximum abundance in September.

Needle-fly, *Leuctra fusciventris,* is only about one half the size of the preceding species; this is the most noticeable difference between them. These Needle-flies are very common and are widely distributed. They are found throughout Britain and Ireland in the stony reaches of both lowland rivers and upland streams, and along the stony shores of lakes. They are abundant on the chalk streams and on limestone rivers. The adults are seen during the late summer and autumn and are perhaps commonest during August and September.

At times trout feed keenly on the spent flies of both this species and the preceding.

Needle-fly, _Leuctra hippopus_: This Needle-fly has a distribution quite like that of the previous species, but its period of emergence is during the spring and early summer. It is widely distributed throughout Britain and Ireland and ranges from the Hampshire chalk streams to the north of Scotland.

CHAPTER 14

DIPTERA

BLACK GNAT

From the time of Ronalds the Black Gnat has been identified as *Bibio johannis* in angling literature. But I think most anglers, at the riverside, call various species of *Simulium* Black Gnats. They do this with good reason. Several of the larger and darker species of *Simulium* superficially resemble *Bibio johannis*. The artificial imitations of the Black Gnats as tied by Halford and Dunne and the pike scale pattern of H. S. Hall catch fish which are feeding on *Simulium* adults floating on the surface. Mr. Dunne's pattern is particularly successful at such times. Halford recommended that his own pattern should be used indiscriminately for trout feeding on Black Gnats, *Bibio johannis*, and on Reed Smuts, *Simulium*.

Even though one artificial pattern at times successfully imitates both Black Gnats and Reed Smuts, it is advisable to differentiate between the natural species, as the habits of species of *Bibio* differ very much from those of *Simulium*. Species of the Black Gnats, *Bibio johannis*, are terrestrial and fall on the water more or less adventitiously, whilst species of *Simulium* are aquatic in their various stages and are found much more frequently.

REED SMUTS

Of the two groups, the Reed Smuts are more important from the angling viewpoint, as trout feed on them more frequently than on the true Black Gnats.

Reed Smuts are known also as Black Flies, and in America they are called Buffalo Gnats. They are very small thickset flies which resemble miniature houseflies in shape, but which have a rather more prominant thorax. The legs are short and the wings are transparent and are held flat along the body, like those of a housefly or bluebottle. In length the flies vary from about one-twelfth of an inch up to a quarter of an inch, and their colour is black or greyish or brownish black. The legs often have brownish or light silver-coloured markings on them.

Nineteen species, many of them uncommon, have been recorded in Britain. The emergence periods of the adults vary, but some or other of them will be found on the wing at least from February until November, and they occur in greatest abundance perhaps from May until August.

The various species are widely distributed throughout Britain and Ireland and, as with other orders of insects, the types of habitat of the larvae of different species vary. They all occur only in flowing water, but, whereas many species are found in weedy lowland streams and rivers of moderate or fast current, others are found only in stony hill burns or rapid upland rivers.

The adult flies lay their eggs on vegetation or protruding stones, sometimes beneath the surface and sometimes above it. When a female desires to oviposit beneath the surface, she crawls down for a short distance, usually less than a few inches, by means of some emerging vegetation or other object, in much the same manner as is adopted by spinners of *Baëtis* species. As she penetrates the surface film a bubble of air clings closely around her, and at some angles of light gives her the appearance of a small silver globule. When oviposition is completed the fly usually returns to the surface and may fly or crawl away, or else may be carried downstream. Trout feed on these spent flies often for hours at a time.

The eggs of those British species which have been studied usually hatch within a week, and a small stumpy wormlike larva emerges. As it grows the larva moults at intervals, and when it has increased in size it can be seen that its body is rather swollen in one half, and that the general colour is dirty cream, pale olive or brownish. The only noticeable appendages are the mouth parts, which include a pair of plume-like brushes, and one medianly situated leg called a proleg, which arises from near the head. The larva (Pl. 28d, p. 129) clings to its support by a posterior sucker and remains hanging or suspended in the current. When in this position it uses its mouth brushes to strain algae and other small food particles from the water. It does not swim but can move about by utilising its proleg and posterior sucker alternatively. It progresses by arching itself into loops in a manner similar to that adopted by the looper caterpillar. That is, the larva extends itself and grips the surface with its proleg and mouthparts, the posterior end releases its hold and is brought forward and grips just posterior to the proleg, and the motion is then repeated.

The larva has a large salivary gland from which it can draw a continuous web, and as it proceeds it releases a continuous strand of this web. When a number of these larvae are established on a leaf, a criss-cross of web will usually be found along the surface of the leaf, showing the peregrinations of the individual larvae. If alarmed, the larvae often release their hold of whatever leaf or twig they are established on and will slide out and remain suspended in the current on a single strand of web. This action often results in their leaving the comparative shelter of a weed bed, and emerging into open water immediately downstream from the weed. At such times they are readily accessible to predatory fish, and trout, at any rate, often take advantage of such opportunities.

Full-grown larvae are from one-quarter to one-third of an inch in length and may be recognised by their size, shape and colour or by their looping method of progressing. With the aid of a magnifying lens the mouth brushes and proleg will be discernible, but little differentiation will be seen between the indistinct segments of the thorax and the abdomen.

Before pupating the larva spins a cone-shaped cocoon. This is attached to the weed with the apex directed upstream and the wider and open end facing downstream. If strands of weed are collected from quick-flowing water of nearly any unpolluted stream during the early summer, large numbers of these cocoons, many with the pupae still in them, will be found. Shortly before the adult fly is due to emerge, gas begins to accumulate beneath the skin of the pupa. A close examination shows that this gas surrounds the contained fly within the pupal skin. It is not known what causes the gas to accumulate or what mechanism is used to collect the gas, presumably from the water.

When the quantity of gas has increased, the pupal skin splits open and the adult fly crawls through the opening. This process occurs under water but the adult fly is not wetted, as it remains enveloped in the bubble of gas which buoys it to the surface. The fly emerges at the surface quite dry and can fly away at once.

Trout feed on Reed Smut larvae, on the emerging adults, and on the adults perhaps during, and certainly after, oviposition. The extent to which trout feed on these smuts varies with the river, the time of the year and the particular season. They appear to be of greatest importance on the quick-flowing weedy stretches of small and moderate-sized lowland rivers.

GNATS AND MIDGES

The appearance of Chironomid flies is probably familiar to most lake anglers. They are long-legged gnat-like insects usually with their bodies longer than their wings, and their shoulders somewhat humped. They vary in length from less than a quarter to at least half an inch. The wings are pale greyish or white, and lie close along the body which is usually olive green or black. The flies carry the somewhat misleading vernacular name of midge. The name midge aptly describes some of the smallest species, but the larger species could more appropriately be termed short-winged gnats.

Anglers have bestowed many names on them. In Scotland the dark species are known as Blae and Blacks. In Ireland the forms appearing in the spring are called Duck-flies or Black Flies and the large summer species are called Racehorses or Buzzers. These last two names owe their origin to the habit the flies have of flying rapidly along the top of the water. On Blagdon they are known as Green Midges, or Olive Midges or Blagdon Buzzers. Ronalds termed one of them the Golden Dun Midge, and Leonard West refers to the Ruby Gnat, Olive Gnat and Black Gnat.

It has always seemed to me that these Chironomids have not received as much attention from authors as their importance warrants. This is perhaps because they are of more importance to lake than to river anglers, and little has been written yet about the entomology of lakes. Of all flies which occur on lakes these are the most widely distributed and the most prolific. They will be found on every unpolluted lake in Britain and Ireland, and during the periods of their emergence they are among the most valuable of the natural species which constitute food for trout.

During the spring emergence period, which occurs in the latter part of March or during April, trout follow the pupae as they ascend to the surface, and on many lakes, this results in the first general rise of fish of the year. Trout feed avidly on the pupae which remain

Robert Atkinson

Plate XIa The alkaline waters of the River Wharfe in Yorkshire are rich in fly life. Among the species found on it are the Yellow May Dun, *Heptagenia sulphurea*, Iron Blue, *Baëtis pumilus*, Mayfly, *Ephemera danica*, and the Little Sky-blue, *Centroptilum luteolum*

Plate XIb Another Yorkshire trout river, the Rye, here seen near Helmsley, is noted also for grayling

The Field

Plate XII Among the flies which occur on Tummel, shown here below Loch Rannoch, are the rare Summer Mayfly, *Siphlonurus limnaeanus* and the Grannon, *Brachycentrus subnubilus*

suspended from the surface film for a minute or two prior to emerging as adults. At times the fish will roam around in shoals, and anyone who is then fishing with good imitations of the pupae can have excellent sport. A peculiarity of the flies is that they emerge from deep water, and it is often in the deepest parts of the lake that they are most abundant and that most trout will be seen feeding on them. No lake angler can afford to ignore these flies, although their value will vary on different waters.

APPEARANCE AND HABITS

It is mainly with the large species the angler is concerned, and most of these large species are contained in the genus *Chironomus*. The adults of both sexes resemble each other in their general similarity to long-legged gnats. The head is small and merges into the thorax, which is deep and humped on the dorsal surface. The mesothoracic segment is the largest, and from it arises the single pair of wings, which appear rather small in comparison to the size of the whole insect. The wings are slender and do not reach to the end of the abdomen. The legs are very long and thin, and when the fly is at rest on the surface of the water, they are spread out sideways in a radial fashion from the thorax; at such times the wings lie flat along the abdomen. The abdomen is long and consists of nine distinct segments but, as with all the Diptera, is devoid of cerci.

Male flies differ from the females in that the antennae (which arise from the head) are conspicuous and are plume-like in structure, the abdomen is very slender and tapers little if at all towards the tail end. The last abdominal segment carries the mating claspers or forceps. Female flies are bulkier, the abdomen is noticeably thicker and it tapers slightly.

Chironomids, in common with all flies other than the Ephemeroptera, pass through only one winged stage. There is no dun stage. When the adults emerge from the water they do not alter in appearance, except for a slight darkening of colour, before they mate and die. But Chironomids resemble caddis-flies and differ from Ephemeropterans and stone-flies in that they belong to the Endopterygota, or division of insects in which the young forms pass through both pupal and larval stages, so that they emerge from the eggs as larvae and in this stage feeding and growth takes place. When the larvae (Pl. 28 c, p. 129) are fully grown they pupate, and the pupae, which are active, remain in the water for some days before swimming to the surface in order to allow the contained adult fly to escape. The pupae are fairly easy to recognise. Very superficially, or when removed from the water, they may resemble *Baëtis* nymphs. The resemblance, however, is mainly in the colour pattern, size and general shape. They differ obviously in the arrangement of their various appendages. The pupae have no legs, but the legs and folded wings of the contained adult fly can be seen through the skin in the region of the thorax. The thorax of the pupa is, therefore, extremely bulky and it occupies from a third to a half of the whole length of the insects.

The contained legs and wings are folded underneath the thorax and the pale wings are particularly conspicuous by contrast in dark-coloured pupae. The abdomen is slender and consists of nine segments. The last segment is very small and from it arise two small fan-like bunches of hairs which serve as a tail fin. The insect breathes through tufts of filaments which arise from the thorax. By means of these filaments oxygen is extracted from the water, but diffusion may perhaps also take place through the integument of the body. The pupae of the genus *Tanypus* differ in that they carry two small tube-like respiratory organs instead of the bunched filaments, and in order to utilise these, the insect must rise to the surface of the water and renew its oxygen supply directly from the air.

The larvae of Chironomids are somewhat worm-like in appearance. They consist of a head, three incipient thoracic segments, and nine abdominal segments. The appendages are few, a pair of short false legs on the first and last segments, and several small respiratory protuberances on the last and penultimate segments of the abdomen. These respiratory protuberances somewhat resemble the short legs, but they are not armed with the small hooks which the latter possess. On the head are a pair of small eyes, very short antennae and the mouth parts.

The colour of the larvae is either a rather pale olive or else is a bright blood red. The red species owe their bright colour to the haemoglobin which is contained in their blood and these red *Chironomus* larvae, or blood worms as they are called, are among the very few insects which possess haemoglobin. Most insects, including the olive coloured Chironomid larvae, have clear or faintly yellow or greenish coloured blood; in addition, insect blood contains colourless cells known as haemocytes. In man, and other mammals, the haemoglobin in the blood stream functions as an oxygen carrier. It absorbs oxygen through the thin walls of the lungs and carries it to cells all over the body. In Chironomid larvae the haemoglobin acts in rather a different capacity; it absorbs oxygen but apparently releases it only if the insect is obtaining an insufficient supply from the water. These larvae live in little tunnels which they excavate in the mud at the bottom of lakes and rivers. At times they leave their burrows and swim up towards the surface, possibly with the object of renewing their supply of oxygen.

Owing to the haemoglobin they are able to live under conditions of very low oxygen concentration, and consequently can inhabit the mud at the bottom of the deepest parts of lakes, where few other insects would be able to live. They can also live in waters in which pollution has reduced the oxygen concentration to a very low level. In regard to this it might be mentioned that the presence of these blood worms in a water does not mean that the water has been polluted; it is only when these larvae alone are found inhabiting an area that serious pollution or other causes, which would cause a shortage of oxygen, should be suspected.

The eggs are laid by the flies on the surface of the water, and, among those species which have been studied, are extruded in a long string-like mass contained in a transparent jelly coating. This is attached to some support at the surface, which anchors it securely. With many species the egg-laying habits have not been studied, and it is possible that the eggs of those species which inhabit deep waters away from the shore-line in lakes, either sink or float freely after they have been laid.

The different stages in the life history, which have been considered here in inverse order, occupy in all a year with many species. Other species have shorter life cycles and there may be more than one brood in a single year.

There is a very large number of species of the Chironomidae in Britain and Ireland, and the annual period of emergence of different species varies. At certain times of the year, notably in spring and summer, the emergence periods of a large number of them coincide. These spring and summer maxima vary somewhat in different districts, but the former maximum usually occurs sometime from the middle of March to the end of April and the latter about July.

The spring maximum is probably of greater importance to anglers. During this, on most lakes, there is a period of about two weeks when the flies appear in sufficient numbers to bring on a general rise of trout, and there may then be better fishing than at any other time of the year.

In order to appreciate the value of these flies it should be remembered that in lake fishing one of the difficulties to be surmounted is the considerable distance which often lies between the angler's flies and the trout. One of the advantages of fishing in the shallows is that a trout, even though swimming near the bottom, is yet also near the surface, as the distance which he is able to sink is controlled by the depth of water. Therefore, a fish which is near the bottom can see flies at the surface more easily in shallow than in deep water. And even though he can see them from deep water he is less likely to rise when he must ascend a long distance. When a trout is feeding at or near the surface the depth of the water is not important.

The chief factor contributing to surface-feeding fish is an abundance of flies on the water, aided by pupae or nymphs ascending from the bottom. These conditions obtain during a hatch of fly, and many species of Chironomids are the only flies which emerge in abundance from the deepest parts of the lake.

The diurnal times of appearance of Chironomids vary with the species and the time of the year. During the spring maximum many of the dark-coloured species (Blae and Black) emerge in the forenoon and early afternoon. The females return to the water to lay their eggs in the evening, and during the day large swarms of the male flies will be seen hovering along or some distance inland from the shore-line. Later in the year the main times of emergence are at dusk and perhaps after darkness. Chironomids are also active at dawn.

DISTRIBUTION AND ECOLOGY

Chironomids occur in all types of natural fresh water. They will be found in water barrels, ditches, ponds, lakes, small and large streams and rivers. In general, those whose larvae are olive-coloured (Pl. 28 c, p. 129) are commonest in water which has a moderate or high concentration of oxygen, and the blood-red coloured larvae in water with a lower oxygen concentration. The former species are found in the shallower areas of lakes, in other standing water and in the bottom mud in rivers and streams. In flowing water they occur also among the moss and algae growing on stones, and in such situations are common even in very fast currents.

The blood red larvae of some species live in the mud of lake

Plate 27: STONE-FLIES × 3.75
(a) Early Brown, *Protonemura meyeri*; (b) Small Brown, *Nemoura variegata*

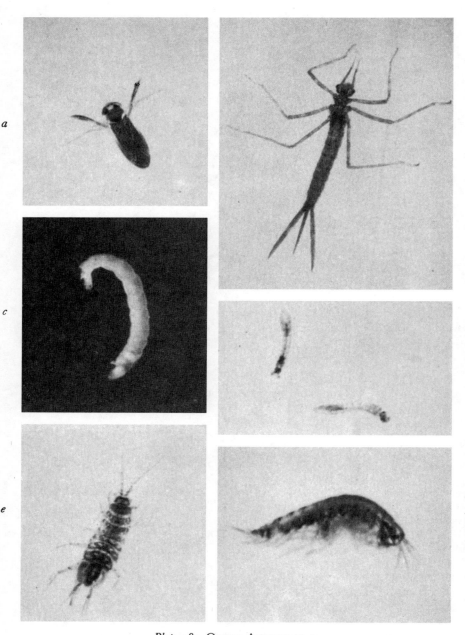

Plate 28: OTHER ANIMALS × 3
(*a*) Lesser Water-boatman, [*Corixa* sp.]; (*b*) Dragon-fly larva; (*c*) Chironomid, Midge larva; (*d*) Two Reed Smuts, *Simulium* larvae; (*e*) Water-louse, *Asellus* sp.; (*f*) Water-shrimp, *Gammarus* sp.

bottoms often in the deepest water, in other standing waters, and also in rivers and streams, and they can withstand considerable pollution.

Little is yet known about the ecology of the larvae of individual species of Chironomids. Lake species are found buried in sand and detritus, in algae covering stones and the submerged portion of reeds and in mud. They inhabit the shallow littoral areas, the sub-littoral areas of moderate depth, and the profundal or very deep areas. All species are selective in the type of habitat in which they live, but some are more severely restricted in this respect than others. Normally those which occur in abundance in the profundal areas in a lake are rare in the littoral zones, and vice versa, but much overlapping in the distribution occurs. Similarly, differences are noticeable in the species found on different types of lake, and from the purely limnological viewpoint Chironomids are important indicators in the classification of lakes. The Chironomids are by no means unique in this respect, as all fauna is of some value. But, owing to the number of different species and to the abundance of many of the species, the Chironomids form probably the most important of all the insect groups for this purpose.

In general, the large olive, and green, and dull crimson coloured midges or buzzers, which include the species *Chironomus viridis* and *C. tentans*, are found only on alkaline lakes. There are many species which are collectively known as Blae and Blacks, and some or other of these are present on both acid and alkaline waters.

PART THREE

FLIES AND FISH

CHAPTER 15

PERIOD FLIES
AND MODERN NAMES

A SUBJECT of considerable interest is the correlation between the older patterns of artificial flies and the natural insects which the tyings were intended to represent. There are innumerable patterns which have long since been discarded. Names such as the Dun Cutte, Great Dun, Moorish-fly and Tawny-fly are now only of historical interest. Patterns such as the Little Pale Blue, Ashy Dun and Orange Dun have only more recently been discarded, and still others, including the Whirling Dun, the Welshman's Button and the Blue Dun appear to be in the process of being dropped.

These old patterns of artificial flies usually carried the same names as did the natural species on which they were modelled, and yet very few of them can be identified with certainty at the present time. This is a peculiar anomaly, having regard to the advances which have been made in entomology during the last century. In order to appreciate the difficulties involved it is necessary to consider the position of systematic entomology preceding and during the period concerned.

The modern system of technical nomenclature of insects dates only from the middle of the eighteenth century, when the great Swedish naturalist Carl Linné brought out his book *Systema Naturae*. In regard to the Ephemeroptera, it is unlikely that angler-entomologists paid attention to the technical names of the flies during the succeeding one hundred years. But towards the end of this period owing to the publication of additional entomological books in England which dealt with the Ephemeroptera it was not altogether surprising to find that in 1836 Ronalds brought out his *Fly-Fisher's Entomology*, although it was not until 1856, when the fifth edition of his book was published, that the technical names of all the species were included and correlated with the angler's names.

Before the appearance of Ronalds's great work, fishing authors used vernacular names only and gave, at the most, only superficial descriptions of the species about which they were writing. Their descriptions were generally combined with, or consisted merely of, descriptions of the artificial imitations, and the natural species was presumably recognised from the colour resemblance which it bore to its artificial counterpart.

It was a free and easy method of identifying flies and, anyway, who was to say that identifications might be incorrect? It was perhaps the age of the angler-naturalist rather than of the angler-systematist.

From a practical angling viewpoint, however, this method of recognising flies had much to commend it. Anglers using it would be inclined to follow the sensible practice of fishing with a fly which looked similar in size and colour to the natural species on the water, and would doubtless name the natural fly after the artificial rather than the other way round.

At such times artificial patterns would take the place of prototypes of natural flies and, in lieu of preserved specimens or coloured illustrations of natural species, they would have been reasonably effective within certain broad limits. For instance, a comparison between an artificial March Brown and an artificial Olive Dun would probably be sufficient to allow the natural March Brown and the Olive Dun to be separated from each other. But it is doubtful if the same could be said for patterns which more closely resemble each other, such as the Yellow Dun and the July Dun.

It is evident from the fishing literature published during the eighteenth and nineteenth centuries that much confusion existed regarding the identification of species. Errors in identification could arise from several causes. (1) An angler reading descriptions of two flies which bore a close resemblance to each other might easily confuse them and transpose their names. (2) Owing to an inadequate

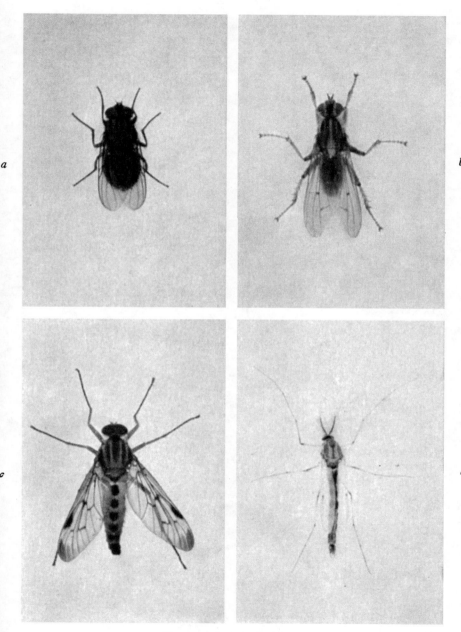

Plate 29: OTHER FLIES × 3
(*a*) House-fly; (*b*) Cow-dung Fly; (*c*) Oak-fly; (*d*) Green Midge, *Chironomus*

Plate 30: OTHER INSECTS × 3
(*a*) Alder-fly, *Sialis lutaria*; (*b*) and (*c*) Ants; (*d*) Hawthorn-fly, *Bibio marci*

or inaccurate description of a species, that species might not be correlated with its name as designated by the author; and (3) owing to differences in the distribution of species an angler living perhaps in the north of England would search in vain in endeavouring to find in his district some species which occurred only in the south of England. In such circumstances it is not unlikely that the name of the fly concerned would be applied to some other species.

There is no reason why at the present time the flies mentioned in these older books should not be identified from the written descriptions with as much accuracy (or inaccuracy) as they were in the past, provided that the reader is familiar with the appearances of the materials which were used in the construction of the equivalent artificial patterns. The only advantages which the older anglers presumably would have had to assist them would have been any additional information which was passed on by word of mouth, and which might not be available now.

There is not likely to be confusion over the identification of such distinctive flies as the Stone-fly, the Yellow Sally, the Iron Blue Dun, the March Brown, etc., but many other species are extremely difficult to place. For instance, the name Whirling Blue Dun has obviously been applied to several species by different authors, and, whilst it is probable that Ronalds's Whirling Blue is a synonym for the Large Dark Olive Dun, *B. rhodani*, which appears in the autumn, it would be very problematical indeed if many of the other species coming under the name could be identified with much certainty.

In identifying these older flies use can be made of the following data, some of which will be contained in the description being considered:—

(1) The colour, size and shape of the natural fly as may be described.

(2) The shape, as judged from the manner in which it is recommended that the materials should be attached to the hook, such as a wing lying close to the body or tied upright. The size, judged from the size of the hook used.

(3) The habits of the fly as they may be described, and its seasonal and diurnal times of appearance.

(4) On what river or rivers, or in what part of the country, it occurs.

In the absence of other examples I quote my own experiences in this connection.

Before becoming interested in systematic entomology I identified natural species from the descriptions in the older angling books, chiefly from Ronalds, Francis Francis, Aldam, Hansard and Brookes.

I know now that, among the species concerned were (1) *Baëtis rhodani*, (2) *B. scambus*, (3) *B. atrebatinus*, (4) *Centroptilum luteolum*, (5 and 6) *Ephemerella ignita* (male and female). These flies I separated respectively as follows:—

(1) Blue Dun (for the flies which appeared in the spring), Whirling Dun (of Ronalds) for the same species as it appeared in the autumn.
(2) July Dun (of Francis Francis).
(3) Dark Olive Dun.
(4) Sky Blue Dun.
(5) Indian Yellow.
(6) July Dun (of Ronalds).

Now, after twenty years, I am still of the same opinion, but have added the following to the list:—

(7) *Procloëon rufulum* (Pale Evening Dun).
(8) *Baëtis vernus* (Yellow Dun, Medium Olive Dun).
(9) *B. tenax* (Medium Olive Dun).
(10) *B. bioculatus* (Pale Watery Dun). This last, of course, from Halford.

I found that the only satisfactory way to correlate the duns with the older descriptions was to examine specimens freshly caught off the water, and in such matters the hackneyed statement that "the riverside is the only true school for the angler" is eminently correct.

It is advisable also when making identification to take into consideration variations in the size, colour and habits of the species which may occur during the season and in different rivers. In this connection it would be desirable in those cases in which an author gives the name of the water and the time of the year on which a certain fly is found, to verify what species occur on that water at the present time. As an instance, it might be mentioned that Ronalds states that the Orange Dun and the Dark Blue Dun or July Dun are favourite flies on the River Dove. It is probable that the Orange Dun is the male Blue-winged Olive Dun, and that the July Dun is the female of the same species. This is substantiated to some extent by the fact that the Blue-winged Olive is evidently common on the Dove, as Mr. Mosely records it from there for every month from April to November inclusive.

Many of the older dressings of such flies as the July Dun, the Pale Evening Dun and the Sky Blue Dun are still used by wet fly anglers, and for practical reasons it is, therefore, of advantage to be able to correlate these older patterns with appropriate natural species. In cases where several authors apparently applied the same vernacular name to different species, preference has been given to the author whose name and reputation as an angler-entomologist has been most generally recognised.

Included in the list of the names of flies are several species which do not appear to have received common names previously, and for any of these species which are of importance to anglers common names have been proposed. Some of the names on the list have been in verbal use for many years but have not, so far, appeared in print.

In compiling these vernacular names, it has been borne in mind that the most natural and useful name is one which describes some obvious characteristic either of the appearance or else of the habits of the species concerned. Nearly all the existing vernacular names of natural species are of this type; for instance, August Dun, Olive Dun, Stone-fly, Sedge. Entomologists usually follow the same system in compiling technical names, except that the names are adopted from either Latin or Greek words. For instance the generic name *Centroptilum* is composed from two Greek words which refer to the spur-like shape of the hind wings of the flies concerned.

Alder — *Sialis* spp. (Pl. 30 a, p. 133).

Angler's Curse — *Caenis* spp., dun (Pl. 12 b, p. 77) or spinner (Pl. 20 b, p. 97).

August Dun — *Ecdyonurus dispar* (Pl. 12 a, p. 77).

Black Drake — *Ephemera danica*, male spinner (Pl. 1 e, p. 16).

Black Gnat — *Bibio johannis*. In practice the name is applied to many small black flies.

Blue-winged Olive Dun — *Ephemerella ignita*, dun (Pl. 11 a, b, p. 76).

Blue-winged Pale Watery Dun — *Centroptilum pennulatum* (Pl. 11 c, d, p. 76).

Brown May Dun—*Heptagenia fuscogrisea*.

Caperer — *Halesus radiatus* (Pl. 23 c, p. 108), *H. digitatus* (and *Sericostoma personatum*, Pl. 24 a, p. 109).

Cinnamon Sedge — various species of *Limnephilus* and other medium- or large-sized sedge flies with cinnamon coloured wings of which *L. lunatus* is typical. *Stenophyllax stellatus* is another (Pl. 23 d, p. 108).

Claret Dun — *Leptophlebia vespertina* (Pl. 13 d, p. 80).

Cow-dung Fly — *Scopeuma stercoraria* (Pl. 29 b, p. 132).

Creeper — Nymph of the large stone-flies (Pl. 3, p. 32).

Dark Dun — *Heptagenia lateralis* (Pl. 12 c, p. 77).

Dark Olive Dun — *Baëtis atrebatinus*, dun.

Downlooker — *Leptis scolopacea* (Pl. 29 c, p. 132).

Early Brown — *Protonemura meyeri* (Pl. 27 a, p. 128).

February Red — *Taeniopteryx nebulosa*.

Grannom — *Brachycentrus subnubilus*.

Gravel Bed — *Anisomera burmeisteri*.

Great Red Spinner — spinners of *Rhithrogena haarupi*, *Ecdyonurus venosus*, *E. torrentis*, *E. dispar* (Pl. 21 c, p. 100).

Greendrake — *Ephemera danica* — dun (Pl. 1 b, c, p. 16).

Grey Drake — *Ephemera danica* — female spinner before oviposition (Pl. 1 e, p. 16).

Grey Flag
Grey Sedge } — *Hydropsyche* spp. (Pl. 25 b, p. 112).

Halford's Welshman's Button—*Sericostoma personatum* (Pl. 24 a, p. 109). This fly is called the Caperer on the Test.

Hawthorn — *Bibio marci* (Pl. 30 d, p. 133).

Iron-blue Dun — *Baëtis pumilus* (Pl. 6 a, b, p. 49), *B. niger*.

Jenny Spinner — *Baëtis pumilus* (Pl. 14 c, p. 81), *B. niger*, male spinners.

July Dun — formerly was *Ephemerella ignita*, female dun (Pl. 11 b, p. 76). Now is apparently *Baëtis scambus* (Pl. 8 c, d, p. 65) in the south of England.

Lake Olive Dun — *Cloëon simile* (Pl. 13 a, b, p. 80).

Large Amber Spinner — *Centroptilum pennulatum*, female spinner (Pl. 19 c, p. 96).

Large Claret Spinner — *Leptophlebia vespertina*, female spinner.

Large Dark Olive Dun — *Baëtis rhodani* (Pl. 6 c, d, p. 49).

Large Dark Olive Spinner — *Baëtis rhodani*, male (Pl. 14 a, p. 81).

Large Green Dun — *Ecdyonurus insignis* (Pl. 9 a, b, p. 68).

Large Green Spinner — *Ecdyonurus insignis* (Pl. 15 d, p. 84).

Late March Brown — *Ecdyonurus venosus*.

Little Amber Spinner — *Centroptilum luteolum*, female spinner (Pl. 17 d, p. 92).

Little Claret Spinner — *Baëtis pumilus* (Pl. 14 d, p. 81), *B. niger*, female spinners.

Little Sky-blue Dun (Pale Watery Dun) — *Centroptilum luteolum* (Pl. 8 a, b, p. 65).

March Brown — *Rhithrogena haarupi* (Pl. 7 p, p. 64).

Mayfly — Three species of *Ephemera*, namely *E. danica*, *E. vulgata* and *E. lineata*, of which the first (Pl. 1, p. 16) is by far the commonest and most important. The last named is so rare that it can have no value as an angling fly.

Medium Olive Dun — *Baëtis vernus*, *B. tenax*.

Midges — Blae and Black
    Buzzer
    Duck-fly } — Species of Chironomidae, more particularly those which occur on lakes and ponds. (Green Midge, Pl. 29 d, p. 132).
    Green Midge
    Olive Midge

Murragh — *Phryganea grandis* and *P. striata* (Pl. 2, p. 17).

Needle-fly } — Stone-fly species of the genus *Leuctra*, including
Needle Brown } the common *L. fusciventris*.

Oak-fly — *Leptis scolopacea* (Pl. 29 c, p. 132).

Olive Duns — A generalised name which is applied to the olive-bodied subimagines of *Baëtis*, namely *B. rhodani* (Pl. 6 c. d, p. 49), *B. vernus*, *B. tenax*, *B. atrebatinus*, *B. scambus* (Pl. 8 c, d, p. 65), and at times to the dun of *Rhithrogena semicolorata* (Pl. 9 c, d, p. 68).

Olive Upright — *Rhithrogena semicolorata*, dun (Pl. 9 c, d, p. 68).

Pale Evening Dun (Pale Watery Dun) — *Procloëon rufulum* (Pl.10 b, p. 69).

Pale Watery Dun — A composite name for the following species:— *Baëtis bioculatus* (Pl. 10 a, p. 69), *Centroptilum luteolum* (Pl. 8 a, b, p. 65), *Procloëon rufulum* (Pl. 10 b, p. 69). These three species are somewhat similar in colouring; *Baëtis scambus* (Pl. 8 c, d, p. 65) is usually darker in the wing and more olive coloured in the body and it has, therefore, been grouped with the Olive Duns.

Pond Olive Dun — *Cloëon dipterum*.

Purple Dun }
Purple Spinner } — *Paraleptophlebia cincta* (spinner Pl. 18 a, p. 93).

Red Spinner — Female spinner of *Baëtis rhodani* (Pl. 14 b, p. 81). In practice the name is applied to nearly any spinner which has a red coloured body.

Reed Smut — *Simulium* spp. (Pl. 28d, p. 129).

Sherry Spinner — spinner of *Ephemerella ignita* (Pl. 19a, b, p. 96).

Silverhorns — Species of the genera *Mystacides* and *Leptocerus* (Pl. 25a, p. 112) which have very long pale-coloured antennae.

Small Dark Olive — *Baëtis scambus*, dun (Pl. 8c, p. 65).

Spent Gnat — Spinner of *Ephemera danica* (Pl. 1e, f, p. 16), which has fallen spent on to the water. The name is often shortened to "Spent" and is sometimes applied to the spinners at any stage of their short existence.

Stone-fly — Any adult fly of the order Plecoptera (e. g. Pl. 26, p. 113). The large species which are used as a bait by anglers include *Dictyopterygella recta* and *Perla carlukiana*.

Summer Mayfly — species of *Siphlonurus* (Pls. 13c, p. 80; 20a, p. 97; 21a, b, p. 100).

Turkey Brown — *Paraleptophlebia submarginata*, dun.

Water-louse — *Asellus* spp. (Crustaceans) (Pl. 28e, p. 129).

Water-shrimp — *Gammarus* spp. (Crustaceans) (Pl. 28f, p. 129).

Willow-fly — *Leuctra geniculata* (Pl. 26c, p. 113).

Yellow Evening Dun ⎫ — *Ephemerella notata* ⎰ (Pl. 7c, p. 64).
Yellow Evening Spinner ⎭ ⎱ (Pl. 18c, p. 93).

Yellow May Dun ⎫ — *Heptagenia sulphurea* (Pl. 7a, b, p. 64).
Yellow Hawk ⎭

Yellow Sally — Stone-fly, *Isoperla grammatica* (Pl. 26a, b, p. 113).

Yellow Upright — *Rhithrogena semicolorata* — spinner (Pl. 18d, p. 93).

The following comments refer mainly to the origins of the less well known or new vernacular names used in describing various species.

Blue-winged Pale Watery Dun — This is the name originally used by Mr. Skues for *Centroptilum pennulatum* and it is, I think, one of the most accurate descriptive names extant. The wings of the fly are a pronounced blue, very similar to those of the Blue-winged Olive, and the fly otherwise is the colour of a Pale Watery Dun. This name also has precedence over subsequent names proposed for this species.

Brown May Dun — Refers to the colour of the dun and to its seasonal time of emergence, and is in keeping with the name Yellow May Dun which is applied to the allied species *Heptagenia sulphurea*.

Dark Dun — Refers to the general colour of the fly which is nearly a true dark dun (not a blue dun).

Dark Olive — Refers to the colour of the dun which, though very similar to the Large Dark Olive, *Baëtis rhodani*, is smaller in size.

Grey Flag — The name used in the midlands of Ireland for species of the caddis flies belonging to the genus *Hydropsyche*. Probably so named because of the flies' habit of resting on the flags which border many of the limestone rivers.

Lake Olive — Dun or Spinner, refers to the habitat of the species. *Cloëon simile* is the only Olive which is common on large lakes and it seldom occurs in flowing water.

Large Amber Spinner — Refers to the size of the spinner and the body colour.

Large Green Dun   ⎱ — Refers to the size and general colour of
Large Green Spinner   ⎰   the flies.

Little Sky-blue — This fly was obviously well known in the middle of the last century, as it is described by Francis Francis and Ronalds as well as by earlier writers back to the time of Brookes in the late eighteenth century. From its description it seems obvious that it is one of the species now called Pale Wateries, and, judging from its description, habits and colour, particularly the colour of its wing, it seems most probable that it is *Centroptilum luteolum*. The wing of this species is an attractive fine shade of pale sky blue, particularly when examined in the early evening light.

These two species, *Centroptilum pennulatum* and *C. luteolum*, were most aptly named Spurwings by Mr. F. E. Sawyer, and the name is descriptive of the appearance of the hind wings of the flies when examined under a strong lens or a microscope. But these hind wings are so small that very few people could see them with the unaided eye, and they could not possibly see the minute spur-shaped projection on the wings which is only one-eightieth of an inch in length. So that, even though the name Spurwing is very suitable for anyone examining the flies under a microscope, it is of no use to an angler who requires to identify the flies at the riverside. It is largely for this reason that preference is given here to the alternative names which appear more suitable for the purpose for which they are required.

Olive Upright — This name is being used to describe the dun of the Yellow Upright, *Rhithrogena semicolorata*. The name "Olive" refers to the colour of the dun which is rather a pale olive coloured fly, and the name "Upright" is retained in order to keep the association with the Yellow Upright which is widely known.

Pale Evening Dun — Refers to the normal diurnal time of emergence of the dun and to its pale colour.

Pond Olive — Refers to the typical habitat of the nymph and the colour of the dun.

Purple Dun — Refers to the colour of the dun.

Purple Spinner — This name is used more for the purpose of keeping its association with the dun, rather than with the object of describing the colour, although both the male and the female spinners have a slight purplish tinge.

Small Amber Spinner — This name refers to the size of the spinner and the body colour.

Summer Mayfly — Refers to the period of emergence of the dun, and to the similarity which it bears in size and colour to the Greendrake.

Yellow Evening Dun — Refers to the diurnal time of emergence of the dun, and to its colour.

Yellow Evening Spinner — Refers to the diurnal time of flight of the spinner and to its colour.

Plates 31: ARTIFICIAL FLIES

c

(a) (l. to r.) (1) Westmeath Large Fly; tied in 1791 for use on Loughs Sheelin, Kinail, Ennel and lakes in general. (2) & (3) Flies tied about 1850; Pattern Fly for L. Sheelin; Golden Olive for L. Sheelin; (4) (5) & (6) Flies tied in 1789 by Thos. Cummess near Kilbreda (Kilbride) for Lough Mask: Fly tied to ten strands of twisted horsehair; lightly dressed Golden Olive type fly on single strand of gut of approximately ¼ drawn thickness; nondescript fly with very thin upright wings of brown mallard.

(b) Flies tied by Cornelius Gorman, Ennis, Co. Clare in 1791. The seven large-sized patterns for Lough Mask; the two smaller patterns for use in Inchiquin Lough, Co. Clare, for the month of July. The Limerick hooks on which these flies are dressed are sharper than the average present-day hooks.

Plate 31: Artificial Flies very slightly enlarged
See full caption opposite

Plate 32: ARTIFICIAL FLIES very slightly enlarged
See full caption opposite

CHAPTER 16

TASTES OF FISH

SEVERAL REASONS have been suggested to explain why fish rise
to artificial flies, and by far the most important of these reasons
is that the fish mistake the flies for something edible. Trout, in
common with most animals, are selective feeders, that is, they eat
only certain foods and they select the food they require. It is obviously necessary that they should be able to do this, as otherwise
they would eat any sort of small particle floating on the water.
The points of interest to anglers are (1) How critical are trout in
their selection, and (2) what senses do they use in discriminating?

We know from autopsies that trout are sufficiently critical to
differentiate between insects or other food organisms and inanimate
particles such as pieces of leaves or chips of bark which may be on
the water. We know that when there is a number of different types
of insects on the surface, trout may feed on them apparently indis-

---

Plates 32: ARTIFICIAL FLIES

(a) (l. to r.) (1) (4) & (7) Bought at Stockbridge 1816. (3) & (8) Flies for
White Trout at Kinvara, Co. Galway; tied by Hynes at Gort, 1797. (2)
(5) (6) & (9) Flies for Kiltartan River, 1810; of these flies nos (6) & (9) are
patterns of Greendrakes with the wings tied forward.

(b) (l. to r.) (1) — (6) Modern Flies: (1) Yellow Wasp; wet dressing of
Greendrake as used on Lough Mask. (2) Golden Olive as used on larger
Irish limestone lakes (3) Claret and Yellow, modern dressing of Westmeath
Large Fly (see Plate 31) (4) Gosling; wet fly dressing of Greendrake as
used on Lough Melvin (5) Spent Greydrake or Spent Gnat as used on
Irish limestone lakes and rivers (6) Greydrake tied cocked, an excellent
pattern for the late afternoon or early evening (7) Olive Quill dry fly dressed
with wings tied forward (8) Brown Sedge-fly (9) Lunn's Particular dressed
to lie flat on the water (10) Red Spinner tied with hackle point wings as
a wet fly (11) Pupa of Chironomid or Duck-fly.

criminately. As a sample autopsy on a fish feeding in this manner, the following is a list of the organisms found in the stomach of a trout of 2½ lbs. caught one afternoon in May in Co. Galway:—
6 Greendrakes, 5 small red sedges, 2 large black terrestrial beetles, 6 small beetles, several small black flies, 4 Blue-winged Olive nymphs, at least 12 Olive Duns, some of which appeared to be only partly hatched, some smaller Ephemeropterans, both duns and nymphs, and one sedge pupa.

The variety and types of food organisms found in a fish feeding in this manner are largely dependent on the assortment available, and on the relative numbers of each type present. When one type predominates on the water, it may or may not predominate among the assortment found in the trout's stomach. Fish feeding in this manner are usually described as general feeders. These fish are relatively easy to catch, or to rise, as they will usually rise to any one of a large assortment of artificial flies which is well presented to them.

In contrast to this, fish may concentrate on one type of food organism and ignore others. This may occur when the type selected is available in greater numbers than any other type. It frequently happens when fish are feeding on *Caenis* species, or on Spent Gnats or Blue-winged Olives. But it also apparently happens at times when the type selected does not predominate on the water. I say "*apparently* happens" here only because an observation of this nature is difficult to prove and not because I doubt the truth of the statement.

I have often noticed in autopsies performed on trout that one or more food organisms may be grouped in layers or sections in the stomach. In several fish killed during a mayfly season on Lough Sheelin, the lower portion of their stomachs contained only mayfly nymphs, and the upper portion only Spent Gnats. These fish obviously had been feeding first on the nymphs and then on the Spent Gnats, and had ignored Greendrakes and many other flies including sedges and small spinners which were on the water at the same time. In regard to fish caught in a river in July, I have found the upper portion of the stomach full of Sherry Spinners, and the lower containing other food organisms, often a varied assortment.

Apart from observations such as these, it has many times been demonstrated under laboratory conditions that fish have a keen sense of discrimination. But to what extent is not so easy to ascertain.

It is reasonable to assume that trout can recognise insects by some or all of the following factors—colour, brightness, shape, trans-

lucency and action. Of these factors most has been written about
the colour, and in this connection I quote hereunder some extracts
from the most modern work I know of on the subject, namely *The
Vertebrate Eye, and its adaptive radiation* by G. L. Walls. Mr. Walls's
opening paragraph on the colour vision of fishes is as follows:—

"The reader's suspense, if any, may as well be relieved at once
by the flat, if somewhat back-handed, statement that no fish is
known *not* to have colour vision. But the angler can take little
comfort from the fact. As will appear shortly, he cannot predict
whether a red fly will attract or violently repel the fish he is after.
In fact, there is every reason to think that a dry fly, or a floating
plug of any colour, is seen by the fish merely as a dark silhouette
whose form is much more important than its hue. Much though
we may know of the colour vision of laboratory fishes, and infer
as to the colour vision of game species, when it comes to wet flies
and plugs the old rule still holds: What they'll take, they take,
and what they won't, they won't."

Mr. Walls then gives a brief account of the more important
experiments which were carried out in order to prove or disprove
that fish had colour vision. The two chief research workers were
Carl von Hess and Karl von Frisch. Hess maintained the negative
and Frisch the positive view. As a result of the experiments conducted
by these and other workers, Mr. Walls points out that it is apparent
that fish can experience colour as a sensation quality apart from
brightness, and that colour seems to lie between brightness and form
(shape) as regards its attention value. Brightness (tone) differs from
colour as follows: a pale red and a darker red which are of different
brightness may be the same colour; and conversely two different
colours, say medium-red and -blue, may be of the same brightness.

In regard to the contention that "a dry fly or a floating plug of
any colour is seen by the fish as a dark silhouette whose form is much
more important than its hue," I think that this quite ignores the
relative translucency of the two objects, and also the angle at which
the sun is shining on the water and on to the objects.

As far as our present knowledge goes, we know that fish discriminate, we know that they discriminate by some or all of the factors
mentioned, but we do not know the relative values of these factors.
Until further research yields more information it is reasonable to
assume that fish recognise flies much as we do ourselves, in other
words by its colour, brightness, shape, translucency and actions.

CHAPTER 17

A NOTE ON SURFACE TENSION

THERE ARE several properties of water which exert a considerable influence on aquatic organisms. Of these, surface tension is perhaps the most important.

The surface tension of water is due to the manner in which water molecules cohere at the surface. In water, the molecules exert an equal attraction on each other from all directions; at the surface the downward attraction of the molecules is not compensated for by any equivalent upward attraction, with the result that the layer of molecules at the surface which forms the surface film is in a specially elastic state.

The surface film's reactions to any body with which it comes into contact vary with the nature of surface of the body. Some substances repel water and others attract water. Those which repel water—for instance, paraffin wax, or grease—are said to have *hydrofuge* properties, and molecules of water are attracted to each other more strongly than they are attracted to molecules of the substance being considered. This attraction of the water molecules to each other is called *cohesion*. When a substance, for instance, clean glass, attracts water, the water molecules are attracted to the molecules of the substance (in this case glass) more powerfully than they are attracted to each other. This is known as *adhesion*. But molecules are extremely small, for instance a molecule of water is formed from the combination of two hydrogen atoms and one oxygen atom (H_2O) and is only about one fifty-five-millionth of an inch in diameter; consequently, if the surface of a body which attracts water is covered with even an infinitely thin layer of some hydrofuge or water-repellant substance, such as grease or oil, then the body will repel water.

When a body of this nature comes into contact with the surface film, the water is repelled, and the surface film assumes the position shown in Fig. 6a. Owing to the cohesion of the water molecules and to the elastic properties of the surface film, an upward pressure is exerted on the body which is quite distinct from any buoyancy which is caused by the displacement of water. Consequently when a nymph swims to the surface and the dorsum of the thorax of either the nymph or of the emerging fly has water-repellent properties, the water partly recedes from this hydrofuge surface, and the surface tension firmly retains the nymph in position and prevents it from sinking while the fly is emerging.

When a small water-repellent object is placed on the surface of the water, it will similarly be supported by the surface tension. The weight of the object will press the surface film downwards as shown in Fig. 6a, but the object actually will not touch the water, as a very thin layer of air will lie between the two surfaces. It is for this reason that a needle can be floated on the surface, and removed again without getting wet. Similarly, when a dun is resting on the surface its feet and legs, which appear to be touching the surface, are not really in contact with it. It is for the same reason that a female spinner can crawl down beneath the surface and emerge again without getting wet. As the spinner descends, a very thin film of air interposes between the fly and the water and completely surrounds her while she is submerged. In order to counteract first the upward thrust of the surface film, and then the buoyant effect caused by the water displacement, the spinner has to crawl down by means of some solid support. When she releases her hold on the support, she is immediately buoyed upwards and usually emerges at the surface again quite dry.

The ease with which objects are supported by the surface tension is affected by impurities either dissolved in the water or else contained in the surface film. The strength of the surface film is reduced by organic substances in solution. Also the presence of scum on the surface greatly reduces the efficacy of a water-repellent body. When a nymph endeavours to penetrate the surface where scum is present, the scum clings to the thorax of the nymph and thus reduces its hydrofuge properties. Similarly, scum is liable to wet the legs or other portions of a fly resting on the surface, so that when the fly endeavours to take flight it is unable to do so. Once a substance has got wet, the adhesion of the water molecules to the molecules

A. E.   L

of the substance causes the water to rise slightly upwards above the surrounding surface. See Fig. 6 b. When this occurs, the surface tension exerts a downward pull on the substance. Consequently ephemeropterans and other flies can emerge and take flight from the surface most easily under conditions which result in a high surface tension and absence of scum. Incidentally, all dry fly anglers know how easily a greased line sinks when there is scum on the water. When this occurs, the line does not require to be regreased

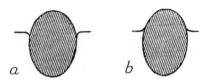

FIG. 6

Diagrammatic figure to illustrate the reaction of (a) water-repellent and (b) non-water-repellent bodies when partly submerged

In fig. (a) the water surface, illustrated by the two short lateral lines, is repelled from the surface of the body and has a buoyant effect on it. In fig. (b) the water clings to the body and tends to submerge it.

in order to make it float again, it is necessary only to rub it with a cloth in order to remove the scum and fine particles of dirt which are clinging to it.

Surface tension exerts an inward pull and this is very noticeable in the formation of drops of water. Owing to this force the drops are globular in shape, and it is easily demonstrated that the force of this inward pull increases accordingly as the drops get smaller. Because of this, when insects get wet as a result of being caught in the surface, and then are lifted from it, or succeed in crawling ashore, they appear extremely helpless. The water which clings to them acts as a stretched elastic membrane and presses their wings and other appendages tightly against their bodies. Similarly, when an artificial fly dressed with soft hackles is removed from the water, the surface tension of the drop of water which clings to the fly presses the hackles close against the body. But as soon as the fly is returned to the water the hackles open again and assume their normal position.

CHAPTER 18

FLIES AND FISH

EPHEMEROPTERANS

IN THIS chapter flies are considered from a more wholly angling viewpoint than in previous chapters, and they are treated more or less in the chronological order of their normal times of emergence. Each of the three main orders is considered in turn, and the remaining orders are grouped in so far as species found in flowing water are concerned. Flies occurring on lakes, reservoirs and ponds are dealt with separately.

Large Dark Olive, *Baëtis rhodani* (Pl. 5 a, p. 48, 6 c, d, p. 49, 14 a, b, p. 81):
One of the easiest flies to identify, and a suitable species to use as a standard unit of size, is the Blue Dun of the older authors, but now called the Large Dark Olive Dun. These flies are easy to identify because during the late winter and early spring they are the only ephemeropterans which are likely to be seen on the water. At this time of year their dull grey wings (which are usually relieved by a faint olive-yellow colour and so may appear of a warmer shade) are about one half inch in height. Their bodies are a dark drab olive or olive-grey, and between the wings the upper surface of their thoraces are a dull grey or bluish grey. Most spring salmon fishermen probably know them well, as they are usually on the water for an hour or two each side of mid-day, during February and March. As the flies drift down the river they hold their wings upright and usually touching, and at such times they are frequently likened to miniature yachts, for their large forewings act in much the same way and somewhat resemble the mainsail on a boat. In bleak weather they may remain on the water for quite a considerable time, but if the morning is warm and sunny they soon take flight for such shelter

as the river bank may afford them. Wet fly anglers fishing rapid turbulent streams will perhaps notice them in the air more often than on the water, as the rate of the current carries them past quickly, and the nature of the surface of turbulent water makes it easier for them to leave the surface than does the more adhesive quality of the surface of more placid streams.

These flies are widely distributed throughout Britain and Ireland, and should be found on the moderate-paced and quick-flowing stretches of all rivers in these islands (if they are not too heavily polluted). Owing to their wide distribution, their abundance, and to the fact that they appear many weeks earlier than other species and are therefore easy to identify, they have received many names in different localities. Most of the names describe the artificial imitations also. The better known of the alternative names are Blue Dun, Blue Upright, Hare's Ear, Dark Olive Quill.

The most effective artificial patterns to use when the Large Dark Olives are hatching are probably the Hare's Ear and the Rough Olive (the latter tied according to Halford or Skues). For dry flies, the Gold Ribbed Hare's Ear or the Hackle Hare's Ear are excellent patterns for fish feeding in the actual stretches of a river from which the Olives are hatching. On the calmer and more placid reaches of flats to which the Olives are carried by the current, but from whose depths they do not hatch, the Rough Olive appears to be the better pattern.

Trout at times differentiate between the Rough Olive and the Hare's Ear under conditions which make it difficult to ascertain the cause. For instance, in even-flowing water a number of fish may accept one of the patterns for a period, and then other fish on the same stretch may refuse that pattern and rise freely to the other pattern. It seems possible that the fish at times concentrate on the ascending nymphs and on nymphs which are in the process of hatching, and that at such times they accept the Hare's Ear in preference to the Rough Olive. It has been suggested by several authors, and I think correctly, that fish mistake the Gold Ribbed Hare's Ear for a hatching fly. Another alternative is that the trout differentiate between the male and the female Large Dark Olives (the female dun is noticeably more yellow-olive coloured than the male), and accept the two patterns as representations of the two sexes.

In the south of England, where the Medium Olive, *Baëtis vernus*, is relatively common, the Hare's Ear is a favourite pattern during

March and April. But it seems that the Gold Ribbed Hare's Ear is a good fly to use either wet or dry when the fish are feeding on any of the olive-coloured species of *Baëtis*. And at times it is successful even for fish feeding on the Iron Blue Dun, *Baëtis pumilus*.

There are several dressings for the Hare's Ear; the pattern which I personally find most successful is the Hackle Hare's Ear tied with a shining grizzled or golden brown cree cock's hackle in place of the usual blue dun hackle.

Owing to the rather indefinite nature of the colour of ephemeropterans, it is difficult to assess or describe the colour differences which take place in individuals of various broods of any one species during the season. Not the least of the difficulties is caused by variation in the ability of people to recognise or differentiate between close shades of colour. It is well known that a painter, or anyone whose work has to do with colours, developes a keener and more critical coloursense than individuals whose eyes have not been trained to perceive fine colour differences. In consequence, where one angler considers two flies to be obviously different in shade or colour, another may quite fail to see any difference in them.

Individuals of any species of Ephemeropterans may be expected to differ somewhat in colour, depending on the time of the year they have emerged and the locality in which they have been found.

Some insects from the south and south-east of England are somewhat lighter in colour than individuals of the same species from the north of Britain and from Ireland. (This is apparent with many animals, including butterflies and moths.) To compare Ephemeropterans from such widely separated localities is not very easy, as the specimens will not retain their original colours after they have been killed.

Last autumn I was able to make colour comparisons from memory between some of the species from the south of England and from Ireland. During the year I had been collecting specimens in Ireland, and I spent a considerable time throughout the season examining them in connection with the colour descriptions which I was continuously checking. During the autumn, while in Somerset and Wiltshire, I examined all the ephemeropterans which I could catch and was able to make the following comparisons. Examples of the July Dun, *Baëtis scambus*, from limestone rivers in the midlands and east of Ireland were similar to specimens from the River Kennet, but were very slightly darker than a few specimens caught in Somerset. Blue-winged Olives from the Kennet were larger and slightly more vivid in colour than specimens from Somerset or than most specimens from Ireland, but, contrary to this, specimens of the Large Dark Olives, *Baëtis rhodani*, from the Kennet were darker (and larger) than the specimens which hatch in Ireland in the autumn. The Kennet Large Dark Olives appeared to me to be identical with the normal large dark forms which appear in Ireland during the spring. These Large Dark Olives appearing in the autumn on the Kennet do not tally with Ronalds's description of the Whirling Blue Dun, but the autumn specimens found in Ireland agree very closely with Ronalds's description, the slightly smaller size and more ginger colour (in comparison with the spring forms) being most noticeable.

I did not have an opportunity of examining freshly caught specimens from the north of England, but in so far as I can ascertain they closely resemble specimens from Ireland.

Apart from slight differences which occur in the colours of species from widely separated areas such as have been described here, slight variations may occur between specimens from low and high altitudes, but these latter variations are not significant in so far as angling interests are concerned, as the trout in the high altitudes are nearly always small and are much less exacting in the choice of patterns than are the heavier fish in lowland waters.

Red Spinner (Pl. 14b, p. 81):

The female spinner of the Large Dark Olive is one of several female spinners which are or could equally well be called Red Spinners if they were judged only by their colour. But by virtue of their early appearance in the year, extended season, wide distribution and general abundance, the female spinners of the Large Dark Olive are the most important of these Red Spinners.

In common with the spinners of several other species of *Baëtis* these Large Dark Olive Spinners crawl down under the water when laying their eggs, and consequently trout must often see them some distance beneath the surface. When oviposition is completed, those spinners which do not die beside their eggs ascend to the surface either by crawling or by floating. Many of those which float up do not succeed in penetrating the surface film, and consequently they get carried downstream beneath the surface. This renders them susceptible to the very slightest sub-surface currents or down-tow, and every little eddy will cause them to sink momentarily. These spinners which are kept beneath the surface will present quite a different appearance from spinners floating on the surface, and they can be imitated very satisfactorily by a wet fly the dressing of which included in Appendix D, p. 243.

Dry fly patterns are successful when they lie flat on the surface and Lunn's Particular is one of the most satisfactory of them. An excellent alternative pattern is the seal fur spinner described by Mr. Skues, particularly when the hackle is flattened underneath the hook. During March, April and part of May trout feed on the Red Spinners in the afternoon and early evening, and later in the year often in the early morning as well as the evening. The spinners will be found in greatest numbers on or below fairly fast stretches of the river in which there are rushes, weeds or stones protruding above the water, but they need not be expected in cold weather.

March Brown, *Rhithrogena haarupi* (Pl. 7d, p. 64):

In many parts of Britain and Ireland the March Brown is unknown; in other parts it is present but is seldom seen, but on some rivers it is of first importance and appears in tremendous numbers. Since a large number of different authors have quoted the Usk as being a river on which the fly appears in unusually big swarms, it probably represents the most suitable type of habitat for the species. The fly can be expected in the latter part of March and may be found until the end of April, and on those rivers on which it is prolific it is a very important species for the angler. The duns hatch most freely at about mid-day and in the afternoon during warm weather, and, as they normally appear in spasmodic, concentrated swarms, the rise of fish, probably to the nymph, is intense but irregular. The nymphs live on smooth stones in fast-flowing water, and the duns emerge at the surface of the water in or below the more rapid parts of rivers. When quick-flowing water enters a pool, a proportion of the hatching flies may float some distance before leaving the water, and at such times I have occasionally seen trout feeding on the duns; more normally, however, they concentrate on the nymph, and a good imitation of the nymph is most valuable.

It seems possible that the usual tyings of the wet artificial patterns of March Browns do not owe their widespread popularity to any resemblance which they bear to the natural duns. For the artificials are very successful on rivers where the natural species are unknown, and it is apparent that trout at times accept them as something other than as imitations of the March Brown. Part of their attractiveness may lie in the resemblance which they undoubtedly bear to the Water-louse, *Asellus* sp. During the spring months, when the wet fly patterns are most successful, the Water-louse forms a very important food organism for trout on many rivers.

The colour of the March Brown nymph is in general a dark bronze green, and a good makeshift imitation can be made from the ordinary lake fly dressing of the Sooty Olive or Green Olive (tied with seal's fur and a brown Mallard wing) by cutting the wing short (to about one-third of its normal length) and clipping off or otherwise partly flattening the hackle underneath, and then by flattening the stump of the wing between the fingers, and pulling the remnants of the hackle out sideways.

A more specific dressing of the nymph is included in the appendices.

Iron-blue Dun, *Baëtis pumilus* (Pl. 6 a, b, p. 49):

This is an extremely common fly and usually abundant where it occurs, although it is not as common as is the Large Dark Olive. It will first be seen in late April and reaches its maximum abundance in May. During this month, and more particularly in the first two or three weeks, trout feed on it with avidity, and, as has often been observed, will at times take it to the exclusion of all other flies which are on the water.

Trout feed on the ascending nymph, on the nymph at the surface, and on the fully hatched dun. The floating pattern which I find most successful appears to be taken for the emerging fly. It is tied with a mole's fur body, and white cock hackles fibres for tail, and three of the tiny feathers from the throat of a cock jackdaw for hackles. In spite of the soft nature of these hackles the fly floats very well but does not sit high on the water. It is a good pattern also when there is a mixture of Iron-blues and Smuts or Black Gnats on the water. An alternative pattern is one in which a blue-black cock's hackle of the colour of the wings of the natural fly is substituted for the jackdaw hackles, and dark purple quill for the mole's fur body.

For wet flies, a Snipe and Purple or the mole's fur pattern tied with a single jackdaw throat hackle are effective.

The Iron blues and the Large Dark Olives appear in greatest abundance during cold weather, particularly after a sudden fall in temperature. On days in which there is a bitter east or north wind, accompanied often by hail showers, they will sometimes hatch in incredible numbers. And during April or May one should not postpone a fishing trip if the weather is very cold and unpleasant, under the assumption that it will be too cold for a hatch of fly. In cold weather Ephemeropterans are inclined to remain for a long while on the water before taking flight and consequently excellent dry fly fishing can be enjoyed (?) under such conditions, as the fish will then be encouraged to feed on the fully hatched fly rather than on the nymph. In contrast to this, March Browns which hatch in warm weather normally remain on the water for a shorter period and the trout then usually concentrate on the nymph.

Iron-blue Duns may be seen at any time during the summer months, but the fish pay much less attention to them once May has passed. The flies comprising the broods which appear in the summer are smaller in size and generally less numerous. In autumn they increase again in numbers and are often quite plentiful in October. At this time of the year the duns are rather less vividly coloured than they are in the spring.

An alternative name for the dun in the north of England is Dark Watchet and in the midlands of Ireland it is sometimes called the Blue Blow. This latter name is probably a corruption of the Yorkshire name Blue Bloa.

Iron-blue Spinners, *Baëtis pumilus* (Pl. 14 c, d, p. 81):

Of the two sexes of the Iron-blue Spinners the male fly or Jenny Spinner is the more conspicuous and widely known, but the female, which is called the Little Claret Spinner, is the more important fishing fly.

Like the Red Spinners, the Little Claret Spinners lay their eggs by crawling down under the water by means of some protruding object, usually in either fast-flowing or medium-paced water, and after they have oviposited, most of them are carried downstream by the current. The spinners are of course in greatest abundance in May, and they will be on the water in the morning, afternoon or early evening, as they are one of the species which oviposit at any time during the day. If, after a few days of cold weather, which is conducive to a hatch of duns but is a deterrent to any activity by spinners, the temperature rises, a very big fall of the spinners should be expected. When this occurs during the period that the Iron-blue hatch is at its maximum, a strong rise of fish nearly invariably follows. It is at such times that a well-tied Houghton Ruby or seal's fur bodied Little Claret Spinner is of particular value. When these spinners are plentiful on the water they get carried downstream to the deep slow-flowing quiet stretches of the river, where the largest trout will often be seen feeding on them.

The Jenny Spinner is one of the few male spinners which are quite often found on the water. These spinners hover from the water's edge inland for any distance up to at least twenty or thirty yards. In the sunshine they form tremendous swarms which extend for a great height into the air, and they will be seen hovering from 8 or 9 a. m. until the late afternoon. At such times, when a cross wind has been blowing from the side of the river on which most of the swarms are located, I have seen a continuous stream of these male spinners on the water for several hours at a time. Trout at times feed on them keenly and when doing so they tend to ignore other species. Halford's Jenny Spinner is an excellent pattern to use when the natural fly is on the water, but the hackle should be either tied flat or else clipped underneath in order that the pattern may lie flat on the surface.

Yellow May Dun, *Heptagenia sulphurea* (Pl. 7 a, b, p. 64):
Owing to their vivid yellow colouring individuals of this species are probably the most conspicuous of all the ephemeropterans. When viewed against a medium-toned or dark background, such as the dark reflection of the opposite bank on the water, one of these duns will be plainly visible at a distance at which many of the more sober-coloured flies would not be seen at all. It is perhaps partly for this reason that they have gained the reputation of being of little use as an angling fly, for it can be often and easily seen that the sparse hatches which take place on many days in May evoke little or no response from the trout. But the same could probably be said of any fly which is on the water in only small numbers, for instance a sparse hatch of Blue-winged Olives will often drift down the river quite unheeded by the trout during the afternoon, but later in the evening, when the flies become more plentiful, the fish may feed on them avidly.

Yellow Evening Dun, *Ephemerella notata* (Pl. 7 c, p. 64):
This fly superficially resembles the Yellow May Dun so closely in size and colour and in the season of its emergence that it could quite appropriately share the same common name. In fact, it is

reasonably certain that anglers who are familiar with the natural fly do call it either by that name or else, erroneously, call both species the Yellow Sally. But as the two species differ in habits in many respects, and in the appearances of their respective nymphs, it is of advantage to be able to differentiate between them. Of the two, the Yellow Evening Dun is more important as an angling fly.

The Yellow Evening Dun is in season from about the middle of May until the middle of June. It starts to hatch at dusk, the duns seldom appearing before sunset, and continues for about an hour. In this it resembles the Blue-winged Olive, and the trout feed on it just as keenly as they do on that latter species. It resembles the Blue-winged Olive also in size and structure, but of course differs extremely in colour. Trout feed on the nymph, the dun and the spinner; when fishing a river on which the species is abundant, it is advisable to carry patterns to represent each of the three stages.

On suitable warm evenings an hour or two before the duns appear, the female spinners may be seen flying along the river, usually upstream, and after they have oviposited they fall spent on the water. At such times, when the flies are sufficiently numerous to bring on a rise of fish, an imitation tied with a yellow amber-coloured seal's fur body and a honey dun hackle has proved effective. Imitations of the nymph and the dun are included in the Appendix, but, apart from these patterns, the ordinary wet fly dressing of the Yellow May Dun can be very deadly when fished in the dusk in fast-flowing water.

Although the species has been recorded from only comparatively few rivers in Britain and Ireland, it is probably widespread in moderate-paced or rather fast-flowing limestone rivers. Owing to the late hour of its emergence, the resemblance which it bears to the Little Yellow May Dun, *Heptagenia sulphurea*, and the short season during which it occurs, it must have been overlooked on many waters.

Pale Watery Duns:

This generalised vernacular name covers at least five different species. Whether or not it is necessary for anglers to differentiate between all the species, is of course a matter of opinion, but some of the species differ considerably in colour and/or in size, and close attention will show differences in the appearances and habits of all five species. The species concerned are *Baëtis bioculatus* (Pl. 10a, p. 69), *B. scambus* (Pl. 8c, d, p. 65), *Centroptilum luteolum* (Pl. 8a, b,

p. 65), *C. pennulatum* (Pl. 11c, d, p. 76), and *Procloëon rufulum* (Pl. 10b, p. 69). The name Pale Watery Dun is retained for the first of these species and alternative names are used for the other four species.

I have seen the **Pale Watery Dun,** *Baëtis bioculatus* (Pl. 10a, p. 69), on the River Kennet, but have not fished for trout which were feeding on it, and consequently have been unable to assess from personal experience the value of the appropriate artificial patterns. Judging from the appearance of the insects, which are perhaps more watery-coloured than most of the other species, either the Little Marryat or the Blue Quill would perhaps be a suitable fly to use. But this is pure conjecture. Fishing authors seem always to group this species with some of the other Pale Wateries when dealing with artificial patterns. In appearance the natural duns lie between *Baëtis scambus* and *Centroptilum luteolum.* This species is common on the chalk streams, but is rare or absent from the north of Britain and Ireland.

Any females of the **Pale Watery Spinner,** *Baëtis bioculatus* (Pl. 18b, p. 93), which I have captured have been of a dark golden-brown colour, but I have not had experience of trout feeding on the species, and I have been unable to isolate this fly from the writings of other angling authors. Possibly Mr. Skues's Little Amber Spinner or the imitation of the golden-brown coloured spinner of Mr. Dunne are the best artificials to use when this fly is on the water. There should be no difficulty in identifying and studying the species on those streams, mainly in the south of England, where the insect is common.

Small Dark Olive, *Baëtis scambus* (Pl. 8c, d, p. 65), is like a very small Olive Dun and is apparently the species which is known as the July Dun in the south of England. It is the darkest and most olive-coloured of the five Pale Wateries, and at times one cannot help wondering how it came about that Halford included it among the Pale Wateries. Perhaps the greyish watery tint in the bodies of some of the paler coloured male duns influenced his decision. In all species of *Baëtis* the bodies of the male duns tend to be less strongly coloured than those of the corresponding females, and in the Olives and Pale Wateries the greenish-olive shade of the abdomen of the females becomes more greyish-olive in the males, due presumably to the absence of the contained eggs within the body of the latter. Similarly, the last two or three segments of the abdomens of male duns (and spinners) contain the genital organs, and these segments in comparison with the first six or seven segments are more opaque and more strongly coloured.

These Small Dark Olives are very common and are widely distributed throughout Britain and Ireland. Although they have been recorded as early as February, I have personally never found them until towards the end of April. They are common in May but are less conspicuous at that time than later in the summer in July and August. This is perhaps because there are so many other species on the water in May which are absent or less numerous in July.

Imitations of the larger Olive Duns, but tied on number oo and ooo hooks, are successful when these small Olives are on the water. The best patterns are perhaps a Gold Ribbed Hare's Ear and the July Duns as dressed by Mr. Skues or Mr. Dunne. The nymphs resemble the Large Dark Olive nymphs but differ in that their wing cases are not of so dark a brown and their bodies are more yellow-olive.

Small Dark Olive Spinner, *Baëtis scambus*, female (Pl. 16, p. 85): These small reddish-brown or olive-brown spinners differ from the female spinners of other species of *Baëtis* in that the body is usually tinged with green-olive. This green-olive is, of course, much subdued and hidden by the typical brown colour, but it is noticeable on female spinners captured while flying over the water prior to ovi-positing. The veins of the wings are very dark, and the flies are easy to recognise owing to these two features and their small size. The most successful imitation of the spent spinner which I know of is Lunn's Particular tied on a oo or ooo hook.

Sky-blue Dun, *Centroptilum luteolum* (Pl. 8a, b, p. 65): This Pale Watery occurs on lakes as well as rivers throughout Britain and Ireland and is probably the commonest of them. During late April and May and in September and October the duns emerge during the mornings and afternoons, but in the warmer months, particularly during bright weather, they delay their appearance until dusk. They are fairly easy to recognise once they have been identified, as their wings are of the same peculiar shade of very pale blue as the feathers on the upper surfaces of the wings of terns and several sea gulls. The colour of their bodies varies from a pale luminous olive-green to pale honey colour.

During stormy weather in May and September when these flies are on the water in the afternoon, they frequently are blown over so that their wings become caught in the surface film, and then large numbers of them may be seen floating downstream with their wings stretched out in the normal position of a spent fly. Fish often become particular at such times, and will accept only a pattern tied in a spent fashion, such as Lunn's Winged Yellow Boy, or an appropriately tied hackled pattern. But when fish are feeding on the hatched fly, which is sitting up on the surface, a well cocked pattern is more successful. I have often found a Blue Quill or a Blue Quill Variant effective; and Mr. Sawyer's Summer Spurwing looks attractive and, I am told, is a good pattern, but I have not used it yet.

The dressing which I have found to be the most satisfactory is composed of a very pale dyed heron herl body, a wing made up of fibres from a breast feather of a pale blue dun hen bunched and tied forward, and supported by a honey dun cock's hackle, and with fibres of the hackle for the tail.

Little Amber Spinner, *C. luteolum* (Pl. 17 b, p. 92), is the female spinner of the preceding dun. The body is a pale russet or reddish-amber on the dorsal surface but is a very pale yellow underneath, and the wings are colourless. The seal's fur bodied Little Amber Spinner or Mr. Dunne's female Pale Watery Spinner are both at times good patterns for fish feeding on these spinners; so is a Lunn's Winged Yellow Boy if it is tied so that it will lie flat on the water. On some lakes and on many rivers the trout feed very keenly on this spinner; on occasions I have even seen the large fish on some of the Irish limestone lakes feeding on it in preference to the Spent Gnats (of *Ephemera danica*) which were on the water at the same time. It has many times been found in the stomach contents of trout which had been caught on Spent Gnats, and which were apparently feeding indiscriminately on both the Gnats and this particular spinner.

The male spinners of this fly hover over the edge of the water and so they are frequently found on the surface. On a river, when a cross wind is blowing, a continuous stream of these spinners will sometimes be seen floating downstream, and if the fish are feeding on them, a most excellent imitation to use is Halford's Male Pale Watery Spinner, but the hackle should first be cut, or otherwise flattened, underneath the hook. When this pattern is correctly tied, it is a sufficiently good imitation (to our eyes) to allow the natural fly to be recognised from the artificial.

Blue-winged Pale Watery Dun, *C. pennulatum:* Dressings of both dun and spinners of this species are given by Mr. Dunne in *Sunshine and the Dry Fly*, and doubtless these patterns are as acceptable to the trout as most of his other patterns when used at the proper time. A more recently devised imitation of the dun is the large Summer Spurwing of M. F. E. Sawyer, who gives an interesting account of the habits and appearance of the fly on the River Avon. One would imagine that these flies, both in the dun and in the spinner stages, would be appreciated by the trout on rivers where the species is common, and it is, therefore, surprising that the fly is mentioned so seldom in books on fly fishing.

It obviously is common locally, for Mr. Dunne, in speaking of it, records that "at the latter end of June in 1923 I found the surface of the Kennet and Avon canal at Hungerford absolutely covered with both male and female spinners of this same large species." (Dun Pl. 11 c, d, p. 76; spinner 19 c, p. 96.)

Pale Evening Dun, *Procloëon rufulum* (Pl. 10 b, p. 69): This is another species which the modern books on angling flies appear to have overlooked. The species must be well known to many anglers but it probably has been confused with *Baëtis bioculatus* and *Centroptilum luteolum*. It has often been pointed out since the time of Halford that the male spinners of *B. bioculatus* can be recognised by their bright yellow turbinate eyes, but I have never seen it mentioned in angling entomological books that the male spinners of *P. rufulum* also have bright yellow turbinate eyes, and that the flies are of similar size and are paler in colour than *B. bioculatus*. The Pale Evening Dun is a species which one feels sure Halford would have regarded as a Pale Watery had he known it, and indeed his dressing of the female Pale Watery Dun is, I think, a better imitation of this dun than it is of any of the species which he grouped as Pale Wateries. The body of the natural fly is a very pale yellow, and the wings are paler than those of any other species of ephemeropteran except *Caenis*.

The duns emerge from the slow-flowing reaches of rivers, and they are extremely common in July and August. Although they

are wide widely distributed throughout Britain and Ireland they are perhaps less plentiful on the chalk streams than elsewhere. On many
of the slow-flowing limestone rivers in Ireland, they are the commonest
of all the Pale Wateries, and it is likely that they are also plentiful
in suitable habitats in England.

Patterns which prove successful are Halford's Pale Watery Dun
female, Flight's Fancy, and a pale edition of Lunn's Yellow Boy. As
its name implies, it is chiefly an evening fly, particularly during hot
weather; in fact, it sometimes emerges too late to be of much use to
a dry fly angler.

Pale Evening Spinners, *Procloëon rufulum* (Pl. 17 c, d, p. 92): At
times equally important as the preceding. The female spinners are
quite similar in appearance to the females of *Centroptilum luteolum*
although paler and more yellow in colour, and Lunn's Winged
Yellow Boy or Halford's Pale Watery Spinner make satisfactory
imitations, provided they are tied so as to lie flat on the surface.
The male spinners fly so late in the evening that I have seldom
seen them on the water, but Halford's male Pale Watery Spinner
should be a reasonably good imitation.

Greendrake, *Ephemera danica* (Pl. 1 b, c, p. 16): This is the commonest and most widespread of the two species (three, to be strictly
accurate) of Greendrake. It is slightly paler and perhaps more
greenish coloured in the wing than *E. vulgata* and, owing to its wide
distribution, it is by far the most important of the three species as
far as the angler is concerned.

In recent years the numbers of Greendrakes have become much
reduced in many rivers, owing to pollution and drainage, and one
seldom now sees the tremendous hatches of fly which were described
by writers in the last century. Often on rivers the mayfly season
has very little effect on the fishing, and many anglers, during the
time that the Greendrake is on the water, will kill all their fish on
sedges or other small flies. But there are still some rivers, probably
more in Ireland than in England, on which the advent of the mayfly
is conducive to some of the best fishing in the year. Nowadays the
wet fly and the natural species are seldom used on rivers, and most
fish are killed on the artificial dry Greendrake.

There are innumerable patterns of Greendrake obtainable, probably more than of any other fly. The patterns which I personally

find most successful are Mr. Dunne's Pale Mayflies and a hackled pattern dressed with a French partridge hackle dyed in picric acid. There is also a good pattern of a drowned Greendrake of Locke's which is tied in the same manner as a Spent Gnat. These flattened Greendrakes are sometimes very useful, as it frequently happens that there may be a considerable number of the freshly hatched flies floating down the river in a spent fashion, as a result of having allowed their wings to get caught in the surface film.

Grey Drake and Spent Gnat (Pl. 1 f, p. 16): One of the most effective of all the mayfly patterns is the Grey-Drake, tied with a cuckoo cock's hackle and dressed as a cocked and not as a spent fly. It is particularly useful in the afternoon or early evening when the imagines are mating. Immediately after mating, many of the female spinners fly over the water and alight on it and drift downstream with their wings held upright. Others may be seen ovipositing and then settling on the water and drifting downstream, often with one wing caught in the surface film. The Grey Drake pattern imitates the flies under both of these conditions, but it is also a good pattern to use at any time during the mayfly season after the trout have been feeding on the spinners.

The male and female spinners differ from each other in that the female is slightly larger and paler coloured and her transparent wings have a distinct blue tinge in them. The wings of the male flies are tinged with brown black. Patterns of the female Spent Gnat are tied with hackle fibre wings of a blue dun or blue cuckoo cock, a white quill body, and either a short fibred ribbing hackle or shoulder hackle of cuckoo cock.

For tying the male Spent Gnat, endeavour to procure a black cock's spade or saddle hackle which has a dark brown sheen in it when viewed against the light. In default, use a black cock's hackle with a few turns of a furnace cock's run through it. This pattern is often of greater value on a lake than on a river as the male spinners are commonly found floating around the shores of suitable lakes.

It is doubtful if any of the Ephemeroptera, other than the Large Dark Olive, is as common and widespread as the **Blue-winged Olive**, *Ephemerella ignita* (Pls. 5b, d, p. 48, 11a, b, p. 76). This fly is as common on limestone rivers as it is on chalk streams, and is widespread on upland rivers and even on hill streams. It is easy to recognise, as it is the only Olive which has three tails, but variations which occur in the colours of male and female duns, as well as in duns from different waters, sometimes cause confusion. The typical colours in the duns of both sexes are seen in specimens from chalk streams and from many limestone rivers. In these, the female flies have olive-green and the male flies dull orange-brown coloured bodies. Specimens from less alkaline waters and from uplands streams, are more subdued and less definite in colour and are usually somewhat smaller in size.

Formerly the Blue-winged Olive was known as the July Dun, and patterns of the July Dun are still used to imitate this species. Confusion arises through the fact that a different fly is called the July Dun in the south of England, where the name is applied to a small dark Olive (probably *Baëtis scambus*, Pl. 8 c, p. 65). The older patterns of the July Dun were dressed with an olive coloured body of some dubbing which was often composed of a mixture of blue and yellow fur. This older tying of the July Dun applied more parti-cularly to the female Blue-winged Olive, and the more orange bodied male dun was almost certainly called by different authors the Orange Dun and the Indian Yellow. Ronalds gives a pattern of the former fly and Aldam describes the latter.

Modern dressings are also of two types, one type having a greenish olive coloured body of dyed seal's fur, heron herl or quill, and the other a body of orange coloured quill or fur. Two of the most consist-ently successful patterns are the Hackle Blue Wing and the Orange Quill. When fish are feeding on the nymph Mr. Skues's dark brown red pattern of nymph tied with cow's hair is at times particularly successful.

On some rivers the duns appear as early as May (they have been recorded even in April), and on limestone rivers in the west of Ireland I have seen quite strong hatches of the flies shortly before the main appearance of the Greendrakes at the end of May. More usually, however, they are not common until towards the end of June, and from then until the latter part of August they can be expected nearly every evening.

The duns will be seen on the water in the afternoon and evening. In the afternoon they appear in very sparse numbers and the male flies often predominate, but in the evening, particulary if the day has been hot and bright, the hatch of fly is concentrated, and for a period of half an hour or an hour the flies may be very numerous. At times they do not appear until it is nearly too dark to recognise them and they may continue hatching for a short while after darkness.

The flies continue during September and October, but trout do not feed on them then with the eagerness which they evinced during the last part of June and all through July. Also, in the late autumn the main hatch often occurs in the afternoon and the concentration of fly in the evening is less noticeable.

On some rivers the Blue-winged Olive provides the best fishing of the year, but on very slow-flowing streams with mud bottoms it is seldom present in sufficient numbers to be of great importance. On such streams the Pale Evening Dun may be common and provide a good substitute.

Both spinners of the Blue-winged Olive, *Ephemerella ignita*, share the name **Sherry Spinner** (Pl. 19a, b, p. 96), but the female spinners are by far the more important for angling purposes. The flies are easy to recognise; they have three tails and the males have chestnut coloured eyes and their bodies are brown-red. The female flies are at first greenish coloured, but after they have shed their eggs their bodies darken and become noticeably reddish, and when spent females are collected from the water their bodies are often nearly of a jam-red colour.

The ovipositing flight of the female spinners has often been described. When the flies are plentiful, they will be seen on fine evenings flying along the river, usually against the direction of the flow of water, in a continuous column. The column is made up of innumerable spinners which arrange themselves in an evenly spaced, loose and open formation, which stretches across the water and often upwards for a considerable height into the air. The column passes along the slow-flowing stretches in a never-ending stream, but when it reaches fast-flowing broken water large numbers of the flies drop down towards the surface, lay their eggs and are then carried downstream.

White Midge, *Caenis* spp. (Pls. 5c, p. 48, 12b, p. 77, 20b, p. 97). These flies are the smallest of all the Ephemeropterans, and they differ from other genera in several respects and are, therefore, easy to recognise. Their wings are very broad, their bodies are short and they possess three tails which in the male spinners are extremely long. Their distinctive shape is well shown on Plates 12 and 20, pp. 77 and 97.

There are five species of *Caenis*, but for angling purposes it is, at the most, necessary to consider only two different types. One of these types, which covers the species *C. moesta* and *C. macrura*, is figured in the colour plate, and, as can be seen from it, the flies are white varied with blackish on the body and on the fore edge of the wings. The other type (which includes the species *C. rivulorum* and *C. horaria*) is smaller and paler coloured, and the darker areas are less noticeable and are of a lighter brown. Normally the black and white type will be seen in the early morning from dawn onwards but usually disappears by eight or nine a.m. The small pale type emerges in the evening, sometimes in the late afternoon but more usually not until an hour or two before sunset. When the flies are on the water they are usually present in very large numbers and trout feeding on them do so with a series of small "sipping" rises. The intervals between rises are so short that the rings of one rise often merge into the rings of the next rise and a continuous disturbance will be seen on the surface. These series of continuous rises will be broken at intervals, presumably to allow the mouthful of flies collected to be swallowed.

When fishing for trout which are concentrating on *Caenis* it is necessary to cast accurately so that the fly floats directly over, or slightly in front of, the fish. At other times fish may move several feet across stream and accept a badly directed fly, but they seldom do this when *Caenis* is on the water.

The duns of *Caenis* (Pl. 12 b, p. 77) differ from other duns in that they cast their subimaginal skins within a very short while, often only a few minutes, after emerging from the water. They are not at all selective in choosing a support on which to rest while moulting, and they will as readily alight on the hands, face or clothes of a conveniently situated angler as on any other object. When the freshly emerged spinner flies away the empty skin of the dun is left adhering to the support chosen, and sometimes one's clothing will become covered with these tiny white exuviae. The flies may be recognised from this habit alone. After moulting, the spinners (Pl. 20 b, p. 97) at once commence hovering and within a short while the females lay their eggs and fall spent on the water.

Fish feeding on the flies (they feed mainly on the spinners) are difficult to catch, but one well-known pattern with which I have many times had success, when the small pale evening species of *Caenis* have been on the water, is Halford's Female Pale Watery Dun. (Alternative patterns are included in the Appendices.)

John Markham

Plate XIIIa A corner of one of the lakes belonging to the Enton Fly Fishers' Club in Surrey shows a typical habitat of the Lake Olive, *Cloëon simile*. Also found here are Silverhorns, *Leptocerus* sp., as well as species of the Large Midges or Buzzers, *Chironomus* sp., and the Little White Midge, *Caenis* sp.

Plate XIIIb Inverbeg Lake in Connemara is noted for its sea-trout, but its waters which lie on, and are fed from, granite and peat, support an extremely meagre population of flies

J. R. Harris

J. R. Harris

Plate XIVa The shallow bays which indent the shore of Lough Sheelin in Co. Cavan support an abundance of caddis-flies and Ephemeropterans. Among the commoner species are found Halford's Welshman's Button, *Sericostoma personatum*, the Little Sky-blue Dun, *Centroptilum luteolum*, the ubiquitous Lake Olive, *Cloëon simile*, and, during May, an incredible number of Greendrakes, *Ephemera danica*

Plate XIVb The turbulent water along the rocky shores of Ennerdale Water provide a suitable habitat for the flat stone-loving nymphs of the Dark Dun, *Heptagenia lateralis*. The Lake Olive, *Cloëon simile*, will be seen emerging further out from the shore-line

John Markham

The early morning angler, if he is on the river by sunrise during June, July and part of August, will depend principally on the larger dark species of *Caenis* to bring on a rise of trout. On many rivers trout feed more freely on these flies between 5 and 7 a. m. than they do on other flies at any time during the day except in the evening, but it is unfortunate that trout feeding in the early morning are often difficult to catch.

August Dun, *Ecdyonurus dispar* (Pl. 12 a, p. 77): which looks like a small-sized March Brown, is seldom on the water in large numbers, and it is doubtful if trout feed on it much. But both Ronalds and Francis Francis speak highly of it, so perhaps it is of importance locally. It occurs only in rivers and lakes which have a hard bottom.

Great Red Spinner, *E. dispar* (Pl. 21 c, d, p. 100): The spinner of the August Dun has a dark mahogany red coloured body. It is a strongly built fly larger than the ordinary Red Spinner, and the males can be recognised in the air by their steady flight. In contrast to the dun, this spinner is a useful fly for angling purposes. Trout which are feeding on Sherry Spinners or on any Red Spinner will usually take any individual spinners of this species which float over them. Occasionally quite a number of these spinners may be on the water together and then the fish feed greedily on them. An imitation on which I have many times killed good fish in limestone rivers is dressed similarly to the Little Claret Spinner but on a number 3 or 4 hook.

Summer Mayfly Spinners, *Siphlonurus* spp. (Pls. 20 a, p. 97, 21 a, b, p. 100), are localised in their distribution, but in some districts during July and August they are quite common. The female spinners adopt an ovipositing flight similar to that of the Sherry Spinners, but they differ very much in size. Spent spinners on the water are nearly as large as Spent Gnats, and a brownish coloured pattern of a Spent Gnat makes quite a good imitation.

SEDGE-FLIES

Grannom, *Brachycentrus subnubilus*, is a caddis-fly which occurs in fairly fast-flowing weedy rivers; in recent years it has become rather less common than formerly. It is found in the south of England and as far north as the Cumberland Eden in April, and it has been recorded from Scotland as late as May or early June.

On those rivers on which it emerges in April it is the earliest appearing sedge fly, and, like other species which are active during the daytime, it is greatly favoured by the trout when it is abundant. The fly emerges at the surface in open water and fish feed on the ascending pupae as well as on the adult flies. There are several dressings of the adult fly, and in his book *Floating Flies and how to dress them* Halford gives a tying of the pupa under the name Grannom "larva".

Grey Sedge or Grey Flag, *Hydropsyche* spp. (e. g. Pl. 25b, p. 112): There are several species of caddis-flies belonging to the genus *Hydropsyche*, which in Ireland are collectively known as Grey Flags. Some of them are rather more brownish coloured than grey, but one artificial pattern seems to be effective in imitating any of them. It is dressed with a grey fur body, grizzled or rusty dun cock's hackle and a woodcock wing.

The flies are found only near flowing water, and during May, at which time they are in greatest abundance, they will be on the water in the daytime as well as in the evening. The male flies hover near bushes or other vegetation alongside the river in the morning and afternoon sunshine, and in the evening the females fly out over the river and often travel upstream for a considerable distance before ovipositing. When spent they get carried downstream on the surface. Trout feed on the flies when they are hatching during the forenoon and evening, and on the spent flies in the evening.

The flies are widely distributed in both Britain and Ireland, and on many rivers they are among the most valuable of all the "angling" flies which occur in May. The imitation is a useful pattern, not only when fish are feeding on the natural flies but also at any time during the season as an alternative to the Red Sedge.

Many species of the genera *Leptocerus* (Pl. 25a, p. 112) and *Mystacides* share the vernacular name **Silverhorns.** Most of the species are of more value on lakes than on rivers, but some of them, including the common Black Silverhorns, *Mystacides azurea*, are at times useful on the very slow-flowing reaches of rivers. The male flies hover over the water and over fringing vegetation in the afternoon and early

evening; the females oviposit on the surface, and on warm evenings
quite a number of spent flies of both sexes will be found on the
still waters of flats and mill heads. Trout feed freely on the flies
when they are plentiful and imitations should be tied in a spent
fashion.

Halford's Welshman's Button, *Sericostoma personatum* (Pl. 24a, p. 109),
is abundant on the River Test, where it is locally called the Caperer;
and it is apparently an important species there during May and
June. Although it is widely distributed throughout Britain and
Ireland, on many rivers it does not appear in very big numbers
and it is no more important than other day-flying sedges.

The two best known imitations are Lunn's Caperer and Halford's Welshman's Button, and these patterns are also effective when
used at any time during the season, whether or not the natural fly
is present. The male flies are easily recognised, as they are medium-
sized dark chocolate-coloured insects, with what appears to be a
very conspicuous and large dark head. The female flies are more
variable in colour and the head appears of normal size.

Silver Sedge, *Lepidostoma hirtum*: I do not know if this species is the
prototype of the Silver Sedge, but it certainly resembles it in colour
and I have, on several occasions, used a small Silver Sedge with
success when this natural sedge-fly has been hatching. The flies
hatch in open water in the late evenings, during May and June,
and on some rivers as late as July and August, and on occasions
the fish feed freely on both the pupa and the hatched fly.

The fly would undoubtedly be of greater importance if it were
not that, very often, other and more attractive flies are on the water
at the same time.

The natural fly has light, plain grey wings, ginger-coloured legs
and a cream or pale-coloured abdomen.

Many species of sedge-flies are collectively known by the name
of **Cinnamon Sedge.** One of these, which Halford used as a model
for his artificial Cinnamon Sedge, is *Limnephilus lunatus*. The name
Cinnamon Sedge is applied to many medium sized sedge flies which
have mottled or plain cinnamon brown wings, and green or brownish
abdomens.

Red Sedge is a name used to describe darker and browner or
more reddish brown coloured species than the preceding. A typical,

and very common, small red sedge, *Tinodes waeneri*, is illustrated on
Pl. 25 c, p. 112. The largest of these red sedges is the Murragh or
Great Red Sedge, *Phryganea*, see Pl. 23 b, p. 108.

Artificials of this species are dressed with a dark hare's ear fur
body, dark red cock hackle and a landrail wing feather or some
dark mottled feather for wings. A large Alder tied on a No. 6 hook
makes a good substitute.

The Caperer, *Halesus radiatus* (Pl. 23 c, p. 108), is a large red or
cinnamon coloured sedge-fly which is common and widespread in
the autumn.

STONE-FLIES

February Red, *Taeniopteryx nebulosa*: apparently absent from
the south of England and from Ireland, this species is found
locally in sluggish rivers during January, February and March. It
is often common where it does occur and is highly spoken of as a
trout fly, for the fish seemingly are fond of it. The fly resembles the
following species except in that the wings are less greyish and the
abdomen is more reddish brown coloured.

Early Brown, *Protonemura meyeri* (Pl. 27 a, p. 128): a small stone-fly
often mistaken for the preceding species. Its habits are different,
however, as it is found in both lowland and upland stony streams
and rivers and it is widely distributed. The greyish coloured strongly
veined wings are plainly seen in the illustration. The body is a very
dark grey-brown or blackish and the legs are a sooty brown.

The flies are found during the spring, from the opening of the
season, and they continue until May or June. They are chiefly of
value to wet fly anglers, and two useful artificial patterns are an
Orange Partridge, tied with a body of deep orange silk, and a hackled
pattern, dressed with a grizzled cock's hackle and a body of dark
hare's fur. This latter pattern is perhaps of most value when it is
used as a top dropper in broken water.

The name **Needle-fly** or Needle Brown is applied to several
species of the genus *Leuctra*. The flies are very small, and when at
rest the wings not only lie along and close to the body, but they are
partially wrapped around it. This gives the flies a very thin appearance. In contrast they are conspicuous when flying.

These species are common and are found all through the season, but they are not of much value to fishermen, except at times on stony hill streams and upland rivers.

Yellow Sally, *Isoperla grammatica* (Pl. 26a, b, p. 113): These flies are conspicuous and easy to recognise owing to their bright yellow colour, but they are seldom of use to anglers. The Small Yellow Sally at times occurs in considerable numbers on stony upland rivers and some authors speak highly of it as an angling fly.

Willow-fly, *Leuctra geniculata* (Pl. 26c, p. 113): This species is in season during the autumn and it is common on many rivers in the midlands and south of England. Trout feed freely on the spent flies, and various authors give different dressings for the artificial.

When these or any of the other small brown coloured stone-flies are in quantity on the water a good pattern to use is one with a body of brown quill and a shining rusty dun or brown dun cock's hackle tied half spent.

Superficially the differences between the Willow-fly, Needle Brown and the Early Brown are slight, and they all are aptly described as small brown stone-flies.

The important Stone-fly, or **Large Stone-fly,** of the fast-flowing stony rivers of the north of England, Scotland and parts of Ireland, represents two different species of *Perla*. These flies are very big; some of the females are nearly two inches in length and are sturdy, strongly built flies.

The larvae or creepers are easily found under stones in fast-flowing water, and they are an excellent bait for trout during April and early May. During late May and early June the adult flies, particularly the females, which are noticeably larger, are used in preference to the creepers. In the north of England these flies are called the Mayfly, and provide some of the best fishing of the year.

Many artificial imitations of these flies have been designed; the earliest known of them dates from the fifteenth century.

As a dry fly the artificial **Alder,** *Sialis* spp., is undoubtedly a most attractive pattern, particularly when it is used while there are few of the Ephemeroptera on the water. But it is obvious that the fish often accept it as something other than an imitation of the natural species, as the presence of the natural fly on the water seldom noticeably affects the success of the artificial. Perhaps the general resemblance which the artificial bears to a dark sedge-fly, a large heavy fly of the blue-bottle type, or to a beetle accounts for its success.

The natural fly (Pl. 30 a, p. 133) is easy to recognise; it resembles a medium sized sedge-fly in shape and size, but its wings are like those of a stone-fly in texture. They are brownish with distinct dark veins and a translucent membrane, and they have not got the somewhat matt appearance of the wings of many sedge-flies.

The species is common in lowland areas during May and the early part of June and is found on bushes or other vegetation bordering lakes and rivers. The flies are terrestrial rather than aquatic, and only get on to the water by accident, either as a result of falling from overhanging herbage or as a result of being blown down by the wind. When the females oviposit they choose herbage near the water's edge and attach their eggs to some leaf or plant stem. The young larvae find their way down to the water and they live in the slow-flowing reaches. They are carnivorous in habit and feed on caddis larvae and Ephemeropteran nymphs and on any other insects which they can catch. When fully developed the larvae crawl ashore and pupate in the ground some distance above the water's edge, and within a few weeks adult flies emerge from the pupal case and seek shelter in the surrounding vegetation.

The true **Black Gnats,** *Bibio johannis*, are terrestrial rather than aquatic species, but during sultry hot weather in May, and also later in the summer, they are often on the water in tremendous numbers. Fish will feed on them consistently and one of the most successful dry fly patterns at such times is Mr. J. W. Dunne's small Black Gnat which is included in his series of Sunshine Flies.

There are many other small black flies which in practice anglers call Black Gnats, and an alternative dressing is one tied with a black hackle, starling wings and a body made of fibres from a rook's wing feather, on a double or treble nought hook.

Among the smaller flies which are sometimes called Black Gnats are the **Reed Smuts** or *Simulium* species. These smuts are present all through the season but are commonest perhaps in May. During hot weather, countless numbers of them will be seen on rivers, flying very rapidly back and forth, close to the surface.

There are many patterns of artificials. Dr. Mottram included five different dressings in his book *Fly Fishing*, and Lunn's Black upright

is at times very effective. A small artificial Black Gnat with its wings cut
down to stumps can at times be used with advantage, if it is fished sunk
just beneath the surface after the manner in which a nymph is used.

House-fly (Pl. 29a, p. 132):

Occasionally during the summer and early autumn one sees on
the water numbers of house-flies and other similar species of Diptera.
They are more noticeable on very slow-flowing rivers, canals and
ponds than on fast streams, and in the absence of other flies trout
may feed quite keenly on them. The imitation of the house-fly is
dressed with a body made up of mixed fibres from both a rook's
and a dark heron's wing feather, a dark grizzled or black hackle
and wings of dark starling, or else two grizzled cock hackle points
tied back over the hook.

LAKE SPECIES

Lake Olive, *Cloëon simile* (Pl. 13a, b, p. 80): this is the Olive Dun
of the lakes. It is exceedingly common and is found throughout Britain and Ireland in the still waters of lakes and reservoirs. The flies
vary somewhat in both colour and size. In the spring they are as
large as or slightly larger and rather darker than the Large Dark
Olive. They differ in that their wings are pronouncedly tinged with
vivid green near the thorax, and in that the green colour is often
conspicuous on the thorax, head and eyes of the fly. At this time
of the year the duns could aptly be named Green Olives.

Later, in the summer and in the autumn, the duns are usually
smaller in size, and paler and more ginger or yellow-olive coloured
instead of dark grey-green. These paler flies could appropriately
be described as Golden Olives.

In the south of England the flies which appear in the autumn
are noticeably smaller and more golden coloured than those found
in Ireland and possibly also in the north of England and Scotland.

There are many dressings of the Lake Olive, and it seems probable that the tyings of those standard Irish lake flies, the Green
Olive and the Golden Olive, were based on imitations of this species.
On the bigger lakes these two patterns are dressed on large hooks,
often on numbers 7 and 8, with the result that the artificial flies are
several times larger than the natural Olive. But, as O'Gorman
pointed out in 1845, in speaking of lake flies, "When the natural

flies come out you must endeavour to be exact in your imitations, more, however, as to the colour of the body and wing than the size, for if you match the kind, a little difference of bigness will not signify, especially in blowing weather."

On some of the smaller limestone lakes the artificial Green Olive and Golden Olive tied on hooks as small as numbers 2 and 3 are used as imitations of the natural Lake Olive. One lake on which the species is of major importance as an angling fly is Lough Glore in Co. Westmeath, and dressings of the patterns used on this lake are given by Gregory Greendrake in *Angling Excursions in the Counties of Wicklow, Meath, Westmeath, Longford and Cavan* which appeared in the year 1832. Some of these patterns are quite effective when trout are feeding on the natural species.

More modern wet fly imitations are provided by Mr. R. C. Bridgett's Rough Olive and by various appropriate shades of the Olive Quill. Nymph patterns are often more successful than patterns of the dun.

The female spinners of the Lake Olives (Pl. 22 d, p. 101) resemble common red spinners and may be seen lying spent on the water, having completed their ovipositing, at any time of the day. They can be successfully imitated by the hackled seal's fur pattern of the red spinner, and by a Pheasant Tail. These patterns are most satisfactory when they are tied half spent, that is with the hackle flattened beneath the hook, but left upright on the upper side of the shank in order to make it easier for the angler to see the fly when it is on the water.

The lee of islands and the calm water along a wooded shore, particularly on one side of a point, are the most likely places to see fish feeding on these spinners. Sometimes they will concentrate on these flies and ignore Greendrakes which are on the water at the same time.

Claret Duns, *Leptophlebia vespertina* (Pl. 13 d, p. 80), are as large as the Large Dark Olives and as dark as the Iron Blue Duns. A closer comparison with the latter flies shows that the wings of the Claret Dun are blacker and that the body is of a darker claret colour. The Claret Duns have three tails.

On some lakes during May, when these flies are in abundance, trout feed very keenly on them and a good dry fly pattern is then indispensable. A useful pattern is dressed with a body composed

Robert M. Adam

Plate XV Among the Ephemeropterans of use to anglers in the calm bays of Loch Rannoch are the Claret Dun, *Leptophlebia vespertina*, and the Lake Olive, *Cloëon simile*

John Markham

Plate XVI Loch Beneveian in Inverness-shire is a type of upland lake where swarms of the darker species of Chironomids known as Blae and Blacks can be expected in March or April

of a mixture of mole's fur and dark claret seal's fur, and a very dark blue dun hackle. The flies commonly occur in Britain and Ireland in bog lakes, but are found also on many limestone lakes. On parts of Lough Mask, for instance, they are exceedingly common and the trout rise freely to them in May.

A dark Claret and Mallard tied with a waterhen's wing feather as substitute for the brown mallard wing makes a good wet fly dressing, and a tying of the peat-coloured nymph is included in the Appendix.

The Claret Spinner is a useful fly when the conspicuously claret-bodied female spinner of the Claret Dun is on the water. The wings of the spinner are nearly colourless and are best imitated with a clear blue dun cock's hackle. These spinners, like those of the Lake Olive, may be seen on the water at any time of the day.

Sedge-flies:

Some lakes abound with different species of sedge-flies, and on calm warm evenings during the latter part of June, July and August heavy rises of trout may occur to sedges. The fish sometimes feed on the spent flies lying on the water, but at other times they concentrate on those flies which can be seen swimming along on the surface.

Fish engaged in this latter occupation may be caught by using an ordinary tying of an appropriate pattern of a dry sedge, and by moving it slightly whenever a trout is seen approaching. But when they are feeding on the spent flies it may be necessary to use a suitable spent dressing. Patterns of both types are included in the Appendix, but owing to the number of different species of sedge-flies which commonly occur on still water, the dressings are generalised and individual species are not imitated.

Sedge-flies vary in size from less than 1 10th of an inch in length to between one and two inches, but the very small species are of little use for angling purposes. Of the medium-sized and large species about 30 occur commonly on still waters, and many of these are extremely common in suitable habitats. Slight differences in the habits or appearance of the flies are not of much consequence. The presence of several closely related species at the same time is an advantage, as the total number of such flies which will be on the water at one time will probably be greater than if only one or two species were present. Normally trout in lakes are inclined to ignore surface food, but a large collection of flies on the surface is one of the most important factors in inducing sulky fish to rise.

Silverhorns are among the more important types of sedge-flies occurring on lakes, ponds and reservoirs. They are small slender caddis flies which have long conspicuous antennae. The antennae are sometimes nearly three times as long as the flies themselves, and in many of the species they are conspicuously ringed with white, hence the vernacular name. In some species the antennae are more drab coloured, and the white or silver markings are not noticeable, but it seems more convenient to group them all under the same common name. The colours of the wings vary from jet black through dark and light brown to grey. One of the species (*Mystacides longicornis*) which has somewhat mottled brown and grey wings is also called the Grouse Wing. The dressing given of the Brown Silverhorns in the imitation in Appendix D, p. 242, (the pattern actually is as much grey as it is brown), is one of the most useful dry flies for evening fishing on any small reservoir or pond on which the natural flies occur.

Both types occur in profusion on some of the large lakes in Ireland, and doubtless in Scotland also. On warm calm evenings in July and August, fish in some of the large limestone lakes in Westmeath and Cavan feed on the various Silverhorns and on other small and medium-sized caddis flies as keenly as on the Spent Gnat during May.

There are many medium-sized dark sedge-flies which are common on lakes and one of the most widely distributed of them is Halford's Welshman's Button.

On lowland limestone lakes medium and large-sized Cinnamon Sedges of the genus *Limnephilus* are sometimes very abundant. These flies often have bright light green abdomens with light red or ginger-coloured thoraces and legs. Patterns dressed with stiff light red cock hackles wound at the shoulder only, and wings of several ginger or waxy cock hackle points tied so as to lie along the body, which should be of pale green quill or herl, are at times very successful.

Dressings of the Murragh and other large dark species are also better if a stiff hackle is not ribbed along the whole body, as it is difficult to hook fish on large flies which are too strongly hackled. One difficulty in tying spent sedges is in using sufficient hackle to keep the flies floating, but not too much, otherwise the fish which rise to it may not succeed in drawing the hook into their mouths. When trout are feeding on spent sedges they make a very small rise, and seemingly barely open their mouths in order to absorb the flies.

Chironomids or Midges:

The Chironomids comprise what is probably the least publicised but is yet the most important, or one of the most important, families of flies in so far as lake anglers are concerned. The systematics of the family are difficult, as not only is there a great number of species involved, but many of the species are ill-defined and, therefore, extremely difficult to identify.

Common names have been applied to a few of the species, or perhaps it would be more correct to say that, in a few instances, a technical name has been correlated with a common name. For instance *Chironomus tentans* and *C. viridis* on Blagdon Reservoir are known respectively as the Olive Midge and the Green Midge (Pl. 29 d, p. 132). But as there are several other species which could equally well be called Olive or Green Midges, and which superficially resemble the two species named, it is probably more reasonable to treat each artificial pattern as representing a group of several similarly coloured species rather than one individual species.

The species which appear in March and April are in general moderate-sized dark species. They include the flies called Blae and Blacks, and some of the species which are called Duck-flies. They are found throughout Britain and Ireland in lakes and reservoirs but they are, of course, much more important on some waters than on others. The flies emerge from deep water, and on some reservoirs it is most marked that most of the fish will be seen rising out of reach of an angler fishing from the shore. Consequently it is advisable, whenever possible, to fish from a boat during the emergence period of these flies.

The main hatch takes place in the forenoon, and the trout feed avidly on the pupae ascending to the surface, and on those suspended from the surface film, just before and while they are hatching. Fish thus engaged can be caught on an ordinary wet fly dressing of the adult fly (a dark Greenwell is sometimes a successful pattern), but more often they will ignore anything other than a dressing of the pupa. The dressing of two pupae, called the Orange Pupa and the Olive Pupa, are included in Appendix D, pp. 245-46, and with both of these patterns I have had some excellent fishing. The value of these patterns is perhaps most apparent on waters which are heavily fished. When using them, two or three are mounted on one cast and they are fished in more or less the same manner as ordinary wet flies, except (as I have always found) that they are more successful if they are moved only slightly and are not drawn quickly through the water. Fish feeding on the pupae tend to swim about near the surface in small shoals and they can be located by their rises. It is always better to locate such feeding fish rather than to fish aimlessly over water where no fish have been seen. This type of fishing is most successful in a wind.

During a flat calm, or in calm sheltered portions of the lake, the flies will sometimes remain for a while on the water before flying to the shore, and when they are sufficiently numerous trout feed freely on them. The larger olive-coloured species are perhaps inclined to remain for longer on the surface than the darker species, but when either species is present one can enjoy some interesting dry fly fishing. On Lough Arrow and other Irish limestone lakes these species are called Duck-flies, and on these large lakes they are in abundance at about the middle of April.

Fish also feed on the adult flies after the flies have returned to the water to oviposit. This generally occurs in the evening, and if there is a wind the best results will probably be obtained with the wet fly. It is advisable to fish on the side of the lake towards which the wind is blowing, as the spent flies will be carried along on the surface, and the greatest concentration of them therefore will be on the lee shore. The artificial pattern of the Hawthorn, or some other black fly with short greyish (starling) wings, is often effective, and the fact that it is fished below the surface does not appear to deter the trout from accepting it.

The species of Chironomids which appear during the summer include the Olive and Green Midges. Many of them are large, being over one half inch in length, and, owing to their habit of flying along the top of the water, they are also called Buzzers or Racehorses. They are more difficult to imitate than the dark spring forms, probably because of their restless habits, but two dry fly dressings which are fairly successful are included among the list of patterns.

These large Olive Midges are found on limestone lakes and ponds. They hatch from the shallower areas of large lakes, where the water is from about two to ten feet deep. In lakes where the water is very clear they emerge also from deeper areas, and in all waters the larvae like a marl or mud bottom. The hatch usually takes place in the late evening, often beginning at about sunset, and may continue for several hours. When the flies are abundant on the water they tend to form into small swarms or clumps; single flies which are restlessly flying along the surface come into contact with one of these swarms and add to its size. On suitable evenings dozens of these clumps, many of them of about the size of a golf ball, will be seen scattered over the water. The clumps assume a rough globular shape and even a light breeze will blow them along the surface. On examination, a clump will be seen to consist of a tangled mass of these large midges clinging to each other with considerable tenacity.

Shortly after the hatch begins fish may start feeding on the single flies, and usually rise to flies moving across the surface in preference to those at rest. When the clumps form they in turn are taken, in preference; and if the clumps are sufficiently numerous the trout may completely ignore single flies. At such times, a fly dressed in accordance with the tying of the midge clump in Appendix D, p. 243, is an excellent pattern. This pattern somewhat resembles a large and very much over-hackled dry Greendrake. In default of this pattern a dry hackled Greendrake makes a fair substitute. When the clumps are not in evidence the hackled Green Midge is effective; but with both patterns their effectiveness is increased if they are dragged slightly on the water when a rising fish is approaching.

Dragon-flies. The nymphs of dragon-flies are aquatic, but in order to allow the adult fly to emerge, the nymph climbs out of the water, usually by upright vegetation. Before coming out, the nymphs of at least some sixteen species swim up to the surface of the water, and then, while remaining just beneath the surface, they swim along until they reach some solid support, by way of which they can leave the water.

On Blagdon Reservoir, and on some of the large Irish limestone lakes, and doubtless elsewhere also, trout feed on these nymphs as they are swimming along, just under the surface. One of the nymphs is shown on Plate 28, p. 129. These nymphs swim in eel-like fashion, and, owing to the undulating movement of their bodies, it would appear difficult to devise a good imitation. I am told, however, that some of the Blagdon anglers have evolved a successful pattern.

A. E.

N

CHAPTER 19

NOTES ON FLY DRESSINGS

M ANY BOOKS have been published on fly-tying, and to describe here details of the fundamentals of the art would be unnecessary. But there are a few points associated with the way in which some of the artificial flies dealt with in the text, or illustrated in the colour Plates, have been dressed to which reference is made.

OLD PATTERNS

Plates 31 and 32a (pages 140 and 141) are of flies which were tied in the eighteenth and nineteenth century. The illustrations are of considerable interest, as these eighteenth century specimens are probably among the oldest trout flies extant. These eighteenth century flies at one time belonged to Richard Gregory, and I have no reason to doubt their authenticity. They had evidently been collected originally by him, as they were in paper folders all of which had either his name or initials transcribed on them. Each of the folders also bore the name and address of the fly tyer and the date. Two of the folders contained flies dressed by Cornelius Gorman, and on one of these was inscribed a letter dated August 1791 addressed to Richard Gregory Esq., and signed by Cornelius Gorman from Ennis.

It is interesting to remember that in his book *The Practice of Angling, particularly as regards Ireland,* which was written by one named O'Gorman, and was published in 1845, the author refers to his fly-tyer Corny Gorman, who dressed flies for Inchiquin and other lakes in Co. Clare, and who contracted the plague (probably cholera) and died in Ennis. It seems not improbable that this Corny Gorman the fly-tyer and Cornelius Gorman, who dressed the patterns illustrated here, were the same person.

An examination of these patterns shows that Corny Gorman had little to learn about tying lake flies. His patterns are beautifully and most neatly dressed. At first glance at Plate 31 b his flies may appear to be somewhat crudely tied, but, if the irregular bend of the hook of any one of the flies is hidden, the finished appearance of the fly at once becomes apparent. The parts of the fly are well proportioned, the body is dressed short (actually it is shorter than that of our modern lake flies), the heads are small and neat, and the whole fly is lightly dressed. Of particular interest are the ways in which the hackles and wings are tied. The hackle on each fly is wound only on the anterior half of the body, and it is in open turns without any additional turns being made at the throat. This gives a different effect from the modern method of winding several turns, if not all of the turns, of hackle at the throat. This older method exposes more of the body of the fly when the fly is viewed from underneath, as the seal's fur and pig's wool which comprise the body are then clearly visible through the hackle. On most of the flies the hackles are dark dun or rusty dun cock of very good quality, and the fibres, which in transmitted light glisten like glass, add considerable lustre to, and intensify the colour of the dubbing on the body. The fur which is used as dubbing is pricked out so that the fibres become nearly as long as and intermingle with the fibres of the hackle. The wings are slightly longer than the hook and are divided. O'Gorman mentions in his book that flies are tied with the wings divided, but later he commenced tying flies without dividing the wing. It is not at all easy to divide mallard wings so that each half of the wing curves slightly towards the hook in the way Corny Gorman tied them, and I have often wondered if the author O'Gorman discontinued the method owing to this difficulty.

These flies are all sober coloured, the bodies being of various shades of brown, turf (peat) colour, cinnamon and green; the wings are of corncrake, brown mallard or grouse. Apart from the details of the dressings, the flies are of considerable interest, as they are examples of lake flies which were designed to resemble natural species. Most modern lake flies are merely lures in that their dressings consist of various combinations of rather gaudy materials, often chosen at random, and the efficacy of the different patterns is ascertained by trial and error. But, as O'Gorman clearly points out, the lake flies which he describes (excluding the gaudy patterns) are copied from the colour, but not necessarily the size, of the natural flies found on the water and on the rushes. He emphasises that it is not important to have the artificial pattern as small as the natural. The flies copied were mostly sedge-flies, and all the patterns of Corny Gorman's are of the type described by the author O'Gorman, and some of them are identical with the dressings he gives.

Modern patterns of gaudy lake flies may have improved, but, at any rate in so far as Irish lakes are concerned, wet fly patterns tied to represent natural flies probably have deteriorated within the past century. But the older type of lake fly tends to persist on Inchiquin and on the other lakes and rivers around Corofin and Ennis. Last year I obtained some patterns tied by a famous local fly-tyer and boatman in Corofin named Frank Egan. He is one of the boatmen mentioned in Barker's book on Co. Clare called *An Angler's Paradise* published in 1929. He was over eighty years of age when he tied pattern no. 3 illustrated in Plate 32b, page 141.

The flies on the lower row on Plate 31a, page 140, are interesting examples of very sparsely dressed lake flies. These flies, as well as the mayflies on Plate 32a, page 141, have their wings tied forwards and then pressed upright and divided, presumably in order to suggest the wings of the natural Greendrake and other upwinged flies. The flies tied by Corny Gorman resemble sedge flies in shape, as the wings closely overlie and extend beyond the body. These wings also are divided, and the hackle occupies about the same proportionate amount of the body of the fly as the thorax and legs of the natural species do. Modern lake flies are usually stereotyped in shape and the wings and hackle slope at the same angle in relation to the body on nearly all patterns. Exceptions to this are found in some of the patterns designed by Mr. R. C. Bridgett and described in his book on lake fishing. Mr. Bridgett dresses flies for use as top droppers with the wings divided, presumably to suggest a fly separating its wings preparatory to taking flight, or else struggling in the surface film.

In lake fishing, as O'Gorman points out, large-sized and gaudy flies are suitable for use during the daytime, particularly in rough water. A sample of a fly of this type is shown on Plate 31a, page 140. But in the evening, or at any other time when fish are feeding on natural species, the best results are obtained by using smaller and more sober-coloured patterns, dressed to imitate the flies on the water.

The practice of tying lake flies to a stereotyped shape, except in the case of gaudy patterns, has little to commend it. It is well to bear in mind that a natural fly can be imitated in shape, colour, size and action. Irrespective of the relative values which we may place on the importance of each of these four factors, the commonsense view would seem to be that all of the four factors should be studied closely. This practice is followed in tying ephemeropteran nymphs, where the bulky thorax, short legs and tails and often the wing cases, are copied. It may be argued that there is no necessity to devise an accurate wet fly imitation of a fully emerged fly, as the natural fly will be seen by the trout only on the surface and that, therefore, it will look different from a sunken fly. But I do not think that this is correct, as I have frequently noticed that trout in a lake will accept a pattern of this type to the exclusion of other patterns, when they are feeding on the appropriate natural insects. It is probable that flies become submerged more readily than may be realised. On the lee shore of a lake I have on occasions seen the water (beneath the surface) impregnated with drowned flies to a depth of several feet. Once a fly has got thoroughly wet and has been enveloped by the surface film very little agitation in the water will cause it to sink further, even though it may be sufficiently buoyant to float up again, and readily does so. Apart from this, trout in a lake may get a different impression of the appearance of a fly floating on the surface when the lake is rough than do trout in the comparative calm water in a river, and the fish may not pay much heed as to whether a fly is above or below the surface film in agitated water.

The oldest specimens of river flies included in the illustrations were tied for sea trout fishing on the Kinvara River, Co. Galway, in 1797 by Hynes of Gort. Except that these are rather crudely dressed they differ little from modern patterns of wet flies. Four of the specimens on Plate 32a were preserved in a folder marked "Flies for Kiltartan River 1810". Two of these are patterns of Greendrakes in which the wings are formed of fibres of a mallard feather dyed yellow and tied upright and divided. In many ways these wings give a more lifelike effect than the whole feather wings which are used on more modern patterns, and, as they were used as wet flies, the fibres forming the wings would move more freely in the water than the fibres in the wings on the later nineteenth century pattern shown.

Flies number 1, 4 and 7 on Plate 32a, p. 141, were enclosed in a folder marked "Flies bought at Stockbridge 1816". This folder had no initials or further particulars on it except that it bore the watermark "Allee 1813". One of these flies is the same as the modern tying of a Black Gnat, and the others are palmer tied with a game hen and a red hackle respectively. The large size of these flies is interesting but is in keeping with Canon Kingsley's remarks about "our large chalk flies". One cannot help wondering if these flies were of the size used by Col. Peter Hawker when he made his big bags of trout on the Test higher up at Longparish.

MODERN DRESSINGS

Dry flies are, broadly speaking, of two types: Those which lie flat on the surface, and often intermingle with the surface film, and represent spent or drowned flies, and those which are sitting cocked up on the surface and which represent flies resting on the surface film but not entangled in it. Usually artificial patterns are most successful if they definitely are of one or other of these types.

Spent patterns are dressed with wings either of hackle points, or hackle fibres or a mixture of both. But they should be constructed so that when the flies are used the wings lie flush with the surface of the water and not, as so often happens with these patterns, with one or both wings held above the surface by the hackle fibres radiating from the shoulder in a sweep's brush fashion. It does not seem to matter if the fibres above the hook are sticking upwards, and these fibres are certainly of advantage as they make a fly easier to see. These points are illustrated in Fig. 7.

The type of upright winged dry fly which is easiest to see on the water, and which I personally find most effective, is one with the wings tied reversed and inclining slightly forwards over the eye. It is tied with either single or double wings, and when the web of the feather forming the wings is laid in position to be tied on, the tip portion inclines over the eye of the hook, and the edge of the web on which the fold lies is uppermost. The web is folded so that the pale sides are touching each other, and when the fly is fished the wings separate and assume an upright position, instead of inclining towards the tail, as usually happens with the normal type of wings. A few turns of tying silk or a turn or two of the hackle in front of the wings helps them to assume an upright position.

When tying a hackled mayfly or other fly which has partridge

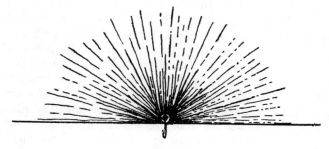

FIG. 7

Hackled dry fly viewed in front elevation floating on water
A fly dressed in this manner with the hackle fibres projecting only sideways
and upwards simulates spent spinners or duns flattened on the water; it has
the added advantage that the angler can see it more easily with the upright
hackle fibres than he could were it tied completely 'spent'.

or other soft-fibred feathers wound in front of a stiffer hackle, the fly will float more easily, and last longer, if the following method is used. The partridge hackle is wound and the fibres are then pressed out over the eye of the fly, and both the tying silk and the stiffer cock's hackle are wound close up against and partly over the roots of these softer fibres.

In general, in the construction of dry flies one is always up against the problem of how much and how stiff a hackle is required to make the fly float. If there is too much stiff hackle on the fly, it becomes more difficult to hook fish. If there is too little hackle, the fly will not float. In this connection it is interesting to remember that the surface tension on some rivers is stronger than on other rivers, and a fly which may easily float on one water will just as readily sink in some other water.

Dry flies dressed with soft hackles are sometimes very effective, provided they can be kept floating. A fly of this type is the Iron-blue Dun. This pattern is tied with two or three of the small hackles from a Jackdaw's throat. These hackles are fragile and somewhat difficult to manipulate, and it is advisable to tie them on "Stewartwise". Two hackles are dealt with at the same time as follows: stroke back the fibres from the tips and tie one of the hackles in at the shoulder (by the tip, of course) so that the stump end is directed towards and sticks out beyond the eye of the hook. The other hackle is tied on in a similar fashion but lying in the opposite direction. When the feathers are being tied in, their out-side surfaces should lie nearest to the hook, both feathers should be fastened to the hook as near to each other as possible, and the tying silk should hang straight down from the point where the feathers are attached. The stalks of the feathers are then pulled back in the opposite direction to that in which they are lying naturally, and the tying silk is held up between them and the stalks are allowed to spring back against the silk. The two stalks and the silk are then spun around each other so that the hackle stalks and the silk are closely twisted together into one cord. The two hackles and the tying silk are then wound as one unit for two or three turns. A third hackle can then be tied in by the tip and wound behind these two hackles.

A LIST OF ANGLERS' INSECTS

PLECOPTERA

FAMILY	GENUS	SPECIES
Perlodidae	*Perlodes*	*mortoni* (Klapálek)
	Dictyopterygella	*recta* (Kemp.)
Perlidae	*Perla*	*cephalotes* (Curt.)
	,,	*carlukiana* Klap.
	Isoperla	*grammatica* (Poda)
	Chloroperla	*torrentium* (Pict.)
Taeniopterygidae	*Taeniopteryx*	*nebulosa* (L.)
Leuctridae	*Leuctra*	*geniculata* Steph.
	,,	*hippopus* Kemp.
	,,	*fusciventris* Steph.
Nemouridae	*Protonemura*	*meyeri* (Pict.)
	,,	*praecox* (Morton)
	Nemoura	*variegata* Olivier

EPHEMEROPTERA

Ephemeridae	*Ephemera*	*danica* (L.)
	,,	*vulgata* (Müll.)
	,,	*lineata* Etn.
Potamanthidae	*Potamanthus*	*luteus* (L.)
Leptophlebiidae	*Leptophlebia*	*marginata* (L.)
	,,	*vespertina* (L.)
	Paraleptophlebia	*submarginata* (Steph.)
	,,	*cincta* (Retz.)
	,,	*tumida* (Bengtsson)
	Habrophlebia	*fusca* (Curtis)

Ephemerellidae	*Ephemerella*	*ignita* (Poda.)
	,,	*notata* Etn.
Caenidae	*Brachycercus*	*harrisella* Curt.
	Caenis	*macrura* Steph.
	,,	*moesta* Bengtsson
	,,	*horaria* (L.)
	,,	*rivulorum* Etn.
	,,	*robusta* Etn.
Baëtidae	*Baëtis*	*bioculatus* (L.)
	,,	*scambus* Etn.
	,,	*vernus* Curt.
	,,	*tenax* Etn.
	,,	*buceratus* Etn.
	,,	*rhodani* (Pict.)
	,,	*atrebatinus* Etn.
	,,	*pumilus* (Burm.)
	,,	*niger* (L.)
	Centroptilum	*luteolum* (Müll.)
	,,	*pennulatum* Etn.
	Cloëon	*dipterum* (L.)
	,,	*simile* Etn.
	Procloëon	*rufulum* (Müll.)
Siphlonuridae	*Siphlonurus*	*armatus* Etn.
	,,	*lacustris* Etn.
	,,	*linnaeanus* (Etn.)
	Ameletus	*inopinatus* Etn.
Ecdyonuridae	*Rhithrogena*	*semicolorata* (Curt.)
	,,	*haarupi* Esb.-Pet.
	Heptagenia	*sulphurea* (Müll.)
	,,	*longicauda* (Steph.) nec. (Etn.)
	,,	*fuscogrisea* (Retz.)
	,,	*lateralis* (Curt.)
	Arthroplea	*congener* Bengtsson
	Ecdyonurus	*venosus* (Fabr.)
	,,	*torrentis* (Kimmins)
	,,	*dispar* (Curt.)
	,,	*insignis* (Etn.)

MEGALOPTERA (NEUROPTERA)

Sialidae   *Sialis*   *lutaria* (L.)

TRICHOPTERA

Phryganeidae	*Phryganea*	*grandis* L.
	,,	*striata* L.
	,,	*varia* F.
	,,	*obsoleta* Hagen
Limnephilidae	*Limnephilus*	*lunatus* Curt.
	Stenophylax	*stellatus* (Curt.)
	Halesus	*radiatus* (Curt.)
Sericostomatidae	*Sericostoma*	*personatum* (Spence)
	Goëra	*pilosa* (F.)
	Brachycentrus	*subnubilus* Curt.
	Lepidostoma	*hirtum* (F.)
Odontoceridae	*Odontocerum*	*albicorne* (Scop.)
Leptoceridae	*Leptocerus*	spp.
	Mystacides	*azurea* (L.)
	,,	*longicornis* (L.)
Hydropsychidae	*Hydropsyche*	*angustipennis* (Curt.)
	,,	*instabilis* (Curt.)
Psychomyidae	*Tinodes*	*waeneri* (L.)

DIPTERA

Bibionidae	*Bibio*	*marci* (L.)
	,,	*johannis* (L.)
Muscidae	*Musca*	*domestica* (L.)
Cordiluridae	*Scopeuma*	*stercorarium* (L.)
Leptidae	*Leptis*	*scolopacea* (L.)

The nomenclature used in the various orders has been taken from the following authors:—

Plecoptera — from H. B. N. Hynes (1940).
Ephemeroptera — from D. E. Kimmins (1942).
Trichoptera — from M. E. Mosely (1939).
Megaloptera and Diptera — from G. S. Kloet and W. D. Hincks (1945).

KEYS TO DUNS AND SPINNERS

How to Use the Keys

THE OBJECT of a key is to simplify the determination of species. By means of a key an individual fly can be named, or at any rate it can be ascertained that the correct name of a fly is one of a few alternatives. Reference is then made to the detailed descriptions, and in the former case the accuracy of the identification can be verified; in the latter case the species should be able to be identified by reference to the detailed descriptions of the few alternatives in question. In other words, the key is a short cut to the correct description and name of a species. The key is used in the following manner.

Refer to number 1 at the top left-hand margin. Under this number are two alternatives and the fly will fit one of them; for it must have either two or three tails (unless of course it has been damaged). If the fly has three tails refer to the number on the right-hand margin, which in this case is number 2. These numbers on the right-hand margin always direct you to the same number on the left margin further down the sheet. Numbers other than those to which you are directed should be ignored.

Suppose that the fly being examined were a *Caenis* species, which is a very small fly with three tails. Then, under number 2 on the left margin you see three alternatives, namely, (a) flies very large, (b) medium-sized flies or (c) very small flies. The only description which fits is obviously the last one, i. e. very small flies. So the other two descriptions are ignored and the number on the right-hand margin opposite to the correct description is followed. This number 4 refers down to number 4 on the left margin. Opposite to this number 4 is a description which obviously fits the fly which is being examined, and this description leads to the name *Caenis* spp. on the right-hand margin. By reference, then, to the detailed description on p. 207 and, of course, to the colour Plate 20b, p. 97, the identification is confirmed.

As a second example, suppose that the fly to be identified were a male Blue-winged Pale Watery Spinner, *Centroptilum pennulatum* (Pl. 19c, p. 96). Then, as this fly has only two tails, number 1 on the left-hand top margin would lead to number 5 on the right. Then, ignoring all other numbers and proceeding to the number 5 on the left it is obvious that this will not lead us to number 6 because the size of the hind wing of the fly being examined is not about one-third of the length of forewings. However, the other alternative fits, as the hind wing is only about one-sixth or less of the length of the forewing, and the fly is medium-sized, so this leads to number 7 on the right and down to number 7 some distance below on the left margin. To proceed further from here it is necessary to use the pocket magnifying glass (x 10 or x 15), and a careful examination of the fly shows that the hind wings are very narrow. With the lens used it may or may not be possible to see the single marginal intercalary veins. The description leads to number 12 on the right and down to the same number on the left margin. As the eyes of the spinner are orange this leads to number 13. Opposite 13 are two descriptions between which it is not difficult to differentiate, and the name of the fly then will be seen on the right-hand margin.

It might be said that the colour plates in the book obviate the necessity for keys or detailed descriptions of the flies, and it is certainly probable that many anglers will never use the keys in making identifications, and will be satisfied to use the plates only. But it should be borne in mind that there are a number of species, either duns or spinners, which are included in the keys but which have not been photographed. Also, a photograph shows the colours of only one side of a fly, and only by reflected light, whereas the detailed descriptions in most cases give the colours, and the variations of the colours, of both sides of the flies, and as seen by transmitted light as well. The colours of the flies as viewed by transmitted light have been included for two reasons. Firstly, so that identification can be made more certain by checking these colours under the alternative lighting conditions, and secondly as a help to fly-tiers when they are dressing or devising artificial imitations.

KEY TO DUNS

1. Flies with 3 tails.   ....   2.

   „   „   2   „   ....   5.

2. Flies, large or very large, wings green-ish-grey with dark brown or black markings.   ....

Greendrake,
Ephemera spp.
(see p. 70 & Pl. 1, p. 16).

Flies, medium-sized.   ....   3.
   „   small or very small.   ....   4.

3. Flies all yellow.   ....

Yellow Evening Dun,
Ephemerella notata
(see p. 72 & Pl. 7 c, p. 64).

Flies with olive-green or brown orange or subdued orange bodies and rather dark blue-grey wings.   ....

Blue-winged Olive,
Ephemerella ignita
(see p. 72 & Pl. 11 a, b, p. 76).

Flies with purplish black bodies and dark bluish black or blackish wings.

Purple Dun, *Paralepto-phlebia cincta* (see p. 74 & Pl. 10 c, p. 69).

Flies with blackish-brown or blackish claret bodies and very dark blue-grey fore wings. Hind wings much paler in contrast.   ....

Claret Dun,
Leptophlebia vespertina
(see p. 73 & Pl. 13 d, p. 80).

Flies with fore wings brown-grey, hind wings scarcely paler in contrast to fore wing. Body dark brownish.   ....

Leptophlebia marginata
(see p. 73).

Flies brownish, with brownish-fawn wings which have very distinct dark bordered cross veins. Pale area devoid of cross veins in centre of wing.   ....

Turkey Brown,
Paraleptophlebia submar-ginata (see p. 74).

4. Flies with very broad wings, usually

whitish often dark along anterior edge. No hind wings. ....   *Caenis* spp. (see p. 71 & Pl. 12 b, p. 77).

5. Very large, large or medium-sized flies with large hind wings.   ....   6.

Very small, small or medium-sized flies with hind wings very small (about one-sixth length of fore wings) or absent.   ....   7.

6. Wings greyish or greenish-grey, long and narrow. Bodies are slender in proportion to their length and are rounded in transverse section.   ....   Summer Mayflies, *Siphlonurus* spp. (see p. 79 & Pl. 13 c, p. 80).

Wings normal length and width, bodies wide, particularly at thorax, and somewhat flattened underneath. These flies are from flat nymphs. ....   8.

7. Fore wings with marginal intercalary veins paired (see Fig. 4a, p. 93). Hind wings oval shaped.   11.

Fore wings with marginal intercalary veins single (see Fig. 4b, p. 93). Hind wings present or absent. ....   12.

8. Flies with a small dark longitudinal streak on the thigh joint of each leg.   9.

Flies without this dark streak.   ....   10.

9. Wings plain bluey-grey. Hind wings paler.   ....   Olive Upright, *Rhithrogena semicolorata* (see Pl. 9 c, d, p. 68).

Wings mottled brownish-fawn.   ....   March Brown, *Rhithrogena haarupi* (see p. 83 & Pl. 7 d, p. 64).

10. Flies all yellow. Eyes black or electric-blue. ....

Yellow May Dun, *Heptagenia sulphurea* (see p. 80 & Pl. 7a, b, p. 64).

Flies with dark plain grey wings. Thorax and abdomen all dark, except for a bright yellow streak on the thorax just in front of each wing root. ....

Dark Dun, *Heptagenia lateralis* (see p. 82 & Pl. 12 c, p. 77).

Flies brownish, wings mottled brownish fawn. Thigh joint of each leg with two distinct light red bands. ....

Brown May Dun, *Heptagenia fuscogrisea* (see p. 82).
August Dun and Late March Brown,

Wings fawn colour either rather mottled, banded or with cross veins of dark brown or blackish. Legs without red bands. ....

Ecdyonurus venosus (see p. 81), *E. torrentis* or *E. dispar* (see p. 82 & Pl. 12a, p. 77).

Wings, greenish varied with blackish. Body green with an oblique black stripe on the side of each segment of the abdomen and a distinctive pattern on underside of each segment (see Fig. 10 a, p. 235). ....

Large Green Dun, *Ecdyonurus insignis* (see p. 81 & Pl. 9 a, b, p. 68).

11. Flies small or very small, wings grey-black or blue-black. Body very dark brownish or bluish-black. ....

Iron-blue Dun, *Baëtis pumilus* (see p. 75 & Pl. 6 a, b, p. 49) and *B. niger*.

Flies with the eyes of the males subdued yellow. Bodies pale olive-green or watery-yellowish Wings medium to pale grey. ....

Pale Watery Dun, *B. bioculatus* (see p. 76 & Pl. 10 a, p. 69).

Flies in which the hind wing is devoid of a costal projection (see Fig. 8 b, p. 215).

Dark Olive Dun, *B. atrebatinus*.

The remaining species of *Baëtis*, namely *B. rhodani* (see p. 74 & Pl. 6c, d, p. 49), *B. vernus*, *B. tenax*, *B. scambus* (Pl. 8c, d, p. 65), and the uncommon *B. buceratus*, are difficult to distinguish from each other in the dun stage as there are no very obvious discriminating features. They all have greyish coloured wings and olive or greyish coloured bodies.

12. Fore wings pale or medium blue-grey. Eyes orange of a brownish or reddish shade. Hind wings minute and slender.　　　　13.

Fore wings variable in colour from grey-white to dark grey, or grey tinged with olive. Hind wing absent. .... 14.

13. Flies usually of medium size. Fore wings medium, blue-grey when viewed obliquely they have a pronounced purplish-blue tinge. Eyes of males subdued orange. Veins in stigmatic area of fore-wing simple, straight, seldom oblique. .... 　Pale Blue-winged Watery Dun, *Centroptilum pennulatum* (see p. 77 & Pl. 11c, d, p. 76).

Flies usually small. Fore wings pale blue-grey or pale sky-blue colour. Eyes of males subdued light red. Veins in stigmatic area of forewing somewhat oblique and usually at least two of them joined. .... 　Little Sky-blue Dun, *Centroptilum luteolum* (see p. 77 & Pl. 8a, b, p. 65).

14. Flies small. Wings greyish-white often tinged with bright green near base. Eyes of males yellow. Body usually pale honey colour or pale yellow. Six to eight cross veins in stigmatic area of wing. .... 　Pale Evening Dun, *Procloëon rufulum* (see p. 77 & Pl. 10b, p. 69).

A. E.

O

Flies medium-sized or small. Wings medium or darkish mouse-grey usually tinged with green or pale yellowish olive along main veins and near wing root. Eyes of males medium or pale olive-green. Nine to eleven somewhat sloping oblique cross veins in stigmatic area of wing. .... Lake Olive Dun, *Cloëon simile* (see p. 78 & pl. 13a, b, p. 80).

Flies usually small. Wings dark grey tinged with olive along main veins. Three to five cross veins in stigmatic area of wing. Eyes of males olive-brown. Pond Olive Dun, *Cloëon dipterum* (see p. 78).

KEY TO SPINNERS

1. Flies with 3 tails. .... 2.

    ,, ,, 2 ,, ... 5.

2. Flies very large. Bodies whitish or cream with dark brown markings, particularly on the posterior segments. Grey Drake and Spent Gnat, *Ephemera* spp. (see p. 54 & Pl. 1f, p. 16).

    Medium-sized flies. .... 3.
    Very small flies. .... 4.

3. Flies with yellow abdomen, bright orange thorax. Eyes of males bright orange. .... Yellow Evening Spinner, *Ephemerella notata.* (see p. 62 & Pl. 18c, p. 93).

    Flies with greenish or red sherry coloured bodies. Eyes of males deep red chestnut. .... Sherry Spinner, *Ephemerella ignita.* (see p. 61 & Pl. 19a, b, p. 96).

    Flies with dark brown-black abdomens, and wings suffused with brown in stigmatic area and often along costal area. *Leptophlebia marginata* Large Claret Spinners,

Flies with dark claret or brown-black abdomens and wings with the membrane colourless. .... *Leptophlebia vespertina* (see Pl. 22b, p. 101) and *Paraleptophlebia submarginata*.

Flies with abdominal segments 2 to 7 in male translucent whitish or faintly suffused with brownish or greyish-mauve. Eyes of male dark brown — Purple Spinner *Paraleptophlebia cincta* (see p. 56).

4. Flies with very broad wings, usually whitish. Tails of males very long. No hind wings. .... *Caenis* spp. (see p. 61 & Pl. 20 b, p. 97).

5. Very large, large or medium-sized flies, with large hind wings. (Hind wings about one-third length of fore wings.) .... 6.

Very small, small and medium-sized flies with hind wings very small (about one-sixth length of forewings) or absent. .... 7.

6. Wings long and narrow. Flies very large. Bodies rounded in transverse section. .... Summer Mayfly Spinners, *Siphlonurus* spp. (see p. 62 & Pls. 20 a, p. 97, & 21 a, b, p. 100).

Wings normal length and width. Bodies wide, particularly at the thorax, and somewhat flattened underneath. Flies may be very large, large or medium-sized. .... 8.

7. Fore wings with marginal intercalary veins paired. Hind wings oval shaped. 11.

Fore wings with marginal intercalary veins single. Hind wings very narrow or absent. .... 12.

8. Body of fly brownish, legs with reddish bands as in dun.   ....

Brown May Spinner, *Heptagenia fuscogrisea* (see p. 59).

Body of fly pale yellow in female. Eyes of male become pale electric blue with age. No reddish bands on legs.   ....

Yellow May Spinner, *Heptagenia sulphurea* (see p. 59 & Pl. 15 a, b, p. 84).

Body of fly all dark, dark reddish abdomen, and black thorax except for a bright yellow streak on the thorax anterior to each wing root.   ....

Heptagenia lateralis (see Pl. 20 c, p. 97).

Flies brownish coloured with a small dark streak on the thigh joint of each leg.   ....

9.

9. Flies large, captured in March, April or early in May.   ....

March Brown Spinner, *Rhithrogena haarupi.*

Yellow Upright Spinner, *Rhithrogena semicolorata* (see p. 58 & Pl. 18 d, p. 93).

Flies medium-sized captured in May, June, July, August.   ....

Flies with dark red, yellowish red or green coloured abdomens, and with a dark red or black streak obliquely crossing the side of each segment. Legs. without red bands or femoral streak.

10.

10. Body of fly dark reddish, often mahogany colour sometimes varied with yellowish red.   ....

Great Red Spinner, *Ecdyonurus venosus, dispar* (see pp. 59, 60 & Pl. 21 c, d, p. 100) or *torrentis.*

Body of fly green. Stigmatic region of fore-wing blackish.   ....

Large Green Spinner, *E. insignis* (see p. 60 & Pl. 15d, p. 84).

11. Male spinners with yellow eyes. Dorsal surface of thorax and of last three

Pale Watery Spinner,

abdominal segments usually dark chocolate or walnut brown. .... *Baëtis bioculatus* (see Pl. 18b, p. 93).

Male spinners with eyes of various shades of dark reddish. ....   13.

12. Eyes of male spinners orange or red. Hind wings present. ....   14.

Eyes of male spinners yellow or olive. Hind wings absent. ....   15.

13. Flies usually of medium size. Tails of both sexes ringed with reddish-brown from base to apex or almost to apex. Veins in wing of female spinners noticeably brown-black. Segments 1 to 6 in abdomen of male spinner translucent greyish or brownish grey. ...   Large Dark Olive Spinner, *Baëtis rhodani* (see p. 55 & Pl. 14a, b, p. 81).

Flies small or very small. Tails white or greyish. Veins in wing colourless or nearly so. Segments 1 to 6 in abdomen of male are pure white, and are in marked contrast to the jet black thorax, and the dark brown colour of the last three abdominal segments as seen from above. Abdomen of female dark red mahogany colour. ....   Iron-blue (Jenny, Little Claret) Spinner, *Baëtis pumilus* (see p. 54 & Pl. 14c, d, p. 81) (or *B. niger*).

Flies small or very small. Tails white or greyish. Veins in wings of female spinners black. Segments 1 to 6 in abdomen of male spinner whitish faintly darkened with yellowish brown. Abdomen of female spinners pale, medium or dark brown distinctly tinged with olive. ....   Small Dark Olive Spinner, *Baëtis scambus* (see p. 55 & Pl. 16, p. 85).

Flies medium or small. Tails greyish or whitish, those of the female being darkened with brown near the base. Segments 1 to 6 of male spinner often of a dark brown similar in colour to the last two or three segments. On other examples the brown in the intermediate segments is less pronounced. ....   Olive Spinner, *Baëtis vernus, B. tenax* (see p. 56).

Flies medium or small. Tails white. Segments 2 to 6 in male spinners translucent whitish tinged with light greenish or olive brown. Veins whitish or colourless. ....   Dark Olive Spinner, *Baëtis atrebatinus* (see p. 56).

14. Flies usually of medium size. Eyes of males cadmium orange. Veins in stigmatic area of fore wing simple, straight, seldom oblique and curved.   Blue-winged Pale Watery Spinner, *Centroptilum pennulatum* (see Pl. 19c, p. 96).

Flies usually small. Eyes of males bright pale red. Veins in stigmatic areas of fore wing somewhat oblique and usually at least two of them joined.   Pale Watery Spinner, *Centroptilum luteolum* (see p. 54 & Pl. 17a, b, p. 92).

15. Flies small or very small. Eyes of males bright yellow. Dorsal surface of thorax and of posterior three abdominal segments amber brown. Abdomen of female pale yellow. ....   Pale Evening Spinner, *Procloëon rufulum* (see p. 56 & Pl. 17c, d, p. 92).

Flies medium-sized or small. Eyes of male olive green. Wings of female colourless except for a faint yellowish tinge sometimes near the wing root. Nine to eleven sloping oblique cross veins in stigmatic area of wing. ....   Lake Olive Spinner, *Cloëon simile* (see p. 58 & Pl. 22 c, d, p. 101).

Flies medium-sized or small. Eyes of male subdued brown-red. Wings of female strongly coloured with amber along the costal and subcostal area. Three to five cross veins in stigmatic area of wing. ....   Pond Olive Spinner, *Cloëon dipterum* (see Pl. 22a, p. 101).

APPENDIX C

DESCRIPTIONS OF EPHEMEROPTERA

The British angler's Duns and Spinners, by reflected and transmitted light.

♂: male
♀: female

EPHEMERA DANICA

♂ ♀ DUN: GREENDRAKE (Pl. 1b, c, p. 16)
Female here described; male very similar but smaller and usually duller in colour.
Wings: variable but usually faintly green or yellowish-green; several brown marks near the middle of the wing; veins blackish.
Thorax: dorsum, brownish-black; venter and sides, olive varied with brown.
Legs: dark yellowish-olive.
Abdomen: faintly yellowish, cream or oliveaceous with a series of brown markings which become predominant on the dorsal surface of the posterior 3 or 4 segments.
Tails: black.
Transmitted light: wings faintly yellowish-green; body pale yellowish becoming brownish in the last 2 segments; tails brown-black.
General appearance: A very large yellowish-bodied fly with grey-green or faintly yellowish-green wings lightly mottled with brownish; three tails.

♂ ♀ SPINNER: SPENT GNAT (Pl. 1e, f, p. 16)
Female (*grey drake*) here described; male (*black drake*) slightly smaller, wings more strongly tinged with brown.

Head and eyes: blackish.

Thorax: dorsum, pitch black; venter, pitch black, varied with grey; sides similar with brownish red mark.

Legs: greyish black.

Wings: membrane transparent, faintly tinged with bluish and carrying few light brown markings; veins brown-black, distinct.

Abdomen: dorsum and venter, segments 1 to 6 translucent white with faint brown markings; last 3 or 4 segments more completely brown.

Tails: brown-black.

Transmitted light: body translucent yellowish white with the last 3 segments of the abdomen medium-brown and the thorax opaque blackish; wings very faintly greyish-blue with dark veins.

General appearance: wings have a faint blue sheen, body white varied with brown posteriorly.

EPHEMERA VULGATA

♂ ♀ DUN: Greendrake

These mayflies differ from the *E. danica* flies in the colour and markings of the abdomen. The dorsal surface of each of the segments 1 to 9 on the abdomen of this species carries a pair of dark brown triangular or longitudinal blotches; and the ground colour is rather dark yellowish or brownish. The blotches on segments 3 to 5 of *E. danica* are extremely small and inconspicuous, and the ground colour of the abdomen is pale yellow.

♂ ♀ SPINNER: Spent Gnat

The difference between the abdominal markings on this species and *E. danica* is even more easily seen on the spinners: the ground colour of the abdomen of this species is olivaceous, and that of *E. danica* is creamy-white.

LEPTOPHLEBIA MARGINATA

♂ ♀ DUN

The wings of these duns are a darkish brown-grey, and the cross-veins are conspicuous owing to dark shading along their edges. The flies are of about similar size to the Claret Dun, *L. vespertina*, but differ in the colour of their wings and in that the cross-veins of the wings of the latter species are not noticeably shaded. They have three tails.

♂ ♀ SPINNER
A dark brown-bodied spinner (with three tails). The wings have brownish veins and are shaded with smoky-brownish in the region of the stigmatic area.

LEPTOPHLEBIA VESPERTINA

♂ DUN: CLARET DUN (Pl. 13d, p. 80)
Wings: very dark grey or grey-blue; hind-wings much paler and more beige-coloured.
Thorax: dorsum, brown-black; venter and sides very similar tinged with purple.
Abdomen: dorsum, very dark and shining, nearly black; central segments grey-blue black, last three segments black-claret or brown-black; venter, dark grey-black.
Legs: darkest brown-black.
Tails: dark grey-brown.
Transmitted light: abdomen segments 1 to 6 grey-black, last three segments very dark claret; legs dark brown, tinged with purple in some lights; tails very similar; wings dark grey-blue.
General appearance: whole fly very dark grey-blue; three tails.

♀ DUN: CLARET DUN
Wings: fore-wings bluish-black, hind-wings buff.
Thorax: dorsum, blackish; venter and sides, purple-brown-black or black-claret.
Abdomen: brownish-black, very dark brown-olive, or very dark claret.
Legs: dark brown-olive.
Tails: blackish-brown.
Transmitted light: abdomen and legs dark brown-olive with a dark claret tinge; wings dark grey-blue; tails mouse-coloured; eyes and thorax blackish and opaque.
General appearance: these duns, both male and female, somewhat resemble very large Iron-blue duns, but are more claret-coloured in the body.

♂ SPINNER: LARGE CLARET SPINNER (Pl. 22b, p. 101)
Eyes: darkest brown-red, nearly black mahogany.
Thorax: dorsum, jet black; venter and sides, varied with dark reddish.

Wings: transparent, with some of the stronger veins tinged with brownish.

Abdomen: dorsum, last three segments dark grey-brown often tinged with purple or claret, intermediate segments dark brownish-claret, joinings paler; venter, somewhat similar but paler.

Legs: dark brown-black.

Tails: buff, faintly ringed with reddish.

Transmitted light: body dark greyish, faintly tinged with purple or brown; wings nearly colourless.

General appearance: a very dark blackish-claret spinner.

♀ SPINNER: LARGE CLARET SPINNER

Eyes: brown-black.

Thorax: dorsum, black; venter and sides, black mixed with mauve or claret.

Wings: transparent colourless, except for some of the stronger veins which are light brown.

Legs: darkest claret-brown.

Abdomen: dorsum, colour of very dark, nearly black, mahogany or black claret, with paler joinings; venter, dark claret-brown, with paler joinings to the segments.

Tails: buff.

Transmitted light: abdomen, dark brown-mahogany or claret-brown with paler joinings; thorax black; legs darkest brown-olive; wings, colourless.

General appearance: a medium or rather large-sized dark claret-bodied spinner with colourless wings.

PARALEPTOPHLEBIA SUBMARGINATA

♂ ♀ DUN: TURKEY BROWN

These are darkish brown-coloured flies with three tails. The membrane of the wings is smoky-grey or fawn colour; the cross-veins are black, and are made more conspicuous as they have a black edging. There is a clear space, of the ground colour of the membrane, in the centre of each of the fore-wings.

♂ ♀ SPINNER: TURKEY BROWN

Eyes: dark purple-brown.

Thorax: dorsal surface jet black.

Abdomen: dorsum, pitch-brown with paler joinings to the segments; venter, light warm sepia-brown with segments 8 to 10 pitch-brown.
Wings: transparent, with the stronger veins amber-brown.
Legs: dark brown or blackish.
Tails: sepia-grey, with darker joinings.

PARALEPTOPHLEBIA CINCTA

♂ ♀ DUN: PURPLE DUN   (♂ Pl. 10c, p. 69)
These duns are very like large-sized Iron-blue Duns; but they have three tails. They usually are slightly tinged with purple.

♂ SPINNER: PURPLE SPINNER   (Pl. 18a, p. 93)
Eyes: brown-black, or purple brown-black.
Thorax: dorsum, pitch-black, with a suggestion of purple; venter and sides, purple-black varied with pitch-brown at the sides.
Wings: transparent, veins faintly brown.
Abdomen: dorsum, segments 1 to 6 translucent white, often tinged with light brown-red or mauve, last three segments very dark brownish, sometimes with a faint trace of purple or grey; venter, intermediate segments translucent whitish, last two or three segments opaque grey or purple-grey.
Legs: whitish, tinged with dark brown-red or mauve.
Tails: subdued white.
Transmitted light: head and thorax black; segments 1 to 6 of abdomen translucent, last three segments dark grey-brown; legs faintly brown-red; wings transparent, nearly colourless.
General appearance: like a large Jenny Spinner with a suggestion of mauve or purple on the body; three tails.

♀ SPINNER: PURPLE SPINNER
This spinner resembles the female Large Claret Spinner *Leptophlebia vespertina*, but differs in that the abdomen is paler and less claret-coloured.

EPHEMERELLA IGNITA

♂ DUN: BLUE-WINGED OLIVE DUN   (Pl. 11a, p. 76)
Eyes: red-brown.
Wings: dark bluish-grey.

Thorax: dorsum, olive-toffee-colour; venter, subdued red-brown.
Legs: olive-grey, becoming dark grey distally.
Abdomen: dorsum, brown orange, sometimes subdued, sometimes
  quite vivid, with the joinings of the segments dark olivaceous,
  last segment yellowish; venter, very similar to dorsum.
Tails: dark grey with distinct brown rings; usually are very limp
  and often rather twisted.
Transmitted light: thorax dusky orange; abdomen brown-orange with
  the joinings brown-olive; legs olive-grey, wings medium-grey.
General appearance: a brown orange-bodied fly with dark blue-grey
  wings; the brown-orange in the body is often very much subdued.

♀ DUN: BLUE-WINGED OLIVE DUN   (Pl. 11 b, p. 76)
Eyes: green-black.
Wings: dark blue-grey, with some of the stronger longitudinal
  veins slightly brown-olive.
Thorax: dorsum, olive-green; venter and sides olive-green varied with
  brownish.
Legs: olive, becoming grey or black distally.
Abdomen: olive-green, varying from a vivid shade to a subdued
  yellowish-olive, often with some of the posterior segments slightly
  red-brown.
Tails: brown-olive-grey with dark rings.
Transmitted light: abdomen olive-green or yellow-olive; thorax more
  opaque brown-olive; legs olive; tails grey dun-colour; wings blue-
  grey.
General appearance: varies from a vivid olive-green-bodied fly, to
  a fly with a yellowish-olive body; wings as in male dun.

♂ SPINNER: BLUE-WINGED OLIVE SPINNER   (Pl. 19a, p. 96)
Eyes: bright chestnut, or bright red-brown.
Thorax: dorsum black; sides black varied with reddish; venter,
  black with a puce tinge and red-brown.
Wings: transparent, with the stronger veins light red-brown.
Legs: yellow-olive, varied brown-amber.
Abdomen: dorsum, dark red-brown or rich dark mahogany-colour,
  with pale segmental joinings; venter, slightly paler red-brown.
Tails: pale amber-olive near the base, becoming nearly colourless
  distally.
Transmitted light: head, thorax and the posterior abdominal segment

opaque dark brown; segments 1 to 7 or 8 rich sherry-colour with distinct pale joinings; legs and tails watery brown-yellow.

General appearance: a red spinner with prominent chestnut-coloured eyes and three tails.

♀ SPINNER: BLUE-WINGED OLIVE (SHERRY) SPINNER

(Pl. 19b, p. 96)

Eyes: drab olive-green.

Thorax: dorsum, brown amber-colour, becoming more pink at the sides; venter, dark amber.

Wings: membrane colourless, stronger veins brownish.

Legs: rather drab olive.

Abdomen: dorsum, brown red or reddish-amber, or nearly lobster-red; venter, more pink-coloured than the dorsal surface.

Tails: grey-olive, ringed with dark brown.

Transmitted light: abdomen translucent pink-amber, becoming more opaque and brown-amber-coloured in the posterior two or three segments; thorax opaque brown; legs dun and olive; tails grey, with distinct dark brown rings.

The colour of the Sherry Spinners varies considerably: the most noticeable variations are in the abdomens of the females. At the time of copulation the abdomen is normally green or yellowish-green, and after oviposition it darkens and usually becomes pronouncedly reddish-brown or more lobster-red. It may darken to a drab yellow-orange, or it may retain its original green or yellow-green in a subdued form.

It is possible that the temperature of the air may affect the colour which the abdomen assumes as the fly becomes spent. I have often noticed on some rivers on which the spent sherry spinners are of the typical red-brown colour in June, July and August, that they darken only to a sort of a drab grey olive-yellow in the later autumn. The more sober coloured spinners are perhaps commoner also in mountainous regions where the air temperature in the summer is considerably lower than it is in the South and Midlands of England and Ireland.

EPHEMERELLA NOTATA

♂ DUN: YELLOW EVENING DUN   (Pl. 7c, p. 64)

Eyes: distinct amber-orange.

Thorax: dorsum, sides and venter, light red-amber.

Wings: membrane milky-grey, suffused with pale yellow in basal and anterior portion; veins distinctly yellow; whole wing appears to be light yellow when viewed from a distance.

Legs: yellowish.

Abdomen: dorsum, pale yellow, last three segments light reddish amber; venter very similar; the abdomen is marked, particularly on the venter with a pattern of very fine lines and dots of dark brown (fig. 10b, p. 206).

Tails: yellowish, ringed with brown.

Transmitted light: body deep yellow becoming orange at the thorax and in the last few abdominal segments; wings whitish-yellow.

General appearance: an all-yellow fly with the thorax light reddish-orange.

♀ DUN: YELLOW EVENING DUN   (Pl. 7c, p. 64)

Head: pale yellow.

Eyes: pale green, sometimes tinged with yellow.

Thorax: dorsum, rather pale or medium red-amber, or red-orange; venter similar, or paler.

Wings: membrane suffused with pale yellow along the costal and subcostal areas, particularly near to the wing root; remainder of wing-membrane palest yellowish-grey; veins pale yellow; the whole wing appears pale yellow.

Abdomen: dorsum, yellow, slightly more pronounced and darker than the wing; venter yellow; there is a pattern of fine dark brown lines and dots visible on the underneath and sides of each segment.

Legs: yellowish, becoming dark grey distally.

Tails: yellowish, ringed with brown.

Transmitted light: wings, pale milky grey tinged with yellow, particularly near front edge; body yellow, becoming more orange or amber-coloured at the thorax; legs faint yellow, becoming grey distally; tails yellowish-grey.

General appearance: very like the Yellow May Dun, *Heptagenia sulphurea*, but of course differs in that it has three tails.

♂ ♀ SPINNER: YELLOW EVENING SPINNER   (Pl. 18c, p. 93)

Male here described; female very similar but abdomen more pronouncedly yellow.

Eyes: medium-orange.

Thorax: dorsum, dark brown-toffee-colour; sides light orange or reddish-amber; venter, orange.

Wings: transparent, colourless, with the stronger veins faintly yellow.

Abdomen: dorsum yellow-olive tinged with grey on segments 2 to 7, segments 8 and 9 opaque brown or brown-olive; venter paler · than dorsum, posterior two segments less strongly-coloured.

Legs: olive-yellow.

Tails: yellowish, ringed with brown-red.

Transmitted light: wings transparent colourless, except for yellowish veins; abdomen translucent pale grey-yellow, becoming opaque in last 2 or 3 segments; thorax orange; legs yellowish.

General appearance: a medium-sized yellowish spinner with three tails.

CAENIS SPECIES

♂ ♀ DUN & SPINNER: ANGLER'S CURSE

(Pls. 12b, p. 77; 20b, p. 97)

All species of *Caenis* may be recognised by their very broad white or whitish wings, their small size and their three tails. The species *C. macrura* and *C. moesta* are as large as Iron-blue duns; their thoraces are generally black, and the abdomens of the male spinners are black or grey-black. The tails of the male spinners are many times longer than the body of the fly. The abdomens of the females are in general flesh- or cream-colour.

The species *C. rivolorum* is marked with light brown instead of blackish, and is very small. The colours of *C. horaria* lie between the colours of these two types.

BAËTIS BIOCULATUS

♂ DUN: PALE WATERY DUN   (Pl. 10a, p. 69)

Eyes: medium lemon-yellow.

Wings: medium or pale greyish.

Thorax: dorsum, brownish toffee-colour; venter pale oliveaceous.

Legs: whitish-olive, fore-legs darker.

Abdomen: dorsum, segments 1 to 7 medium or pale greyish-green-olive, last two segments distinctly more yellowish-olive; venter paler, watery grey-green-olive.

Tails: pale grey.

Transmitted light: abdomen, segments 1 to 7 palest grey-green, segments 8 and 9 yellowish-olive; thorax palest amber; wings and tails palest watery-grey; legs faintly olive.

General appearance: a small pale watery or pale olive-coloured fly with yellow eyes and rather pale grey wings.

♀ DUN: PALE WATERY DUN

Wings: medium grey.

Thorax: dorsum, light brown-olive or subdued amber-colour; sides paler; venter pale yellow.

Legs: fore-legs olive-grey; other legs whitish-olive.

Abdomen: dorsum pale greenish-olive on segments 1 to 7, last segments more yellow-olive; venter paler grey, or light olive.

Tails: pale grey.

Transmitted light: abdomen pale light olive; thorax slightly more amber-coloured; wings and tails palest watery grey; legs lightest olive.

General appearance: a small pale olive-coloured fly with greyish wings.

♂ SPINNER: PALE WATERY SPINNER   (Pl. 18b, p. 93)

Turbinate eyes: primrose to lemon-yellow, with a dark spot.

Lower eyes: blackish-brown.

Thorax: dorsum dark chocolate-brown or dark nut-brown—it appears very dark in contrast to the yellow eyes; sides and venter brown, varied with olive.

Legs: palest olive, nearly grey-white.

Abdomen: dorsum, segments 1 to 6 or 7 translucent white, very faintly tinged with olive or yellowish, last 3 or 4 segments dark nut-brown or very dark brown-olive and similar to the thorax; venter much paler.

Wings: transparent, veins colourless.

Transmitted light: abdomen, segments 1 to 6 or 7 translucent very faintly olive-white, last three segments and thorax opaque olive-brownish; wings colourless; tails transparent, legs palest olive or nearly colourless; eyes yellow.

General appearance: the yellow eyes appear very vivid in contrast to the dark brown thorax; the thorax and last few abdominal segments of the Pale Evening Spinner *Procloëon rufulum* are of a much lighter brown.

♀ SPINNER: PALE WATERY SPINNER

Thorax: dorsum medium olive-brown or toffee-colour; venter very similar; sides varied with paler and darker markings.

Legs: palest watery-olive.

Abdomen: dorsum, segments medium golden-brown, distinctly paler at the joinings; venter faint watery-olive with last two segments whitish and opaque.

Wings: transparent, veins colourless.

Tails: greyish-white or white.

Transmitted light: abdomen, segments 1 to 7 faintly translucent golden-brown, with last two segments and thorax pale toffee-colour and opaque; legs palest watery-olive; wings colourless; tails greyish-white.

General appearance: a small brown-bodied spinner.

BAËTIS SCAMBUS

♂ DUN: SMALL DARK OLIVE DUN   (Pl. 8c, p. 65)

Eyes: subdued brown-red.

Abdomen: usually more watery-coloured than in female.

Thorax: very similar to female.

Legs: ,,   ,,   ,,   ,,
Tails: ,,   ,,   ,,   ,,

General appearance: a very small darkish-olive dun; some of the males are smaller even than the larger species of *Caenis*.

♀ DUN: SMALL DARK OLIVE DUN   (Pl. 8d, p. 65)

Wings: medium or rather dark blue-grey.

Thorax: dorsum, brown olive; venter greenish-olive; sides varied with brown.

Legs: pale yellow-olive; feet grey-black.

Abdomen: dorsum medium or pale greenish-olive, last two segments more yellow-olive; venter grey-green-olive, last two segments paler yellowish.

Tails: pale grey or buff; straight and held wide apart.

Transmitted light: thorax and abdomen; pale or medium green-olive with the last two abdominal segments slightly more yellowish; wings pale blue-grey; legs pale olive; tails pale greyish.

General appearance: is as small or smaller than the Iron Blue Dun, and resembles a minute Large Dark Olive with rather more blue in the wings and a more vivid olive-coloured body.

A. E.   P

♂ SPINNER: SMALL DARK OLIVE (PALE WATERY) SPINNER

(Pl. 16, p. 85)

Eyes: reddish-brown.

Thorax: dorsum black or brown-black; venter dark brown, varied with brown and olive at the sides.

Wings: transparent, veins colourless.

Legs: femora olive, fading to grey on the tibiae and tarsi.

Abdomen: dorsum, first segment and last three segments dark olive-brown, other segments translucent greyish-white tinged with olive; venter, last three segments opaque brownish, other segments as dorsum.

Tails: translucent grey.

Transmitted light: abdomen translucent watery-grey, with last three segments more opaque brownish or brown-olive; thorax opaque dark brown-olive; legs palest olive; tails and wings colourless.

General appearance: resembles the Large Dark Olive male spinner in colour.

♀ SPINNER: SMALL DARK OLIVE SPINNER   (Pl. 16, p. 85)

Eyes: blackish.

Thorax: dorsum dark greenish-brown; venter and sides paler than dorsum.

Wings: transparent, with conspicuous blackish veins.

Abdomen: dorsum of various shades of brown mahogany-colour distinctly tinged with olive-green—the olive-green becomes less pronouned with age; venter paler, often olive-green.

Legs: greenish-brown-olive.

Tails: greyish, darker at base.

Transmitted light: body and legs brown, more or less tinged with green-olive; tails grey; wings colourless, with brown-black veins.

General appearance: a small red spinner with a pronounced tinge of olive on the body, and dark veins in the wings.

BAËTIS VERNUS

♂ DUN: MEDIUM OLIVE DUN

Eyes: subdued medium brownish.

Wings: medium or rather pale smoky-grey, with the grey colour sometimes reduced by the faintest tinge of yellowish-olive.

Abdomen: dorsum medium or rather pale watery-yellow-olive; venter pale olive.

Tails: pale grey.

Legs: palest olive, becoming dark grey at the tips.

Transmitted light: abdomen pale greenish-olive, with the last few segments more yellowish and opaque; wings and tails very pale grey.

General appearance: this fly is of about similar size to, or is only slightly smaller than, the male Large Dark Olive Dun *B. rhodani*; but it is very noticeably paler in the wing and it has a brighter and more conspicuously olive-coloured body.

♀ DUN: MEDIUM OLIVE DUN

Wings: smoky grey as in male fly.

Abdomen: a bright rather luminous olive-colour which varies in different specimens from a yellowish to a greenish-olive.

Tails: grey or creamy grey.

Legs: pale olive, becoming greyish-black distally.

Transmitted light: the abdomen is a pale translucent yellowish-olive; the thorax more opaque; wings and tails very pale grey; legs faintly olive.

General appearance: slightly lighter in colour than the male dun; and the olive colour of the body is more pronounced.

♂ SPINNER: MEDIUM OLIVE SPINNER

Eyes: brownish-red.

Thorax: dorsum black; sides varied with olive and brownish.

Abdomen: dorsum, all segments may be dark brown or olive-brown, or central segments may be paler, and of a more translucent greyish-olive-colour than the brown on the last three segments; venter pale greyish-green or greyish-olive.

Wings: transparent, colourless, with some of the longitudinal veins brownish.

Tails: nearly white.

Transmitted light: eyes reddish-brown; thorax black; abdomen with segments 2 to 6 or 7 translucent brownish-olive, with pale joinings, last segments opaque brownish.

General appearance: owing to the additional brown tinge in the central segments of the abdomen, these spinners are darker in the body than the male Large Dark Spinners, *B. rhodani*.

♀ SPINNER: MEDIUM OLIVE SPINNER
Thorax: black or brown-black on dorsal surface varied with yellowish-brown on the sides.
Wings: colourless.
Abdomen: dorsum yellowish or olive-brown with paler joinings; venter paler with last two segments nearly yellow.
Tails: white darkened towards their bases.
Legs: pale greyish-olive, varied with blackish at the tips.
General appearance: a yellowish-brown bodied spinner with colourless wings.

BAËTIS TENAX

♂ ♀ DUN: MEDIUM OLIVE DUN
These duns quite closely resemble the duns of *B. vernus*, but specimens from upland streams are slightly darker in the wings, and rather less vividly coloured in the bodies, as well as being smaller than specimens of *B. vernus* from the south of England.

♂ SPINNER: MEDIUM OLIVE SPINNER   (Pl. 19d, p. 96)
Eyes: chocolate brown.
Thorax: dorsum black; venter black; sides varied with dark brown, red and olive-grey.
Wings: membrane and veins colourless.
Legs: greyish-olive, becoming grey-black distally.
Abdomen: dorsum rather dark olive-brown but translucent, last four segments slightly darker and opaque, joinings translucent pale greyish; venter slightly paler, with last three or four segments opaque and more yellowish.
Tails: whitish or greyish-white, very faintly ringed near base.
Transmitted light: body translucent, and coloured with pale grey or olive-brown, last four segments opaque.
General appearance: these spinners differ from most of the *Baëtis* male spinners except *B. vernus*, in that the central abdominal segments are rather more strongly coloured.

♀ SPINNER: MEDIUM OLIVE SPINNER
A pale reddish-brown-bodied spinner with colourless wings and greyish-white tails.

BAËTIS RHODANI

♂ DUN: LARGE DARK OLIVE DUN   (Pl. 6c, p. 49)
Eyes: dusky brick-red.
Wings: dull grey with a pale ginger or indistinct brown-olive colour
  in the stronger veins; in some specimens the faint ginger colour
  appears to give warmth to the whole wing, in other specimens the
  wing appears devoid of ginger or brown-olive.
Thorax: dorsum dull dark grey, often permeated with a faint tinge
  of olive; sides varied with greyish and amber or brown-olive
  markings; venter rather dull grey and pale brownish-olive.
Legs: fore femora green olive, other femora rather lighter olive;
  fore tibiae grey, other tibiae pale greenish-grey; all tarsi dull black.
Abdomen: dorsum dark or medium-grey tinged with olive-green, last
  segment more yellowish-olive and not so dark—this shade slightly
  permeates the penultimate segments joinings pale watery grey;
  venter, first segment dull watery olive, segments 2 to 8 dull watery
  grey, 9th segment tinged with yellow.
Tails: dull grey or greyish-green with dull reddish rings which are
  more pronounced near the base.
Transmitted light: head and thorax opaque but faintly brownish-
  olive; abdomen pale dull grey with the last three segments more
  opaque and showing a yellowish-amber tinge; tails watery-grey;
  legs grey-olive; wing medium greyish.

♀ DUN: LARGE DARK OLIVE DUN   (Pl. 6d, p. 49)
Wings: dull grey, as in male, with the longitudinal veins faintly
  ginger or olive-coloured.
Thorax: dorsum dull blue-grey, sometimes tinged with amber-olive;
  sides rather greenish-olive interspaced with fine irregular brown-
  black lines; venter as in male.
Legs: all femora greenish-olive; all tibiae grey-green-olive; all tarsi
  dull blackish.
Abdomen: dorsum fairly dark or medium olive-green or brownish-
  olive-green; venter paler and more watery-olive than dorsum.
Tails: darkish grey with indistinct rings.
Transmitted light: thorax opaque but faintly brownish-olive; abdomen
  and legs a greyish-yellow or brownish-olive.
General appearance: the colours of the Large Dark Olives, both male
  and female, differ appreciably during the year; the flies which

appear in the late winter and spring are usually darker than those which emerge in the autumn, and on rivers which show a high summer temperature the autumn flies may become more ginger coloured. During the summer months I have found specimens of these *Baëtis rhodani* duns in which the body was a pale luminous olive and was very similar to, and almost as pale as, the body of *B. vernus* which is a Medium Olive.

♂ SPINNER: LARGE DARK OLIVE SPINNER   (Pl. 14a, p. 81)
Eyes: dark reddish-brown.
Thorax: dorsum pitch black and shining; sides dark reddish-brown; venter black varied with reddish-brown.
Legs: anterior pair, dark grey or dark greyish-olive; median and posterior legs paler watery-olive, becoming grey to blackish distally.
Abdomen: dorsum, segments 2 to 6 transparent greyish, often infused with light brownish-olive or faint greenish-olive, last 3 or 4 segments dark brown, or olive-brown or very light mahogany-colour; venter paler and more greenish-grey.
Wings: transparent, colourless membrane, with dark longitudinal veins.
Tails: palest grey, ringed with reddish-brown.
Transmitted light: eyes dark mahogany; thorax dull blackish; abdomen, last three segments amber-brown, other segments translucent greyish-white, very faintly tinged with reddish or orange or olive at joinings of the segments; tails pale grey; legs watery-olive, anterior legs darker; wings transparent colourless, veins rather dark brownish.
General appearance: the largest of the *Baëtis* spinners; the tails are noticeably ringed with reddish and the intermediate abdominal segments are of a greyish colour.

♀ SPINNER: LARGE DARK OLIVE (RED) SPINNER (Pl. 14b, p. 81)
Head and eyes: brown-black.
Thorax: dorsum pitch black; sides reddish varied with paler markings; venter dark brown, varied with pitch black.
Abdomen: dorsum dark mahogany with paler joinings, last two segments varied with paler red; venter grey-brown-olive, third last segment nearly primrose.
Legs: very dark brown-olive.
Wings: membrane colourless, veins dark brown.
Tails: dark grey-brown, with reddish-brown rings.

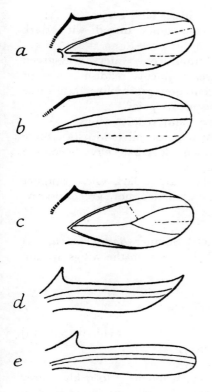

FIG. 8

Hind wings of some species of *Baëtis* and *Centroptilum*:

a) *Baëtis rhodani*,
b) *B. atrebatinus*,
c) *B. pumilus*,
d) *Centroptilum luteolum*,
e) *C. pennulatum*

In fig. (b) the costal projection, which is clearly seen on the other four wings, is almost completely suppressed. Fig. (a) superficially resembles the hind wings of several other species of *Baëtis*.

Transmitted light: body dark brown-mahogany; tails dark grey; legs dark brown-olive; wings colourless dark brown veins.

General appearance: a dark red-bodied spinner with dark veins in the wings.

BAËTIS ATREBATINUS

♂ ♀ DUN: DARK OLIVE DUN

These duns are quite like the Large Dark Olive Duns *B. rhodani*, but the abdomen is often tinged with a dark dusky-amber; the tails are dark grey with dark reddish joinings; wings dark grey.

♂ SPINNER: DARK OLIVE SPINNER

Eyes: dark reddish-brown on top, sides much paler.

Thorax: dorsum pitch black; venter and sides very dark brown.

Legs: femora green-olive; tibiae paler olive; tarsi grey.

Wings: transparent colourless, veins sometimes tinged with dark brown-olive.

Abdomen: dorsum, segments 1 to 7 translucent watery grey-green with paler joinings, last two or three segments reddish-brown or amber-brown; venter dark translucent grey-green-olive, last three segments more opaque, joinings of segments paler.

Tails: translucent grey-white, with very faint reddish rings.

Transmitted light: thorax black; abdomen palest olive with last three or four segments a watery amber-brown; legs pale olive becoming grey distally; tails translucent, colourless.

General appearance: rather similar to the Large Dark Olive Spinner male, but the tails are whiter and the abdomen more greenish-grey.

♀ SPINNER: DARK OLIVE SPINNER

This spinner closely resembles the Red Spinner *Baëtis rhodani*, but differs in that the tails are paler and the veins on the wings are not so dark.

BAËTIS PUMILUS

♂ DUN: IRON-BLUE DUN   (Pl. 6 a, p. 49)

Wings: blackish-grey or blackish-blue-grey.

Thorax: grey-black.

Abdomen: segments 1 to 6 blackish-grey, segments 7 to 9 black-grey tinged with dark brown (more noticeable in some specimens than in others).

Legs: rather dark watery-olive, becoming darker distally.

Tails: black-grey.

Transmitted light: wings and tails darkish blue-grey; abdomen segments 1 to 6 dark blue-grey (darker than wings), joinings paler, segments 7 to 9 opaque very dark brown or subdued dark mahogany-colour; legs greyish-watery-olive.

General appearance: a very small, very dark blue-black fly.

♀ DUN: IRON-BLUE DUN   (Pl. 6 b, p. 49)

Wings: as in male dun, or very slightly paler.

Thorax: blue-grey.

Abdomen: very dark brown-olive.

Legs: dark watery-olive; tarsi blackish.

Tails: dark grey.

Transmitted light: abdomen, dark brown-olive; wings and tails medium to dark blue-grey; legs watery-yellow-olive.

General appearance: similar to, but not quite so dark as, the male dun.

♂ SPINNER: IRON-BLUE (JENNY) SPINNER (Pl. 14c, p. 81)

Eyes: dark reddish-brown.

Thorax: dorsum and venter pitch black.

Wings: transparent, colourless, veins pellucid white.

Legs: anterior pair pale blue-grey; other legs pale greyish-white.

Abdomen: dorsum, first five segments translucent white, last three or four segments dark mid-brown, sometimes tinged faintly with purplish; venter, posterior three or four segments rather dark olive, remainder as on dorsum.

Tails: white.

Transmitted light: eyes and head reddish-brown; thorax black; abdomen, last three segments olive-brown, other segments translucent white; wings colourless; legs and tails nearly colourless, greyish-white.

General appearance: a small white spinner with a black thorax and the last few segments of the body dark brown.

♀ SPINNER: IRON-BLUE (LITTLE CLARET) SPINNER

(Pl. 14d, p. 81)

Eyes: black.

Thorax: dorsum pitch black; venter and sides black interspaced with dark brown-red.

Wings: transparent, colourless, the stronger veins faintly tinged with reddish-brown.

Legs: rather dark olive-brown, becoming more watery-coloured distally.

Abdomen: dorsum dark red-mahogany or dark claret-brown, with the joinings of the segments pale reddish-brown; venter slightly paler than dorsum.

Tails: faint grey.

Transmitted light: thorax pitch-brown; abdomen dark mahogany-colour, with paler joinings; legs medium brown-green-olive; tails translucent grey; wings colourless with the stronger veins slightly brown.

General appearance: a small or very small dark red-mahogany-bodied spinner.

CENTROPTILUM LUTEOLUM

♂ DUN: LITTLE SKY-BLUE (PALE WATERY) DUN   (Pl. 8 a, p. 65)

Eyes: subdued light red-orange.

Thorax: dorsum pale grey-green-amber; venter and sides watery grey or grey-green.

Wings: very pale or pale grey-blue; sometimes faintly tinged with yellow.

FIG. 9

Eyes of *Centroptilum luteolum.*

Abdomen: dorsum varies from a pale watery honey-colour on some specimens, to light olive-grey-green on others, last one or two segments often more yellowish; venter palest grey, faintly tinged with greenish.

Legs: watery-grey, faintly tinged with yellowish proximally.

Tails: pale grey.

Transmitted light: body palest watery-grey, becoming more opaque and slightly amber-coloured at the thorax; wings pale blue-grey; legs pale grey, tinged with olive.

General appearance: the flies which appear in the late spring are generally larger, and have more olive-green-coloured bodies than the pale honey-bodied specimens which are common during the summer.

♀ DUN: LITTLE SKY-BLUE (PALE WATERY) DUN   (Pl. 8 b, p. 65)

Wings: pale blue-grey, sometimes with a faint tinge of yellow-olive near the base of the wing.

Thorax: dorsum honey-colour or pale greyish-brown; venter paler and tinged with green-olive.

Abdomen: dorsum watery-honey-colour or greenish-olive; venter pale straw or greenish-olive.

Legs: palest olive.

Tails: whitish.

Transmitted light: abdomen pale honey-colour; thorax more opaque; legs pale yellowish-olive; wings pale blue-grey.

General appearance: some specimens resemble a small olive, as the abdomen is green-olive, others have a more pale honey-coloured abdomen; the green olive-coloured specimens appear to be commonest in April and May, and the honey-coloured ones in the warmer months of the year.

♂ SPINNER: LITTLE SKY-BLUE (PALE WATERY) SPINNER

(Pl. 17a, p. 92)

Eyes: bright light red on top and on sides; the edge of the top is circumscribed by a thin greyish-white line.

Thorax: dorsum dark toffee-colour; sides paler; venter dark toffee or dark olive-brown.

Wings: colourless, veins pellucid.

Legs: femoral joints pale olive; tibial and tarsal joints watery-grey.

Abdomen: dorsum, segments 2 to 6 or 7, translucent watery-white, each segment being tinted with pale reddish-amber, posterior two or three segments reddish-brown-amber; venter transparent pale greyish-white on segments 1 to 6 or 7; last two or three segments opaque white, slightly tinged with light brown or yellowish.

Tails: watery white.

Transmitted light: eyes light red; thorax brownish-olive; abdominal segments 1 to 6 translucent white, remaining segments pale brown-amber-colour; wings colourless; legs and tails translucent greyish-white.

♀ SPINNER: PALE WATERY (LITTLE AMBER) SPINNER

(Pl. 17b, p. 92)

Eyes: blackish.

Thorax: dorsum olive-amber, or brownish amber; venter and sides very similar, but varied with paler markings.

Wings: transparent and colourless; veins colourless.

Legs: faintly olive.

Abdomen: dorsum yellowish-brown, becoming brown-amber when spent; venter yellowish-white, last two segments amber.

Tails: pale yellowish-white.

Transmitted light: abdomen amber-colour; more opaque at thorax; legs and tails cream, or legs faintly olive; wings transparent colourless.

General appearance: an amber-brown-bodied fly with colourless wings.

CENTROPTILUM PENNULATUM

♂ DUN: BLUE-WINGED PALE WATERY DUN   (Pl. 11c, p. 76)

Eyes: subdued orange.

Wings: grey-blue, rather more bluish than the wings of the Blue-winged Olive Dun; the front edge of the wing (that is the costal and sub-costal area) is slightly darker than the remainder of the wing.

Thorax: dorsum rather dark greyish or greenish-grey, posterior portion amber-coloured; venter and sides greenish-grey, varied with paler areas.

Legs: greyish.

Abdomen: dorsum greyish or greenish-grey, sometimes faintly amber-tinted; venter greyish-white or pale grey-green-white.

Tails: grey.

Transmitted light: abdomen, segments 1 to 7 pearly-grey (the colour of pale grey heron-herl) with the posterior two segments more yellowish-amber; thorax grey or faintly amber-grey; tails and legs pale grey; wings grey-blue.

General appearance: a large pale watery with rather dark bluish wings.

♀ DUN: Blue-winged Pale Watery Dun   (Pl. 11d, p. 76)

Wings: very similar to those of male dun.

Thorax: grey faintly tinted with greenish, paler at sides

Abdomen: greyish white along the sides becoming distinctly brown amber colour on dorsal surface: venter, whitish darkened to watery grey posteriorly.

Legs and tails: watery grey.

Transmitted light: thorax greyish, abdomen whitish becoming darker posteriorly: legs and tails, watery grey: wings grey-blue.

General appearance: resembles the male dun: the wings of the male and female duns are of a peculiar shade of blue which is particularly noticeable when the wings are viewed obliquely in a lengthwise direction: the blue then takes on a purple tinge which is deepest along the front edge.

♂ SPINNER: Blue-winged Pale Watery (Large Amber) Spinner
(Pl. 19 c, p. 96)

Eyes: deep vivid orange.

Thorax: dorsum brownish-olive; venter somewhat similar, sides paler.

Wings: colourless.

Abdomen: dorsum, segments 1 to 6 translucent, nearly colourless, with faint reddish markings, last 2 or 3 segments light brown-red; venter pale pellucid whitish-grey, last three segments opaque.

Legs: palest grey.

Tails: greyish-white.

Transmitted light: wings, legs, tails translucent, nearly colourless; thorax and last three abdominal segments faintly brownish-red; other abdominal segments pellucid.

General appearance: very similar to the male spinner of *C. luteolum*, but is larger and has orange instead of light red eyes.

♀ SPINNER: BLUE-WINGED PALE WATERY SPINNER

Eyes: greenish-grey.

Thorax: dorsum, colour of pale india-rubber (a pale olive-amber-shade); venter and sides rather similar, with reddish markings.

Wings: membrane and veins colourless, except for portion of the stronger veins near the wing-root which may be reddish-amber.

Legs: palest olive-grey.

Abdomen: dorsum reddish-amber, toning to a light cream-olive-colour at the sides; venter pale, rather translucent, whitish-olive becoming more opaque in the posterior 2 or 3 segments.

Tails: palest grey.

Transmitted light: abdomen whitish, faintly suffused with pink, last three segments and thorax more opaque and less white; wings glassy; legs faintly white-olive; tails colourless.

General appearance: a large reddish-amber-bodied spinner with colourless wings.

CLOËON DIPTERUM

♂ ♀ DUN: POND OLIVE DUN

Male here described; female is very similar but differs in that the costal area of the wings is slightly olive and the abdomen is brown or reddish-grey-olive.

Eyes: brown-amber.

Wings: dark bluish grey, rather like the wings of the Blue-winged Olive.

Thorax: dark olive-amber.

Legs: olive-yellow, becoming blackish distally.

Abdomen: dorsum dark grey-olive or dark grey-amber—the amber is more pronounced in last three segments; venter grey-olive.

Tails: dark grey.

Transmitted light: body translucent grey-brown, becoming darker, more reddish and opaque, at thorax and in last few abdominal segments.

General appearance: a dark, rather grey-brownish-coloured olive.

♂ SPINNER: POND OLIVE SPINNER

Eyes: bronze-olive.

Thorax: dorsum black.

Wings: transparent and colourless, not marked along anterior border as in female.

Abdomen: dorsum reddish-brown on last few segments, intermediate segments more translucent of a reddish-grey colour (variable); venter greyish with pale joinings.

Legs: dark olive, varied with brown, and becoming grey distally.

Tails: grey with dark rings.

♀ SPINNER: POND OLIVE SPINNER   (Pl. 22a, p. 101)

Eyes: pale viridian greenish.

Thorax: dorsum medium green-olive, with two pale olive streaks crossing it lengthways; sides greenish-olive with fine irregular reddish markings; venter pale green-olive, tinged with red.

Wings: conspicuously marked along the front edge (the costal area) with reddish-amber; remainder of the wing transparent, colourless with somewhat dark veins.

Legs: pale olive, becoming dark brown or opaque distally; there are usually faint amber-red marks on at least the fore femora.

Abdomen: dorsum, ground colour yellowish, overlaid by a pattern of reddish or amber-red markings; venter quite similar.

Tails: pale olive, with dark brown rings.

Transmitted light: abdomen and thorax composed of a mixed pattern of pale red and yellow-olive; wings transparent, with a band of amber along the front edge; legs pale olive-straw-colour; tails faint yellow-brown.

General appearance: body yellowish and brown or red mixed; the front edges of the wings are distinctly marked with reddish-amber.

CLOËON SIMILE

♂ DUN: LAKE OLIVE DUN   (Pl. 13a, p. 80)

Eyes: medium brown-olive or green-olive.

Wings: membrane dark grey, tinged with bright green near to the wing-root and the main veins greenish-olive; or else the membrane paler grey tinged with yellowish-amber and the stronger veins yellowish—giving to the whole wing a ginger shade.

Thorax: dorsum dark grey-olive or greenish-olive; venter and sides brown-olive, varied with grey-olive.

Abdomen: dorsum dark or medium brown-olive or dark amber-rubber-colour or greenish-brown; venter dark grey-brown-olive, sometimes more green-olive-coloured, last segment paler olive.

Legs: medium to pale olive, becoming blackish distally.

Tails: medium grey.

Transmitted light: abdomen greenish or greenish-amber-olive, with the posterior three segments more opaque; wings grey, tinged with green or yellowish-olive; legs greenish-olive; tails dark grey.

General appearance: the duns vary from a dark and decidedly green-olive fly in the spring, to a smaller and paler brown-olive fly in the autumn.

♀ DUN: Lake Olive Dun (Pl. 13b, p. 80)

Wings, thorax, legs and tails: very similar to the male duns.

Abdomen: dorsum dark or medium olive, tinged with brownish; venter rather dark greyish-amber or brownish-olive.

Transmitted light: abdomen medium brown-olive, with the posterior two segments more opaque and more orange-coloured; wings grey, faintly (or at times strongly) shaded with olive; legs green or yellowish-olive; tails grey.

General appearance: the female duns vary in colour in the same way as the males do, but the females are perhaps on the whole slightly more olive-coloured.

♂ SPINNER: Lake Olive Spinner (Pl. 22c, p. 101)

Eyes: olive-green.

Thorax: dorsum purple-black; sides varied with pale orange or straw-coloured markings; venter purple-black.

Wings: membrane transparent and colourless, except where it is tinged with light olive near the wing-roof; stronger veins tinged with brown-olive.

Legs: dark grey-olive.

Abdomen: dorsum dark red-brown-olive with the most posterior segment a paler brown; venter, segments 1 to 6 dark grey-olive often slightly tinged with purple, joinings paler, segments 7 to 9 paler brown.

Tails: grey, tinged with red, particularly near to the base.

Transmitted light: thorax opaque brown-black; abdomen brownish, tinged with olive; legs olive-grey; tails grey; wings transparent but showing olive colour near their base; the smaller autumn forms appearing in warm districts are somewhat paler.

General appearance: a brownish red spinner.

♀ SPINNER: Lake Olive Spinner   (Pl. 22d, p. 101)

Eyes: brownish-black.

Thorax: dorsum brown olive; venter brown-olive, varied with greyish-olive at sides.

Wings: transparent, but tinged with olive-green near the basal portion of costal area.

Legs: brownish-olive.

Abdomen: dorsum dark amber-brown or reddish-brown-olive; venter darkish grey-olive with last two segments paler.

Tails: palest watery-olive, with reddish-brown rings which are more pronounced proximally.

Transmitted light: body amber-brown with paler joinings; thorax more opaque; tails reddish.

General appearance: a medium-brown spinner.

PROCLOËON RUFULUM

♂ DUN: Pale Evening Dun

Eyes: somewhat subdued yellow.

Thorax: dorsum palish honey-colour; venter and sides a watery-honey-colour.

Wings: greyish or bluish-white, often with a tinge of vivid green near the base.

Abdomen: dorsum pale honey or pale yellow, in some lights tinged with pale rusty-red; venter paler than dorsum, a watery-honey-colour.

Legs: palest olive, becoming slightly darker distally.

Tails: pale dun-colour.

Transmitted light: body very faint watery-honey-colour; thorax more opaque; wings palest grey; legs very faintly olive-tinted.

General appearance: a very pale or whitish Pale Watery Dun.

♀ DUN: PALE EVENING DUN (Pl. 10b, p. 69)

Eyes: pale-viridian green with small black dots.

Head: yellowish.

Wings: pale grey-white, with the basal portions of the stronger veins near to the wing-root often of a vivid light green.

Thorax: dorsum palest toffee- or amber-colour—there is usually a small vivid green mark on this surface of the thorax; sides also pale toffee- or pale amber-colour; venter similar to sides but paler.

Legs: very pale lemon-yellow, becoming slightly brownish distally.

Abdomen: dorsum pale lemon-yellow, each segment marked with two pale red-amber-coloured blotches and often has two fine green lines, posterior two segments not darker; venter palest lemon- or watery-yellow, very faintly tinged with grey, posterior two segments pale grey-green.

Tails: watery-grey.

Transmitted light: head, thorax and abdomen palest lemon-yellow; legs and tails transfused with yellow; wings palest grey.

General appearance: a very pale Pale Watery Dun with a pale yellow body.

♂ SPINNER: PALE EVENING SPINNER (Pl. 17c, p. 92)

Eyes: lemon-yellow with a movable dark spot; lower eyes greeny-blue with black spots.

Thorax: dorsum light brown-olive, turning darker with age to rather dark brown-amber; sides, rather light greenish-olive; venter light or medium greenish-olive.

Wings: colourless, veins translucent.

Legs: femora are pale olive; and the other segments are a transparent watery-grey.

Abdomen: dorsum, segments 1 to 5 translucent and nearly colourless with two faint light red blotches on each segment, last three or four segments brown-amber or golden-brown; venter, segments 1 to 5 transparent, nearly colourless, last three segments dirty-white.

Tails: watery-white or colourless.

Transmitted light: the legs, tails and first five segments of the abdomen appear translucent and nearly colourless; thorax and last three or four abdominal segments are a dirty white or faintly amber; eyes lemon- or olive-yellow, wings transparent colourless.

General appearance: differs from the male spinner of the Pale Watery *Baëtis bioculatus* in that the thorax and last few abdominal segments are a much lighter brown and that the intermediate abdominal segments are faintly suffused with rusty-red.

♀ SPINNER: PALE EVENING SPINNER   (Pl. 17d, p. 92)
Eyes: pale blue-green.
Thorax: dorsum pale brown-olive or amber-olive; venter pale watery-olive.
Wings: transparent, colourless, veins pellucid.
Legs: femora faintly olive; other joints transparent watery-grey.
Abdomen: dorsum, first five segments pale straw-colour, each segment marked with two light red-amber blotches and with very fine dark brown lines, last three segments slightly darker; venter watery-olive with last three segments more opaque.
Tails: translucent watery-grey.
Transmitted light: legs palest green-olive proximally; remainder of legs and tails translucent and nearly colourless grey; abdomen, olive-straw-colour with the last two or three segments and the thorax opaque, of pale straw tinged with brown-olive.
General appearance: a very pale yellowish-bodied spinner with colourless wings.

SIPHLONURUS LACUSTRIS

♂ ♀ DUN: SUMMER MAYFLY DUN
These duns resemble the duns of *S. linnaeanus* (p. 227) but differ in that their wings are a plain grey or olive-grey and have not got the pale shading noticeable in the wings of that species.

♂ ♀ SPINNER: SUMMER MAYFLY SPINNER   (Pl. 20a, p. 97)
Male here described; female similar but somewhat less strongly coloured.
Eyes: dark brown, without the conspicuous circumscribed white lines on *S. linnaeanus*.
Thorax: black on dorsal surface, varied with brownish and yellowish on the sides.
Abdomen: dorsum dark brown with pale joinings; venter dark grey-olive-green.

Legs: greenish-black.
Wings: transparent, with dark brown veins.
Tails: pale with dark joinings.

SIPHLONURUS LINNAEANUS

♂ ♀ DUN: SUMMER MAYFLY DUN (Pl. 13c, p. 80)
Eyes: grey-green.
Thorax: brownish-green.
Wings: grey, varied with yellowish-olive near the base of the fore-wings and along the posterior edge of the hind-wings; veins distinct but not strongly coloured.
Abdomen: greenish-grey varied with brownish and olive markings.
Legs: olive-brown.
Tails: greyish.
Transmitted light: the abdomen is greenish-grey of various shades; wings medium to rather dark grey; legs brown-olive.
General appearance: in the distance these flies resemble Greendrakes in size and colour.

♂ ♀ SPINNER: SUMMER MAYFLY SPINNER (Pl. 21a, b, p. 100)
Male here described; female is somewhat similar but the thorax and abdomen are more grey-green coloured.
Eyes: dark red-brown with two narrow white bands circumscribing the edges.
Thorax: dark brown-olive with pale markings an the sides.
Abdomen: dorsum dark brown often with a suggestion of purple and green intermingled; venter brownish-green-olive; each segment has rough V-shaped markings of dark brown.
Wings: colourless with dark brown or blackish veins.
Tails: pale grey-green with red-brown rings.
Transmitted light: body brownish-green, becoming more yellow-brown towards the tail.
General appearance: a brown-bodied spinner of similar size to a Spent Gnat, but with only two tails.

RHITHROGENA SEMICOLORATA

♂ DUN: OLIVE UPRIGHT DUN (Pl. 9c, p. 68)
Eyes: brown-black, often tinged with olive.

Wings: medium to rather dark blue-grey; hind-wings slightly paler and more buff-coloured.

Thorax: dorsum watery-grey-green; venter and sides grey-green varied with pink.

Abdomen: dorsum dusky-grey-green or brownish-grey-olive, joinings paler; venter watery-grey-green or palest olive-green.

Legs: watery-olive with a small dark brown streak on each femoral joint; tarsi dull grey.

Tails: grey or grey-buff, sometimes brownish proximally.

Transmitted light: abdomen watery-green-brown-olive or pale olive-grey-green, joinings paler on dark specimens; thorax opaque grey-green; legs pale olive; tails grey; wings rather clear grey or grey-blue, somewhat similar to those of the Blue-winged Olive.

General appearance: the flies vary somewhat in appearance, some specimens being less grey-green than others; when freshly hatched they are a pale grey-green-olive but they darken rapidly to a rather dark greyish.

♀ DUN: Olive Upright Dun   (Pl. 9d, p. 68)

Eyes: blackish-brown.

Thorax: dorsum grey-green or olive-amber; venter olive, varied with dull pink or amber.

Wings: medium or dark blue-grey; hind-wings paler and more buff-coloured.

Legs: pale olive, with femoral streak dark brown or brown-black.

Abdomen: dorsum bronze, or bronze-olive, or grey-green-olive with paler joinings; venter whitish-olive or pale greenish-olive, posterior three or four segments often darker.

Tails: pale grey-buff, often more amber-coloured proximally.

Transmitted light: legs and tails watery-olive; abdomen pale greenish-olive or faintly yellowish-olive; wings dark grey or blue-grey.

General appearance: freshly-emerged duns vary considerably in colour; some resemble a large pale olive, others are darker with more bronze-coloured bodies when viewed from above, and with wings of a darker grey; the colour of the flies darkens rapidly.

♂ SPINNER: Olive (Yellow) Upright Spinner (Pl. 15c, p. 84)

Eyes: brown-black or bronze-brown.

Thorax: dorsum brown-olive; venter and sides subdued brownish.

Wings: transparent colourless, veins dark brown, costa and subcosta paler brownish; membrane sometimes tinged with brownish-amber near to the base of the wing.

Abdomen: dorsum dark brown or olivaceous brown with pale whitish joinings; venter brown-grey-olive, joining pale and last two segments yellow-brown.

Tails: brown-grey.

Legs: yellow-brown, becoming darker distally with dark femoral streak.

Transmitted light: body pale grey-brown-olive with paler joinings, last two segments opaque richer brown; thorax opaque brown; tails pale greyish-brown; legs pale grey-brown-olive; wings colourless with stronger veins brownish.

General appearance: a subdued brown-coloured spinner.

♀ SPINNER: OLIVE UPRIGHT SPINNER

Eyes: grey-black.

Thorax: dorsum medium or rather pale brown-amber; venter paler than dorsum; sides varied with a few irregular nearly white markings.

Wings: transparent, colourless, veins faintly brownish.

Legs: pale amber, with a slight tinge of olive; there is a small dark brown longitudinal mark on each femur.

Abdomen: dorsum, segments 1 to 6 medium reddish-brown with pale joinings, posterior three segments darker brown; venter pale grey-olive tinged with light brown, last three segments more reddish-brown.

Tails: palest amber or buff, faintly ringed.

Transmitted light: head, thorax and legs pale amber-brown; abdomen last two or three segments reddish-amber, other segments slightly paler; tails, ginger.

General appearance: a brown-bodied spinner of medium size.

RHITHROGENA HAARUPI

♂ DUN: MARCH BROWN (Pl. 7d, p. 64)

Eyes: dark brown-olive.

Wings: membrane fawn or warm buff-colour with very conspicuous blackish-grey cross veins, longitudinal veins are dark brown or brown-olive and are less conspicuous; there are two pale areas in each wing devoid of cross-veins.

Thorax: dorsum dark sooty-brown-olive; sides and venter more dingy in colour.

Legs: dark dingy olive-brown, anterior legs darker than the other legs; a dark spot on the femora of the median and posterior legs is faintly discernible.

Abdomen: dorsum dark brown with joinings of the segments yellowish or faintly green; venter somewhat similar but paler, and with the sides and the joinings of the segments pale greenish.

Tails: dark dingy-brown-grey.

Transmitted light: abdominal segments dirty drab-brown with the joinings much paler and tinged with green-olive; wings grey-fawn with the fawn predominating in the anterior areas; thorax dark and opaque; legs dark grey-green mixed with brown; tails brown-fawn.

General appearance: a drab brown-fawn-coloured fly with a somewhat mottled wing.

♀ DUN: MARCH BROWN

Head: dull fawn-colour.

Eyes: very dark.

Wings: membrane greyish-fawn, cross-veins dark grey or grey-black, longitudinal veins dark brown-olive; there are two pale areas in the middle of each wing as in the male flies.

Abdomen: dorsum dull brown, faintly olive-tinged at times, with paler (nearly straw-coloured) joinings; venter paler and more reddish-brown.

Legs: dark drab greenish-brown, with a dark streak visible on the femora of all three pairs of legs.

Thorax: dorsum dark bronze-brown-olive; sides and venter paler and more sober-coloured.

Tails: dark grey-brown.

Transmitted light: abdomen, segments amber-brown with pale greenish straw-coloured joinings; legs slightly mottled brownish and greyish-olive; tails dark drab-brown or brown-grey; wings pale grey, shaded with darker grey and with fawn nearer to the wingroot.

General appearance: very similar to male dun; sometimes is slightly more greenish coloured.

♂ ♀ SPINNER: MARCH BROWN SPINNER

These spinners are fairly similar in colour to the Olive Upright

Spinner *R. semicolorata* (p. 58) but, of course, are larger in size and appear earlier in the year.

HEPTAGENIA SULPHUREA

♂ ♀ DUN: YELLOW MAY DUN   (Pl. 7a, b, p. 64)
Eyes: black, becoming pale blue with age.
Head: yellow.
Thorax: dorsum yellow-amber with two fine dark lines between the wings; venter and sides yellow, tinged with palest amber.
Wings: membrane and veins yellow.
Abdomen: dorsum yellow-straw with thin dark joinings to the segments; venter pale yellow.
Legs: yellow, tarsi blackish.
Tails: grey-buff.
Transmitted light: body pale straw-yellow with last two abdominal segments and thorax more opaque and deeper yellow; legs primrose; becoming dark grey distally; tails dark grey; wings pale lemonish-yellow.
General appearance: the fly is all yellow and is very like the Yellow Evening Dun, but the amber colour of the thorax is less obviously reddish-amber than in that species.

♂ SPINNER: YELLOW MAY SPINNER   (Pl. 15a, p. 84)
Eyes: blackish, becoming pale blue-green with age.
Thorax: dorsum brown amber; venter and sides primrose varied with pale amber.
Wings: membrane colourless or sometimes tinged with pale yellow; veins dark brown.
Legs: yellow, becoming grey distally.
Abdomen: dorsum dark brown-olive, becoming darker and browner with age, last two segments more amber-coloured; venter, segments 2 to 7 grey-green, posterior three segments primrose.
Tails: yellowish-grey ringed with red-brown.
Transmitted light: thorax and last three abdominal segments reddish-brown; remaining segments of abdomen greyish-green-olive; legs yellow-olive; tails distinctly ringed brownish-red; wings transparent with the anterior edge light green-olive.
General appearance: a dark or very dark-coloured spinner.

♀ SPINNER: YELLOW MAY SPINNER   (Pl. 15b, p. 84)
Eyes: blackish, becoming very pale blue-verditer with age.
Thorax: dorsum light amber; venter and sides pale amber.
Wings: membrane colourless except for a trace of pale lemon-
yellow along the costal area; veins dark brown.
Legs: lemon-yellow, rather darker and more grey distally.
Abdomen: dorsum lemon-yellow, sometimes very pale; venter
palest yellow.
Tails: pale fawn, ringed with red-brown.
Transmitted light: legs and abdomen pale primrose or lemon-yellow;
thorax and last segment of abdomen yellow-orange or pale amber;
tails, pale fawn with red-brown rings; wings colourless except for
tinge of lemon-yellow near anterior border.
General appearance: a very pale yellow or yellowish-white spinner
of medium or large size.

HEPTAGENIA FUSCOGRISEA

♂ ♀ DUN: BROWN MAY DUN
These flies resemble the Late March Brown in size and general
colour but can be recognised by two pale reddish or sherry-coloured
bands on the femoral joints of each of the legs.

♂ ♀ SPINNER: BROWN MAY SPINNER
The male spinner resembles the male Yellow May Spinner, *Heptagenia sulphurea*, but can easily be distinguished from it by the
distinct sherry-coloured bands on the femoral joints of the legs,
as in the dun. The female spinner, which is not nearly so pale
as the female *Heptagenia sulphurea*, also may be recognised by the
femoral bands.

HEPTAGENIA LATERALIS

♂ ♀ DUN: DARK DUN   (Pl. 12 c, p. 77)
These flies are a dark drab dun-colour, their wings being dark
dirty grey and their bodies dull greyish-brown or mid-beige-
brown. The uniform dull colour is relieved by a yellow streak on
the thorax in front of the root of each of the forewings.

Transmitted light: body dull yellowish brown; thorax darker; legs dark brown or yellowish-grey; tails dark greyish; wings dark grey.

♂ ♀ SPINNER   (Pl. 20c, p. 97)
Male here described; female is very similar, may be recognised by the yellow thoracic marks.
Eyes: bronze-black.
Thorax: dorsum pitch-black; venter and sides pitch-black except a vivid yellow mark in front of each wing-root on the thorax.
Legs: very dark brown or blackish.
Wings: transparent, with brown veins.
Abdomen: dorsum variously coloured, olive-brown to bronze or mahogany-brown; venter grey-greeny-brown with distinct yellowish-olive joinings.
Tails: blackish-grey.
Transmitted light: legs greyish-brown; thorax pitch-black; abdomen rather pale bronze-brown; tails drab grey; wings transparent, with male veins amber-coloured.
General appearance: the jet-black thorax and the prominent blackish eyes are in marked contrast to the two small and usually vivid yellow marks on the thorax.

ECDYONURUS VENOSUS

♂ ♀ DUN: LATE MARCH BROWN
These duns are very like the March Brown *Rhithrogena haarupi* in size and colour, but the fore-wings have not got pale areas clearly marked as in that species.

♂ ♀ SPINNER: GREAT RED SPINNER
The spinners of this species are very like the spinners of the August Dun *Ecdyonurus dispar* (Pl. 21c, d, p. 100), but are larger in size; and the colour of the abdomens is not quite such a dark red.

ECDYONURUS TORRENTIS

♂ ♀ DUN
These duns resemble the duns of the Late March Brown *Ecdyonurus venosus*, but differ in that the wings are more or less banded transversely with blackish.

♂ ♀ SPINNER: GREAT RED SPINNER

The spinners, both male and female, resemble the other Great Red Spinners *Ecdyonurus venosus* and *Ecdyonurus dispar*.

ECDYONURUS DISPAR

♂ DUN: AUGUST DUN   (Pl. 12a, p. 77)

Eyes: pitch-brown or pitch-bronze.

Wings: drab yellowish-grey with black cross-veins.

Thorax: dorsum olive-brown, varied with darker brown on the sides; venter reddish-brown.

Legs: brown-olive, becoming blackish distally.

Abdomen: dorsum drab yellowish-brown, with a dark streak on the side of each segment; venter watery yellowish-brown.

Tails: dusky grey-brown.

Transmitted light: body subdued reddish-brown; wings dun or beige-colour; legs brownish-black tinged with olive proximally.

General appearance: a drab brownish-dun-coloured fly.

♀ DUN: AUGUST DUN

Eyes: brown-black.

Wings: drab beige-coloured, sometimes faintly yellowish along costal area; veins brown-black.

Thorax: dorsum pale olive-brown; venter and sides very similar, varied with reddish-brown.

Legs: dark grey-brown.

Abdomen: dorsum drab beige-brown, with a subdued dark oblique line on each side of each segment; venter pale olive-brown.

Tails: grey-black.

Transmitted light: wings greyish-olive-beige; body yellowish or amber-brown; legs dark olive becoming grey-black distally; tails grey-black.

General appearance: a dingy greyish-brown or beige-coloured fly.

♂ SPINNER: GREAT RED SPINNER (OF AUGUST DUN)

                            (Pl. 21c, p. 100)

Eyes: brown-black.

Thorax: dorsum pitch-black; sides varied with dark red-brown; venter pitch-black.

Wings: membrane transparent, with the area near to the wing-root faintly tinged with olive; veins pitch-brown.

Legs: anterior pair very dark brown tinged with olive; other legs dark brown-olive.

Abdomen: dorsum rather dark brown-red or mahogany-colour—on each segment the posterior portion of the dorsal area is very dark and this dark colour extends obliquely forwards and downwards on the sides of each segment—in contrast to these dark streaks the paler areas are more yellowish-red; venter dark reddish-brown.

Tails: very dark and pitch-brown.

Transmitted light: tails, wing venation and anterior legs dark reddish-brown, other legs more yellowish-brown; abdomen dark red-mahogany-colour.

General appearance: a large-sized red spinner with a deep mahogany-red body and strong brown veins in the wings.

♀ SPINNER: GREAT RED SPINNER (OF AUGUST DUN)
(Pl. 21 d, p. 100)

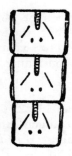

a

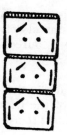

b

FIG. 10

Conspicious marking on ventral surfaces of abdominal segments of (a) *Ephemerella notata* and (b) *Ecdyonurus insignis*.

Eyes: dark olive-brown or greenish-brown-black.

Thorax: dorsum dark toffee-colour; sides varied with subdued yellow-and-red markings; venter dark red-brown or purple-brown.

Wings: transparent membrane, with dark brown-black veins; proximal anterior area faintly olive.

Legs: dark brown-olive.

Abdomen: dorsum similar to male spinner but of a slightly paler red-brown; venter dark reddish-brown, at times faintly tinged with purple.

Tails: dark brown.

Transmitted light: abdomen red-brown or mahogany-colour; legs brownish-olive; tails dark red; wings transparent, colourless, with reddish-brown venation.

General appearance: similar to male.

ECDYONURUS INSIGNIS

♂ ♀ DUN: Large Green Dun   (Pl. 9a, b, p. 68)

Eyes: dark brown-green.

Wings: membrane is greenish-grey, the green or olive being more pronounced in the anterior portion—but the whole wing is darkened by the veins, particularly the cross-veins, which are a brown-black; there are two pale areas containing few cross-veins near the middle of the wing.

Thorax: greenish-grey.

Abdomen: greenish-grey with an oblique black or brown-black stripe on the side of each segment; the arrangement of these stripes is similar to the arrangement on the August Dun and its spinner.

Legs: femora grey-green, other joints and forelegs darker.

Tails: grey-black.

Transmitted light: abdomen and legs greyish-green; thorax darker and opaque; tails dark grey; wings pale grey tinged with olive.

General appearance: the male and female duns closely resemble each other; they look like medium greenish-coloured March Browns.

♂ ♀ SPINNER: Large Green Spinner   (Pl. 15d, p. 84)

The spinners of this species closely resemble the duns in colouring; they differ in that the membrane of the wings is much more transparent, though the veins are very dark: there is a dark clouded patch in each of the fore-wings in the stigmatic area which is most noticeable; and the tails are unusually long.

UNCOMMON SPECIES

There are some species which are extremely rare or are very local in their distribution. Consequently they have not been included in the keys, nor has their distribution or natural history been dealt with in the text. For the sake of completeness, however, some brief notes on these species are set out here. These notes have been compiled mainly from Eaton's *Revisional Monograph* and Mr. Kimmins's *Keys to the British Species of Ephemeroptera*.

Ephemera lineata closely resembles the mayfly *Ephemera vulgata*, in colour and size. Has been recorded from the Thames in June and July.

Potamanthus luteus is rather larger than the Yellow May Dun, *Heptagenia sulphurea*, but resembles it in colour as the wings and the body are yellow. Both the duns and the spinners differ from that species in having a distinct brownish stripe running along the dorsal surface of the body. These flies have been found on a few occasions in the south of England on the Thames in July.

Paraleptophlebia tumida is a species closely related to the Purple Dun, *P. cincta*. The male spinners resemble the spinners of that species in size and colour. Has been recorded from streams in Hampshire and Lincolnshire, in May.

Habrophlebia fusca is probably the commonest of these uncommon species. It is a small-sized species with three tails and rather dark grey wings in the dun, and somewhat resembles the Pond Olive, *Cloëon dipterum*, in colour. The species may be recognised by the shape of the hind wing. The anterior border of this wing has a blunt projection or angle lying in the middle of the anterior edge. Mr. Kimmins records the species from May to September in the Lake District. It is found in streams and rivers, and it is possible that in local areas it may be common enough to warrant its inclusion among angling flies.

Brachycercus harrisella has been recorded on a few occasions in the south of England in June. It closely resembles the larger and dark species of *Caenis*.

Baëtis buceratus is a species which resembles the medium Olives, *B. vernus* and *B. tenax*. Has been recorded from the south of England.

Siphlonurus armatus has been recorded from the west of Ireland and from England but is not common. It somewhat resembles *S. lacustris* but differs in that the last segment of the abdomen is noticeably wider than the preceding segments.

Ameletus inopinatus is about the size of a small March Brown, and is brown in colour. Occurs in high hill streams in June and early July.

Heptagenia longicauda closely resembles the Yellow May Dun in colour, but can be distinguished from it by the light reddish bands on the femoral joints of the legs. A few records from the south of England, in late May and June.

Arthroplea congener: only one record of this species in Britain.

FLY DRESSINGS

DRY FLIES

GREENDRAKE — Cocked pattern.

Shoulder hackles:	French partridge; blue-grey side feather dyed in picric acid and wound in front of a stiff white cock's hackle also dyed in picric.
Rib hackle:	light badger cock, with grey or brown centre.
Body:	raffia dyed yellow.
Rib:	gold wire.
Tails:	cock pheasant centre tail fibres.
Tying Silk:	light-coloured, waxed with white wax.
Hook:	5, 6, 7.

GREENDRAKE — Spent pattern.

Wing hackle:	four or five turns of a spade or saddle hackle from a dun, honey dun, or pale blue dun cock's hackle dyed faintly yellow-green.
Shoulder hackle:	a grizzled or light cuckoo cock's hackle dyed pale yellow; this is either ribbed to the tail or else wound closely behind the wing-hackle, and is then clipped so that its fibres are strengthened.
Body:	pale yellow raffia or quill.
Rib:	gold wire.
Tail:	cock pheasant centre tail fibres.
Hook:	5, 6, 7.

GREY DRAKE — Female. (Pl. 32, p. 141)

Shoulder hackle:	cuckoo cock.
Rib hackle:	cuckoo cock.
Body:	swan herl dyed pale yellow or undyed.

Rib: gold wire.
Tail: fibres of cuckoo cock hackle.
Hook: 4, 5, 6.

SPENT GNAT — Male.
Wing hackle: a spade or saddle-hackle of a black cock which
                     has a dark brown tinge through it; alternatively,
                     a black cock with a cock-y-bonddhu cock wound
                     mostly behind it can be used; tied spent.
Body: white duck quill; this is improved if it is wound
                     over a foundation of thin cork so that the cork
                     shows at the tail.
Rib hackle: badger cock with thin brown or black centre.
Rib: gold wire or fine gold twist.
Tail: cock pheasant tail fibres.
Hook: 5, 6, 7.

SPENT GNAT — Female.   (Pl. 32, p. 14)
Wing hackle: spade or saddle hackle of a medium blue dun or
                     blue cuckoo cock; tied spent.
Rib hackle: short fibred pale cuckoo cock.
Rib: silver wire or fine silver twist.
Body: white quill tied over white floss silk.
Tail: cock pheasant tail fibres.
Hook: 5, 6, 7.

LAKE OLIVE DUN
Wing: dark starling tied forward.
Hackle: green-olive or brown-olive cock.
Body: palest blue heron herl or white swan dyed brown-
                     olive.
Rib: gold wire.
Tail: brown-olive cock.
Hook: 0, 1 or 2.
                     In the spring and early summer the green-olive
                     hackle, heron herl dyed brown-olive and hooks
                     1 or 2 make the best pattern; for the smaller,
                     more amber or golden-olive-coloured variation,
                     which is common in the autumn, use the brown-
                     olive hackle and swan herl with a No. O hook.

LAKE OLIVE SPINNER

Hackle: good quality rusty or pale grizzled dun cock tied spent or half spent.

Body: deep amber or mahogany seal's fur on orange tying silk.

Rib: gold wire.

Tail: rusty dun or reddish cock hackle fibres.

Hook: 0, 1.

CLARET DUN

Shoulder hackle: dark blue dun cock, six or seven turns with a V clipped underneath it.

Body: dark heron herl dyed dark claret, or mole's fur and dark claret mohair mixed on claret tying silk.

Rib: fine gold wire.

Tail: dark blue dun cock.

Hook: 1.

CLARET SPINNER

Hackle: blue dun or rusty dun cock.

Body: very dark claret seal's fur, on claret tying silk.

Rib: fine gold wire.

Tail: dark blue dun cock.

Hook: 1.

PURPLE DUN

Hackle: black cock with a dark blue dun cock run through it.

Body: dark heron herl dyed purple or mole's fur tied on purple tying silk.

Tail: dark blue dun cock.

Hook: 0, 1.

HATCHING IRON-BLUE DUN

Hackle: three jackdaw throat hackles tied at shoulder (see page 183).

Body: mole's fur on claret tying silk.

Tail: white, cream, or pale blue dun cock; three fibres.

Hook: 000, 00, 0.

A.E.   R

SKY-BLUE DUN

Wing:	fibres of pale blue dun hen breast-feather tied in a bunch and inclined slightly forwards.
Hackle:	honey dun or palest ginger cock.
Body:	undyed raffia, palest yellow quill or very pale blue heron herl lightly dyed in picric acid.
Tail:	honey or pale blue dun cock.
Hook:	oo, o.

GREAT RED SPINNER

Hackle:	dark rusty dun cock, tied half spent.
Body:	dark red or claret seal's fur on claret tying-silk.
Rib:	gold wire.
Tail:	dark rusty dun or red cock.
Hook:	2, 3.

YELLOW EVENING DUN

Wing:	bunch of fibres of a pale yellow cock-hackle tied so as to incline slightly forwards.
Hackle:	ginger cock.
Body:	bright orange floss silk or yellow-orange quill.
Rib:	gold wire.
Tail:	ginger cock.
Hook:	I.

YELLOW EVENING SPINNER

Wing:	honey dun or palest ginger cock-hackles tied spent or half spent.
Body:	yellow-orange seal's fur on orange tying silk.
Rib:	gold wire.
Tail:	ginger cock hackle fibres.
Hook:	I.

BROWN SILVERHORNS

Wing:	speckled partridge tail tied to lie along the hook and protrude beyond the bend.
Body:	grey or green seal's fur.
Rib hackle:	brown cuckoo or grizzled cock.
Shoulder hackle:	,, ,, ,, ,, ,,
Rib:	gold wire.
Hook:	o, I, 2.

Murragh or Large Red Sedge

Wing: dark brown speckled hen wing-feather tied to lie close to the hook.

Body: dark grey-black or black-claret mohair or seal's fur.

Hackle: two dark red cock hackles tied in front of wing.

Hook: 5, 6, 7.

Black Duck-fly

Wings: two dun or cream cock hackle points tied sloping backwards along the hook.

Body: black floss silk thickened near shoulder.

Hackle: rusty-black cock tied in front of wings.

Hook: 1, 2.

Olive Duck-fly or Large Olive Midge

Wings: two blue dun or cream cock hackle points tied sloping backwards along the hook.

Body: olive-coloured floss silk or dyed pale green-olive swan herl.

Rib: gold wire.

Hackle: pale grizzled or rusty dun cock tied in front of wings.

Hook: 1, 2, 3.

Large Olive Midge or Buzzer

Shoulder hackle: cream badger cock tied spent fashion.

Rib hackle: cream or pale badger cock.

Body: hare's ear and pale olive seal's fur mixed.

Rib: gold wire.

Hook: 1, 2, 3.

Midge Clump or Swarm

Hackles: three or four stiff cuckoo cock saddle or neck hackles dyed pale olive, wound from head to tail.

Body: Pale Olive swan herl or seal's fur.

Rib: gold wire.

Hook: 4, 5, 6, 7.

GREY SEDGE OR GREY FLAG

Wing·	woodcock wing fibres tied so as to lie close along the hook and protrude slightly beyond the bend of the hook; tied in a bunch.
Body:	grey seal's fur.
Rib hackle:	rusty dun or grizzled dun cock.
Shoulder hackle:	rusty dun or grizzled dun cock; tied in front of wing.
Rib:	gold wire.
Hook:	1, 2, 3.

LARGE CINNAMON SEDGE

Wing:	light brown or brown-yellow speckled hen.
Body:	light green floss, mohair, or quill wound over floss to make it thick.
Rib hackle:	ginger or red cock.
Shoulder hackle:	ginger or red cock.
Rib:	gold wire.
Hook:	3, 4, 5.

SPENT RED SEDGE

Shoulder hackle:	grouse hackle wound in front of a rusty dun cock hackle and both hackles tied in a spent fashion.
Body:	dark hare's fur or dark brown mohair.
Rib hackle:	red cock (or none).
Rib:	gold wire.
Hook:	1, 2.

CAENIS SPINNER (for evening)

Wings:	two palest blue dun or cream hen hackle points tied spent.
Body:	palest yellow or white floss silk ribbed with brown tying silk, or with a strand of light brown horsehair.
Hackle:	honey dun or cream cock flattened underneath the hook.
Tail:	cream cock.
Tying silk:	brown.
Hook:	000, 00.

CAENIS DUN (for evening).

Shoulder hackle:	pale cream cockerel or henny cock tied in by the butt end with some of the soft downy fibres still remaining on the stalk; this is wound slightly towards the tail so as to occupy about one-third of the hook shank.
Body:	cream-coloured herl or floss silk.
Tail:	cream cock.
Tying silk:	brown.
Hook:	000, 00.

CAENIS SPINNER (for early morning).

Wings:	two pale blue dun hen hackle points tied spent.
Body:	palest yellow or cream-coloured floss silk slightly darkened with wax near the tail-end.
Hackle:	pale grizzled or blue dun cock.
Tail:	blue dun cock.
Tying silk:	brown.
Hook:	00, 0.

WET FLIES AND NYMPHS

OLIVE DUCK-FLY PUPA OR LARGE MIDGE PUPA

Tying silk:	yellow.
Tag:	flat silver.
Body:	olive-coloured elastic stretched and wound over the yellow tying silk.
Thorax:	light brown turkey-herl wound at shoulder to occupy about one-quarter to one-third of the hook shank.
Wing-cases:	very small jungle-cock feather tied with the enamelled part lying along the underneath of the thorax.
Hackle:	one or two turns of the stalk of the jungle-cock feather which has badger-coloured hackle fibres.
Hook:	00, 0, 1, 2.

ORANGE DUCK-FLY PUPA   (Pl. 32, p. 141)

>Similar to the preceding except that the tying silk used is hot orange and the thorax is dark brown turkey herl.

Hook: 1, 2, 3.

GREEN SEDGE PUPA

Body: tail half light green floss silk tied thickly.
Thorax: brown ostrich-herl or copper-coloured peacock-herl, wound to occupy about half of the hook shank.
Wings: very short brown mallard tied to reach only to the end of the thorax.
Hackle: two turns red hen or cock.
Swimming legs: two cock pheasant tail-fibres tied sloping back towards the tail, underneath the hook.
Hook: 2, 3, 4.

RED SPINNER   (Pl. 32, p. 141)
Wings: two blue dun or rusty dun hackle points tied upright and sloping slightly backwards and separated.
Body: brown-red or claret seal's fur, tied thinly on red tying silk.
Rib: gold wire.
Hackle: red cock; two turns at most.
Tail: red cock.
Hook: 0, 1, 2.

HARRY LONG-LEGS

Body: fibres of cock pheasant-tail or brown turkey-tail wound as herl.
Rib: gold wire.
Legs: six fibres of cock pheasant-tail feather, knotted and tied in on top of the hook, two at the head and four at the shoulder.
Hackle: rusty dun cock, a few turns at shoulder and then wound to the tail end, and held in place by the gold wire which is wound up over it to the head.
Hook: 5, 6, 7.

BLACK DUCK-FLY

Body:	black silk or wool wound thickest at shoulder, and tied with crimson or claret silk.
Hackle:	black cock.
Wing:	starling secondary tied short, divided and inclined towards the tail.
Hook:	1, 2, 3.

DISTRIBUTION MAPS

THE DISTRIBUTION maps are intended mainly to show the relative distribution of various species. Very little collecting of ephemeropterans has been carried out in comparison with the intensive work done on such orders as the Lepidoptera, and consequently it is not possible to show an exact distribution of even one species. But even though the complete distribution of none of the species is known, some idea of the relative distribution of species can be gleaned from the records which are available.

The maps have been compiled mainly from records very kindly supplied by Mr. Kimmins of the Natural History Section of the British Museum, from unpublished records of the late Roland Southern compiled while he was Inspector of Fisheries for Ireland, from various entomological publications and from my own collector's notes.

Much additional information could have been included in these maps if use had been made of innumerable records kindly supplied by numerous anglers and if all published records had been included. If this had been done, however, it is possible that many inaccuracies would have appeared. It was therefore reluctantly decided not to include any records of species where there was any possibility that inaccurate determination of species had been made.

In cases where a number of records in any one vice-county were available only one or at most two of the records (depending on the size of the vice county), have been recorded by dots on the maps.

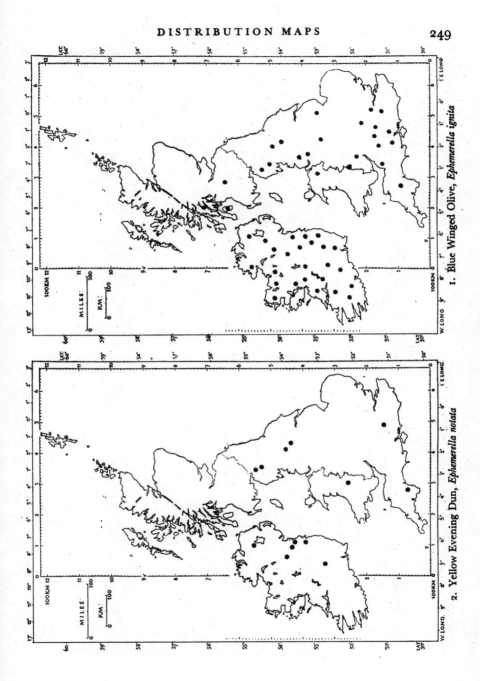

1. Blue Winged Olive, *Ephemerella ignita*

2. Yellow Evening Dun, *Ephemerella notata*

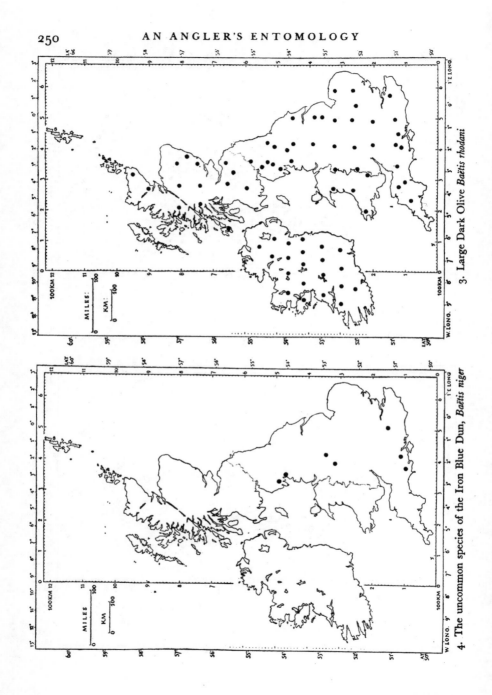

3. Large Dark Olive *Baëtis rhodani*

4. The uncommon species of the Iron Blue Dun, *Baëtis niger*

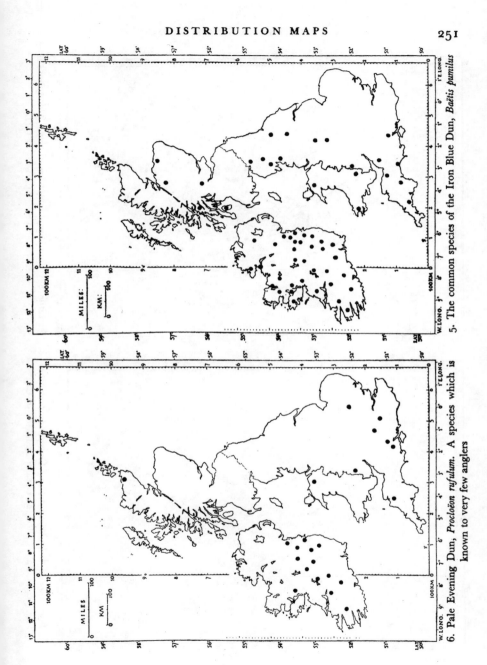

5. The common species of the Iron Blue Dun, *Baëtis pumilus*

6. Pale Evening Dun, *Procloëon rufulum*. A species which is known to very few anglers

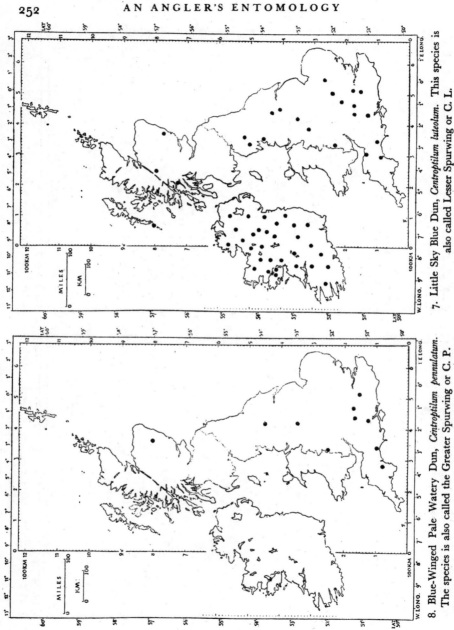

7. Little Sky Blue Dun, *Centroptilum luteolum*. This species is also called Lesser Spurwing or C. L.

8. Blue-Winged Pale Watery Dun, *Centroptilum pennulatum*. The species is also called the Greater Spurwing or C. P.

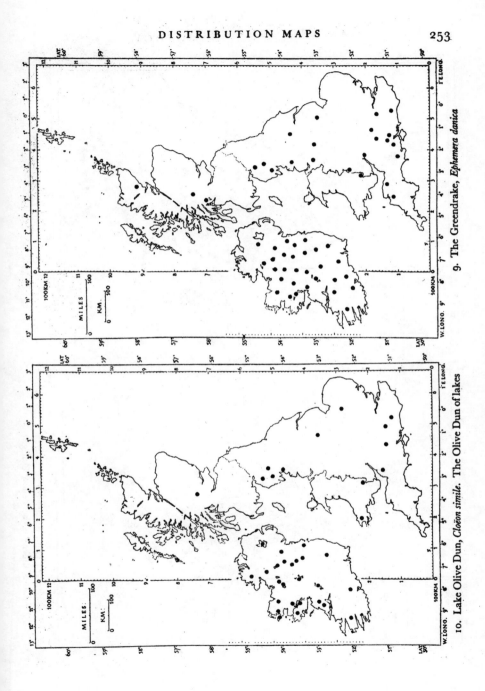

9. The Greendrake, *Ephemera danica*

10. Lake Olive Dun, *Cloëon simile.* The Olive Dun of lakes

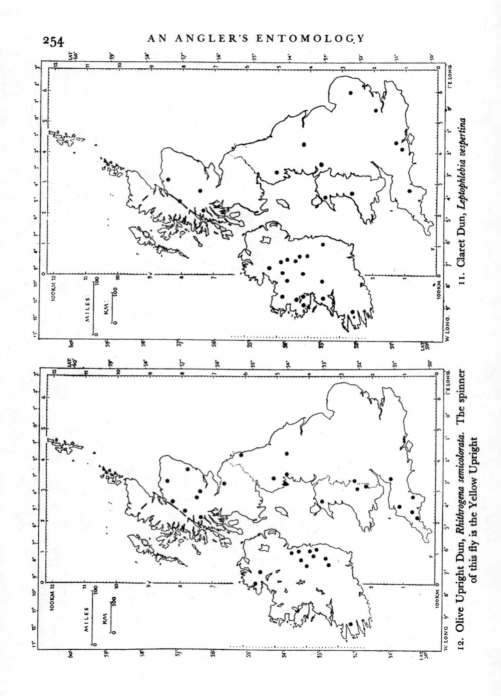

11. Claret Dun, *Leptophlebia vespertina*

12. Olive Upright Dun, *Rhithrogena semicolorata*. The spinner of this fly is the Yellow Upright

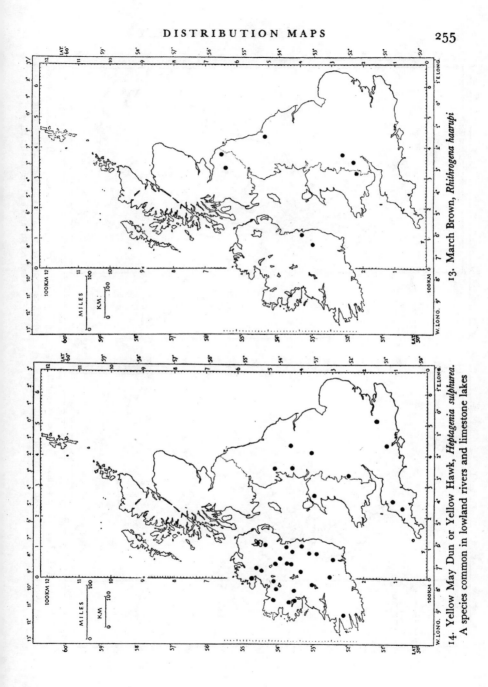

13. March Brown, *Rhithrogena haarupi*

14. Yellow May Dun or Yellow Hawk, *Heptagenia sulphurea*. A species common in lowland rivers and limestone lakes

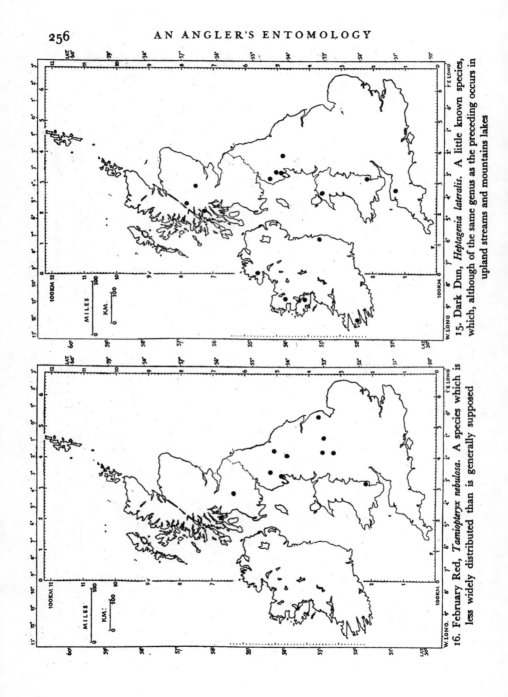

15. Dark Dun, *Heptagenia lateralis*. A little known species, which, although of the same genus as the preceding occurs in upland streams and mountains lakes

16. February Red, *Taeniopteryx nebulosa*. A species which is less widely distributed than is generally supposed

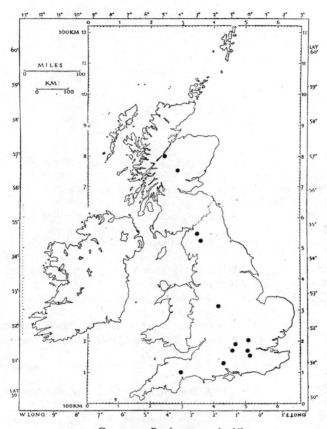

17. Grannom, *Brachycentrus subnubilus*

BIBLIOGRAPHY

ALDAM, W. H. (1876). A Quaint Treatise on Flees and the Art of Artyfichal. Flee Making. London.

ALLEN, K. R. (1938). Some Observations on the Biology of the Trout (*Salmo trutta*) in Windermere. *J. Anim. Ecol.* 7: 333—49.

BARKER, F. D. (1929). An Angler's Paradise. London, Faber & Faber.

BERNERS, DAME JULIANA (1496). Treatyse of Fysshynge with an Angle, *in* The Boke of St. Albans. Westmestre (Westminster). Wynkyn de Worde (facsimile London, 1880).

BRIDGETT, R. L. (1924). Lake Fishing in Theory and Practice. London, Jenkins.

BROOKES, R. (1799). The Art of Angling. London. 54—80.

DODDS, G. S., AND HISAW, F. L. (1924—25). Ecological Studies of Aquatic insects. *Ecology*, 5: 136—48, 262—71; 6: 123—37, 380—90.

DUNNE, J. W. (1924). Sunshine and the Dry Fly. London, Black. 1—136.

EATON, A. E. (1883—88). A Revisional Monograph of Recent Ephemeridae or Mayflies. *Trans. Linn. Soc.* (*Zool.*), Ser. 2, 3: 1—352.
(1871). A Monograph on the Ephemeridae. *Trans. Ent. Soc. London, 1871*: 1—158.

FOSTER, D. (1886). The Scientific Angler (3rd edition). London, Bemrose. 117—60, 213—58.

FOX, H. MUNRO, SIMMONDS, B. G., AND WASHBURN. R. (1935). Metabolic Rates of Ephemerid Nymphs from Swiftly Flowing and from Still Waters. *J. Exper. Biol. 12*: 179—84.

FOX, H. M., WINGFIELD, C. A., AND SIMMONDS, B. G. (1937). Oxygen Consumption of Ephemerid Nymphs from Flowing and from Still Waters in Relation to the Concentration of Oxygen in the Water. *J. Exper. Biol. 14*: 210—18.

FRANCIS, F. (1880). A Book on Angling (5th edition). London, Longmans Green. 189—246.

FROST, W. E. (1942). River Liffey Survey III. The Fauna of the Submerged Mosses in an Acid and an Alkaline Water. *Proc. Roy. Irish Acad. 47 B*: No. 13.
(1943). The natural history of the Minnow, *Phoxinus phoxinus*. *J. Anim. Ecol. 12*: 139—62.

GREENDRAKE, GREGORY (1832). The Angling Excursions of Gregory Greendrake in the Counties of Wicklow, Meath, Westmeath, Longford and Cavan. Dublin.

HALFORD, F. M. (1886). Floating Flies and how to dress them (2nd edition). London. 81—115.

(1913). The Dry-Fly Man's Handbook. London, Routledge.

HANSARD, G. A. (1834). Trout and Salmon Fishing in Wales. London.

HEWITT, E. R. (1948). A Trout and Salmon Fisherman for Seventy-five years. New York, Scribners.

HILLS, J. W. (1934). River Keeper. London, Bles. 1—227.

HOFFMANN, C. H. and others (1946). Field Studies on the Effect of DDT on Aquatic Insects. *U. S. Dep. Agric. Bur. Ent.* E-702. (20 pp. mimeod bulletin.)

HUMPHRIES, C. F. (1938). The Chironomid Fauna of the Grober Plöner See, the Relative Density of its Members and their Emergence Period. *Arch. Hydrobiol. 33*: 535—84.

HYNES, H. B. N. (1940). A Key to the British Species of Plecoptera (Stoneflies). *Sci. Publ. Freshw. Biol. Assoc.* No. 2: 1—39.

IMMS, A. D. (1942). Outlines of Entomology. London, Methuen. 1—184.

KIMMINS, D. E. (1941). Under Water Emergence of *Hept. lateralis. Entomologist, 74*: 169—70.

(1942). Keys to the British Species of Ephemeroptera with Keys to the Genera of the Nymphs. *Sci. Publ. Freshw. Biol. Ass.* No. 7: 1—64.

KLAPÁLEK, F. (1909). Ephemerida. Die Süsswasserfauna Deutschlands. Jena, G. Fischer, vol. *8*: 1—32.

KLOET, S. AND HINCKS, W. D. (1945). A Check List of British Insects. Stockport, Kloet and Hincks.

KROGH, A. AND ZEUTHEN, E. (1941). The Mechanism of Flight Separation in some Insects. *J. Exper. Biol. 18*: 1—10.

MACAN, T. T. AND MACAN, Z. (1940). Preliminary note on the Ephemeroptera and Plecoptera of the Hampshire Avon and its Tributaries. *J. Soc. Brit. Ent. 2*: 53—61.

MELLANBY, H. (1938). Animal Life in Fresh Water. London. Methuen. 115—215.

MIALL, L. C. (1903). The Natural History of Aquatic Insects. London, MacMillan. 1—395.

MOSELY, M. E. (1939). The British Caddis Flies. London, Routledge. 1—320.

(1921). The Dry-fly Fisherman's Entomology. London, Routledge. 1—109.

MOTTRAM, J. C. (n. d.). Fly Fishing: Some New Arts and Mysteries. London, The Field.

NEEDHAM, J. G., TRAVER, J. R., AND HSU, Y. (1935). The Biology of Mayflies. New York, Comstock. 1—759.

OGDEN, J. (1879). On Fly Tying. Cheltenham.

O'GORMAN (1845). The Practice of Angling, particularly as regards Ireland (2nd edition). Dublin.

PERCIVAL, E. AND WHITEHEAD, H. (1926). Observations on the biology of the mayfly *Ephemera danica* Mull. *Proc. Leeds Phil. Lit. Soc. 1*: 136—48.

RAWLINSON, R. (1939). Studies on the Life History and Breeding of *Ecdyonurus venosus* (Ephemeroptera). *Proc. Zool. Soc. London*, *109*: 377—450.

ROUSSEAU, E. (1921). Les Larves et Nymphes Aquatiques des Insectes d'Europe. Bruxelles, Lebègue. 164—959.

RONALDS, A. (1836). The Fly-Fisher's Entomology. London.

(1856). The Fly-Fisher's Entomology. (5th edition), London, 55—132.

SAWYER, F. E. (1945). Two British Spurwings. *Salmon and Trout Mag.* No. 114: 150—58.

SCHOENEMUND, E. (1930). Eintagsfliegen oder Ephemeroptera. Die Tierwelt Deutschlands und der angrenzenden Meeresteile, Jena, G. Fischer. *19*: 1—106.

SKUES, G. E. M. (1921). The Way of a Trout with a Fly. London, Black.

SMART, J. (1944). The British Simuliidae, with Keys to the species in the Adult, Pupal and Larval stages. *Sci. Publ. Freshw. Biol. Assoc.* No. 9: 1—57.

SOUTHERN, R. Unpublished notes.

ULMER, G. (1929). Eintagsfliegen (Ephemeroptera) *in* Brohmer, Ehrmann and Ulmer: Die Tierwelt Mitteleuropas, Leipzig, Band IV, Lief 1 b; 1—44.

WALLS, G. L. (1942). The Vertebrate Eye, and its Adaptive Radiation. Michigan, Cranbrook Inst. Sci.

WALTON, IZAAK (1653). The Compleat Angler, or the Contemplative Man's Recreation. London.

WELCH, P. S. (1935). Limnology. New York, McGraw-Hill. 1—471.

WEST, L. (1921). The Natural Trout Fly and its Imitation. Liverpool, Potter. 1—163.

WHITNEY, R. J. (1939). Thermal resistance of Mayfly Nymphs from Ponds and Streams. *J. Exper. Biol.* *16*: 374—86.

WIGGLESWORTH, V. B. (1934). Insect Physiology. London, Methuen. 1—129.

WINGFIELD, C. A. (1939). Function of gills of Mayfly Nymphs. *J. Exper. Biol.* *16*: 374—85.

INDEX